A Native Sons R E A D E R

A Native Sons
READER

edited by Edward Margolies

J. B. Lippincott Company
Philadelphia / New York

I should like to express my gratitude to the following persons who helped me put together some of the material in this book: Denise Cannon, Sophie Matthews, Robert Micalizio and Helen Stasiak. Also many thanks to my wife, who typed and made editorial suggestions.

To my mother

Contents

Introduction

This is an anthology for people who do not like anthologies. Briefly, what I have tried to do here, as in my critical study *Native Sons* (1968), is to present a personal selection of pieces by black authors explaining from the point of view of *their* sensibility different aspects of the Afro-American experience in the United States. Obviously no collective experience, by the very multiplicity of its nature, can be fragmented or categorized topically or thematically as I have done without raising serious questions, but I think that categories can serve as useful guidelines in attempting to cope with the complexities of the black experience. Thus, it can be argued that some of the pieces I have placed under one category would be more suitable in another. My response can only be that I have not tried deliberately to distort the implication of any of the pieces but rather have attempted to list them from a variety of points of view, some of which may indeed strike the reader as unusual. Hence, for example, James Baldwin's "The Outing" might quite justifiably have been placed under the heading "City" or "Children" rather than under "Church," but I would suggest that the nature of the religious experience described is an important consideration.

I may as well add too that although my concerns in selecting these pieces have been primarily aesthetic, I think the careful juxtaposition of these pieces within a given category makes its own human (social? historical? psychological? cultural?) comment. I suppose that if the anthologist exercises any art at all, it is in the way he puts things together—or maybe leaves them out.

In any event, I don't intend to enumerate, even if I could. The pieces themselves, their arrangement, the chronology of categories ought to speak for themselves. I believe, like some of Hemingway's characters, that if you talk about these things too much, you lose them.

Finally, what this book is not. It is not a chronological grouping of literary pieces by black writers. It is not a "sampler" of Afro-American literature (whatever that may mean), nor is it a balanced gathering of literary genres intended to prove what black American authors may or may not have accomplished during the half-century. I may as well go further. A number of first-rate pieces by black authors have been deliberately excluded because they do not suit the purposes of this book. Unquestionably, there are other works I would have wished to incorporate but could not, for reasons of space and other hard pragmatic considerations. Nonetheless, I hope that the very paucity of the selections represent, better than a profusion of offerings, a more intensive perception of meanings.

Doubtless, it will be said (and has already been said) by some blacks as well as whites that the white editor or reader cannot possibly understand the black experience. I find statements of this kind tiresome and wonder at the motives of their makers. Good art transcends skin as well as historical and psychological barriers and manages to filter into some of the most unlikely places. At any rate, the pieces contained herein have reached me, and that is why I want to pass them along. Whether or not I would react the same way if I were black, I cannot say. I suspect not, but then I suspect nothing touches any of us, black or white, the same way. In other words, considering the human condition, we had all better be more careful about what we prescribe and what we proscribe.

A more important reason, it seems to me, why a white editor can (and maybe should) put together a collection of this sort is that as an American he has a black identity as well, and to ignore his blackness is to ignore, indeed to deny, himself. I do not mean, however, to imply that the black experience has not been something apart from what the rest of us have undergone. (It is

not necessary to rehearse the differences between the black
man's history and that of other ethnic groups that have come to
American shores.) But the black presence, indeed the black experience, are part of a common American heritage and have
from the very beginning largely determined America's history,
institutions, laws, manners. In our ignorance we have failed to
see how the culture of black communities has permeated all lev-
els of American culture—even to the ways we use language, the
ways we move and dance and listen and sing. We *think* Duke
Ellington and Charlie Parker and John Coltrane even though we
may never have heard them—just as we think William James
and Freud and Marx even though we may never have read
them. Not surprisingly then, black men of letters in this century
—particularly in the last three decades—have begun to articulate their/our experience, and it is incumbent upon white people
in order to know themselves to receive this kind of experience
not only implicitly, instinctively, as has been done in the past
with sounds, rhythms, movements, but consciously, deliberately,
as befitting the skilled arrangement of words into feelings and
ideas. The present anthology does not pretend to be an embodiment of black literary expression; its editor would, however, feel
that his book has achieved some modicum of success if it were
to suggest the possibilities of that expression.

A Native Sons **READER**

I Roots

It is an accepted fact that Americans have an identity problem. White European immigrants have come to these shores because they felt alienated or at the very least dissatisfied with one aspect or another of their lives in their homeland. For them and their children the dilemma has always been how much of their European heritage they could or should adapt to the changed conditions of an American environment. For blacks, who came to America involuntarily, the problem has been far worse. Not only have they shared a common American insecurity about who they are but, additionally, they have had to overcome the dominant cultural view that they are racially inferior and that their African ancestral homes are shamefully primitive.

It was not until the 1920's that black Northern urban authors began to re-evaluate their African heritage. In part they were responding to a new wave of black nationalism that swept the country as a result of increasing racial and economic tensions in the cities. In part they were converting into pride the bitterness they felt at the broken promises of equality they had fought for in World War I and had expected to find in the North. Obviously their search for roots was at the very least romantic (see Cullen's "Heritage") but, more often than not, it expressed something akin to a kind of mysticism, as in Hughes's "The Negro Speaks of Rivers" or Toomer's "Conversion." Yet for all their well-intended efforts the complexities of an impersonal urban industrial life could not be satisfied by rejoicing in one's négritude or African ancestors. LeRoi Jones, living in New York in the late 1950's, could still describe a kind of emptiness and sadness as in "Genealogy." But it was perhaps William E. B. Du Bois in the early years of the century whose essay "Of Our Spiritual Strivings" still best describes the peculiar psychological dilemma of being black in white America.

3

Langston Hughes

The Negro Speaks of Rivers

I've known rivers:
I've known rivers ancient as the world and older than the flow
  of human blood in human veins.

My soul has grown deep like the rivers.

I bathed in the Euphrates when dawns were young.
I built my hut near the Congo and it lulled me to sleep.
I looked upon the Nile and raised the pyramids above it.
I heard the singing of the Mississippi when Abe Lincoln went
  down to New Orleans, and I've seen its muddy bosom turn
  all golden in the sunset.

I've known rivers:
Ancient, dusky rivers.

My soul has grown deep like the rivers.

Countee Cullen

Heritage

(For Harold Jackman)

What is Africa to me:
Copper sun or scarlet sea,
Jungle star or jungle track,
Strong bronzed men, or regal black
Women from whose loins I sprang
When the birds of Eden sang?
One three centuries removed
From the scenes his fathers loved,
Spicy grove, cinnamon tree,
What is Africa to me?

So I lie, who all day long
Want no sound except the song
Sung by wild barbaric birds
Goading massive jungle herds.
Juggernauts of flesh that pass
Trampling tall defiant grass
Where young forest lovers lie,
Plighting troth beneath the sky.
So I lie, who always hear,
Though I cram against my ear
Both my thumbs, and keep them there,
Great drums throbbing through the air.
So I lie, whose fount of pride,
Dear distress, and joy allied,
Is my somber flesh and skin,
With the dark blood dammed within
Like great pulsing tides of wine

6

That, I fear, must burst the fine
Channels of the chafing net
Where they surge and foam and fret.

Africa? A book one thumbs
Listlessly, till slumber comes.
Unremembered are her bats
Circling through the night, her cats
Crouching in the river reeds,
Stalking gentle flesh that feeds
By the river brink; no more
Does the bugle-throated roar
Cry that monarch claws have leapt
From the scabbards where they slept.
Silver snakes that once a year
Doff the lovely coats you wear,
Seek no covert in your fear
Lest a mortal eye should see;
What's your nakedness to me?
Here no leprous flowers rear
Fierce corollas in the air;
Here no bodies sleek and wet,
Dripping mingled rain and sweat,
Tread the savage measures of
Jungle boys and girls in love.
What is last year's snow to me,
Last year's anything? The tree
Budding yearly must forget
How its past arose or set—
Bough and blossom, flower, fruit,
Even what shy bird with mute
Wonder at her travail there,
Meekly labored in its hair.
One three centuries removed
From the scenes his fathers loved,
Spicy grove, cinnamon tree,
What is Africa to me?

So I lie, who find no peace
Night or day, no slight release
From the unremittent beat
Made by cruel padded feet
Walking through my body's street.
Up and down they go, and back,
Treading out a jungle track.
So I lie, who never quite
Safely sleep from rain at night—
I can never rest at all
When the rain begins to fall;
Like a soul gone mad with pain
I must match its weird refrain;
Ever must I twist and squirm,
Writhing like a baited worm,
While its primal measures drip
Through my body, crying, "Strip!
Doff this new exuberance.
Come and dance the Lover's Dance!"
In an old remembered way
Rain works on me night and day.

Quaint, outlandish heathen gods
Black men fashion out of rods,
Clay, and brittle bits of stone,
In a likeness like their own,
My conversion came high-priced;
I belong to Jesus Christ,
Preacher of humility;
Heathen gods are naught to me.

Father, Son, and Holy Ghost,
So I make an idle boast;
Jesus of the twice-turned cheek,
Lamb of God, although I speak
With my mouth thus, in my heart
Do I play a double part.

Ever at Thy glowing altar
Must my heart grow sick and falter,
Wishing He I served were black,
Thinking then it would not lack
Precedent of pain to guide it,
Let who would or might deride it;
Surely then this flesh would know
Yours had borne a kindred woe.
Lord, I fashion dark gods, too,
Daring even to give You
Dark despairing features where,
Crowned with dark rebellious hair,
Patience wavers just so much as
Mortal grief compels, while touches
Quick and hot, of anger, rise
To smitten cheek and weary eyes.
Lord, forgive me if my need
Sometimes shapes a human creed.
All day long and all night through,
One thing only must I do:
Quench my pride and cool my blood,
Lest I perish in the flood.
Lest a hidden ember set
Timber that I thought was wet
Burning like the dryest flax,
Melting like the merest wax,
Lest the grave restore its dead.
Not yet has my heart or head
In the least way realized
They and I are civilized.

Jean Toomer

Conversion

African Guardian of Souls,
Drunk with rum,
Feasting on a strange cassava,
Yielding to new words and a weak palabra
Of a white-faced sardonic god—
Grins, cries
Amen,
Shouts hosanna.

LeRoi Jones

*Genealogy**

Each morning
I go down
to Gansevoort St.
and stand on the docks.
I stare out
at the horizon
until it gets up
and comes to embrace
me. I
make believe
it is my father.
This is known
as genealogy.

* From "Hymn for Lannie Poo." The title of this selection was
supplied by the editor.

William E. B. Du Bois

Of Our Spiritual Strivings

Between me and the other world there is ever an unasked question: unasked by some through feelings of delicacy; by others through the difficulty of rightly framing it. All, nevertheless, flutter round it. They approach me in a half-hesitant sort of way, eye me curiously or compassionately, and then, instead of saying directly, How does it feel to be a problem? they say, I know an excellent colored man in my town; or, I fought at Mechanicsville; or, Do not these Southern outrages make your blood boil? At these I smile, or am interested, or reduce the boiling to a simmer, as the occasion may require. To the real question, How does it feel to be a problem? I answer seldom a word.

And yet, being a problem is a strange experience,—peculiar even for one who has never been anything else, save perhaps in babyhood and in Europe. It is in the early days of rollicking boyhood that the revelation first bursts upon one, all in a day, as it were. I remember well when the shadow swept across me. I was a little thing, away up in the hills of New England, where the dark Housatonic winds between Hoosac and Taghkanic to the sea. In a wee wooden schoolhouse, something put it into the boys' and girls' heads to buy gorgeous visiting-cards—ten cents a package—and exchange. The exchange was merry, till one girl, a tall newcomer, refused my card,—refused it peremptorily, with a glance. Then it dawned upon me with a certain suddenness that I was different from the others; or like, mayhap, in heart and life and longing, but shut out from their world by a vast veil. I had thereafter no desire to tear down that

veil, to creep through; I held all beyond it in common contempt, and lived above it in a region of blue sky and great wandering shadows. That sky was bluest when I could beat my
mates at examination-time, or beat them at a foot-race, or even
beat their stringy heads. Alas, with the years all this fine contempt began to fade; for the worlds I longed for, and all their
dazzling opportunities, were theirs, not mine. But they should
not keep these prizes, I said; some, all, I would wrest from
them. Just how I would do it I could never decide: by reading
law, by healing the sick, by telling the wonderful tales that
swam in my head,—some way. With other black boys the strife
was not so fiercely sunny: their youth shrunk into tasteless syco-
phancy, or into silent hatred of the pale world about them and
mocking distrust of everything white; or wasted itself in a bitter
cry, Why did God make me an outcast and a stranger in mine
own house? The shades of the prison-house closed round about
us all: walls strait and stubborn to the whitest, but relentlessly
narrow, tall, and unscalable to sons of night who must plod
darkly on in resignation, or beat unavailing palms against the
stone, or steadily, half hopelessly, watch the streak of blue
above.

After the Egyptian and Indian, the Greek and Roman, the
Teuton and Mongolian, the Negro is a sort of seventh son, born
with a veil, and gifted with second-sight in this American
world,—a world which yields him no true self-consciousness,
but only lets him see himself through the revelation of the
other world. It is a peculiar sensation, this double-consciousness,
this sense of always looking at one's self through the eyes of
others, of measuring one's soul by the tape of a world that looks
on in amused contempt and pity. One ever feels his twoness,—
an American, a Negro; two souls, two thoughts, two unreconciled strivings; two warring ideals in one dark body, whose
dogged strength alone keeps it from being torn asunder.

The history of the American Negro is the history of this
strife,—this longing to attain self-conscious manhood, to merge
his double self into a better and truer self. In this merging he
wishes neither of the older selves to be lost. He would not Afri-

canize America, for America has too much to teach the world and Africa. He would not bleach his Negro soul in a flood of white Americanism, for he knows that Negro blood has a message for the world. He simply wishes to make it possible for a man to be both a Negro and an American, without being cursed and spit upon by his fellows, without having the doors of Opportunity closed roughly in his face.

This, then, is the end of his striving: to be a co-worker in the kingdom of culture, to escape both death and isolation, to husband and use his best powers and his latent genius. These powers of body and mind have in the past been strangely wasted, dispersed, or forgotten. The shadow of a mighty Negro past flits through the tale of Ethiopia the Shadowy and of Egypt the Sphinx. Throughout history, the powers of single black men flash here and there like falling stars, and die sometimes before the world has rightly gauged their brightness. Here in America, in the few days since Emancipation, the black man's turning hither and thither in hesitant and doubtful striving has often made his very strength to lose effectiveness, to seem like absence of power, like weakness. And yet it is not weakness,—it is the contradiction of double aims. The double-aimed struggle of the black artisan—on the one hand to escape white contempt for a nation of mere hewers of wood and drawers of water, and on the other hand to plough and nail and dig for a poverty-stricken horde—could only result in making him a poor craftsman, for he had but half a heart in either cause. By the poverty and ignorance of his people, the Negro minister or doctor was tempted toward quackery and demagogy; and by the criticism of the other world, toward ideals that made him ashamed of his lowly tasks. The would-be black *savant* was confronted by the paradox that the knowledge his people needed was a twice-told tale to his white neighbors, while the knowledge which would teach the white world was Greek to his own flesh and blood. The innate love of harmony and beauty that set the ruder souls of his people a-dancing and a-singing raised but confusion and doubt in the soul of the black artist; for the beauty revealed to him was the soul-beauty of a race which his

larger audience despised, and he could not articulate the message of another people. This waste of double aims, this seeking
to satisfy two unreconciled ideals, has wrought sad havoc with
the courage and faith and deeds of ten thousand thousand people,—has sent them often wooing false gods and invoking false
means of salvation, and at times has even seemed about to make
them ashamed of themselves.

Away back in the days of bondage they thought to see in one
divine event the end of all doubt and disappointment; few men
ever worshipped Freedom with half such unquestioning faith as
did the American Negro for two centuries. To him, so far as he
thought and dreamed, slavery was indeed the sum of all villain-
ies, the cause of all sorrow, the root of all prejudice; Emancipation was the key to a promised land of sweeter beauty than
ever stretched before the eyes of wearied Israelites. In song and
exhortation swelled one refrain—Liberty; in his tears and curses
the God he implored had Freedom in his right hand. At last it
came,—suddenly, fearfully, like a dream. With one wild carni-
val of blood and passion came the message in his own plaintive
cadences:—

"Shout, O children!
Shout, you're free!
For God has bought your liberty!"

Years have passed away since then,—ten, twenty, forty; forty
years of national life, forty years of renewal and development,
and yet the swarthy spectre sits in its accustomed seat at the
Nation's feast. In vain do we cry to this our vastest social problem:—

"Take any shape but that, and my firm nerves
Shall never tremble!"

The Nation has not yet found peace from its sins; the freed-
man has not yet found in freedom his promised land. Whatever
of good may have come in these years of change, the shadow of

a deep disappointment rests upon the Negro people,—a disappointment all the more bitter because the unattained ideal was unbounded save by the simple ignorance of a lowly people.

The first decade was merely a prolongation of the vain search for freedom, the boon that seemed ever barely to elude their grasp,—like a tantalizing will-o'-the-wisp, maddening and misleading the headless host. The holocaust of war, the terrors of the Ku-Klux Klan, the lies of carpet-baggers, the disorganization of industry, and the contradictory advice of friends and foes, left the bewildered serf with no new watchword beyond the old cry for freedom. As the time flew, however, he began to grasp a new idea. The ideal of liberty demanded for its attainment powerful means, and these the Fifteenth Amendment gave him. The ballot, which before he had looked upon as a visible sign of freedom, he now regarded as the chief means of gaining and perfecting the liberty with which war had partially endowed him. And why not? Had not votes made war and emancipated millions? Had not votes enfranchised the freedmen? Was anything impossible to a power that had done all this? A million black men started with renewed zeal to vote themselves into the kingdom. So the decade flew away, the revolution of 1876 came, and left the half-free serf weary, wondering, but still inspired. Slowly but steadily, in the following years, a new vision began gradually to replace the dream of political power,—a powerful movement, the rise of another ideal to guide the unguided, another pillar of fire by night after a clouded day. It was the ideal of "book-learning"; the curiosity, born of compulsory ignorance, to know and test the power of the cabalistic letters of the white man, the longing to know. Here at last seemed to have been discovered the mountain path to Canaan; longer than the highway of Emancipation and law, steep and rugged, but straight, leading to heights high enough to overlook life.

Up the new path the advance guard toiled, slowly, heavily, doggedly; only those who have watched and guided the faltering feet, the misty minds, the dull understandings, of the dark pupils of these schools know how faithfully, how piteously, this people strove to learn. It was weary work. The cold statistician wrote down the inches of progress here and there, noted also where here and there a foot had slipped or some one had fallen. To the tired climbers, the horizon was ever dark, the mists were often cold, the Canaan was always dim and far away. If, however, the vistas disclosed as yet no goal, no resting-place, little but flattery and criticism, the journey at least gave leisure for reflection and self-examination; it changed the child of Emancipation to the youth with dawning self-consciousness, self-realization, self-respect. In those sombre forests of his striving his own soul rose before him, and he saw himself,—darkly as through a veil; and yet he saw in himself some faint revelation of his power, of his mission. He began to have a dim feeling that, to attain his place in the world, he must be himself, and not another. For the first time he sought to analyze the burden he bore upon his back, that deadweight of social degradation partially masked behind a half-named Negro problem. He felt his poverty; without a cent, without a home, without land, tools, or savings, he had entered into competition with rich, landed, skilled neighbors. To be a poor man is hard, but to be a poor race in a land of dollars is the very bottom of hardships. He felt the weight of his ignorance,—not simply of letters, but of life, of business, of the humanities; the accumulated sloth and shirking and awkwardness of decades and centuries shackled his hands and feet. Nor was his burden all poverty and ignorance. The red stain of bastardy, which two centuries of systematic legal defilement of Negro women had stamped upon his race, meant not only the loss of ancient African chastity, but also the hereditary weight of a mass of corruption from white adulterers, threatening almost the obliteration of the Negro home.

A people thus handicapped ought not to be asked to race with the world, but rather allowed to give all its time and thought to its own social problems. But alas! while sociologists gleefully count his bastards and his prostitutes, the very soul of the toiling, sweating black man is darkened by the shadow of a vast despair. Men call the shadow prejudice, and learnedly explain it as the natural defence of culture against barbarism, learning against ignorance, purity against crime, the "higher" against the "lower" races. To which the Negro cries Amen! and swears that to so much of this strange prejudice as is founded on just homage to civilization, culture, righteousness, and progress, he humbly bows and meekly does obeisance. But before the nameless prejudice that leaps beyond all this he stands helpless, dismayed, and well-nigh speechless; before that personal disrespect and mockery, the ridicule and systematic humiliation, the distortion of fact and wanton license of fancy, the cynical ignoring of the better and the boisterous welcoming of the worse, the all-pervading desire to inculcate disdain for everything black, from Toussaint to the devil,—before this there rises a sickening despair that would disarm and discourage any nation save that black host to whom "discouragement" is an unwritten word.

But the facing of so vast a prejudice could not but bring the inevitable self-questioning, self-disparagement, and lowering of ideals which ever accompany repression and breed in an atmosphere of contempt and hate. Whisperings and portents came borne upon the four winds: Lo! we are diseased and dying, cried the dark hosts, we cannot write, our voting is vain; what need of education, since we must always cook and serve? And the Nation echoed and enforced this self-criticism, saying: Be content to be servants, and nothing more; what need of higher culture for half-men? Away with the black man's ballot, by force or fraud,—and behold the suicide of a race! Nevertheless, out of the evil came something of good,—the more careful adjustment of education to real life, the clearer perception of the Negroes' social responsibilities, and the sobering realization of the meaning of progress.

So dawned the time of *Sturm und Drang*: storm and stress to-day rocks our little boat on the mad waters of the world-sea; there is within and without the sound of conflict, the burning of body and rending of soul; inspiration strives with doubt, and faith with vain questionings. The bright ideals of the past,— physical freedom, political power, the training of brains and the training of hands,—all these in turn have waxed and waned, until even the last grows dim and overcast. Are they all wrong, —all false? No, not that, but each alone was oversimple and incomplete,—the dreams of a credulous race-childhood, or the fond imaginings of the other world which does not know and does not want to know our power. To be really true, all these ideals must be melted and welded into one. The training of the schools we need to-day more than ever,—the training of deft hands, quick eyes and ears, and above all the broader, deeper, higher culture of gifted minds and pure hearts. The power of the ballot we need in sheer self-defence,—else what shall save us from a second slavery? Freedom, too, the long-sought, we still seek,—the freedom of life and limb, the freedom to work and think, the freedom to love and aspire. Work, culture, liberty,— all these we need, not singly but together, not successively but together, each growing and aiding each, and all striving toward that vaster ideal that swims before the Negro people, the ideal of human brotherhood, gained through the unifying ideal of Race; the ideal of fostering and developing the traits and talents of the Negro, not in opposition to or contempt for other races, but rather in large conformity to the greater ideals of the American Republic, in order that some day on American soil two world-races may give each to each those characteristics both so sadly lack. We the darker ones come even now not altogether empty-handed: there are to-day no truer exponents of the pure human spirit of the Declaration of Independence than the American Negroes; there is no true American music but the wild sweet melodies of the Negro slave; the American fairy tales and folk-lore are Indian and African; and, all in all, we black men seem the sole oasis of simple faith and reverence in a dusty desert of dollars and smartness. Will America be poorer if she replace her brutal dyspeptic blundering with light-hearted but determined Negro humility? or her coarse and cruel wit with loving jovial good-humor? or her vulgar music with the soul of the Sorrow Songs?

Merely a concrete test of the underlying principles of the great republic is the Negro Problem, and the spiritual striving of the freedmen's sons is the travail of souls whose burden is almost beyond the measure of their strength, but who bear it in the name of an historic race, in the name of this the land of their fathers' fathers, and in the name of human opportunity.

II South: Slavery and After

Generally speaking, the black experience in America began in the South, and to a greater extent than is usually supposed remains embedded as a larger frame of reference in the black consciousness—despite the present-day dispersal of Negroes to all sections of the country. Modern black American authors have begun to relive imaginatively their Southern experience not only in terms of their own heritage but in terms of the implications of their heritage for the larger white community. The ramifications of slavery (see the pieces by Hayden, Kelley and Chesnutt) lie obviously central to this experience, and the continuing oppression of Negroes in the modern South (see Toomer and Oliver) betrays the persistence of racial attitudes acquired during the slavery period. But Albert Murray in "Stonewall Jackson's Waterloo" suggests that events that take place beyond the literal confines of the Negro community become part of the black heritage as well. Hence, despite their differences, there are a reciprocity and an interrelationship of ethnic and regional traditions in America. And these ultimately constitute a national American culture shared by all communities.

Robert Hayden

Middle Passage

1

Jesús, Estrella, Esperanza, Mercy:

Sails flashing to the wind like weapons,
sharks following the moans the fever and the dying;
horror the corposant and compass rose.

Middle Passage:
  voyage through death
      to life upon these shores.

"10 April 1800—
Blacks rebellious. Crew uneasy. Our linguist says
their moaning is a prayer for death,
ours and their own. Some try to starve themselves.
Lost three this morning leaped with crazy laughter
to the waiting sharks, sang as they went under."

Desire, Adventure, Tartar, Ann:

Standing to America, bringing home
black gold, black ivory, black seed.

  Deep in the festering hold thy father lies,
  of his bones New England pews are made,
  those are altar lights that were his eyes.

Jesus Saviour Pilot Me
Over Life's Tempestuous Sea

We pray that Thou wilt grant, O Lord,
safe passage to our vessels bringing
heathen souls unto Thy chastening.

Jesus Saviour

"8 bells. I cannot sleep, for I am sick
with fear, but writing eases fear a little
since still my eyes can see these words take shape
upon the page & so I write, as one
would turn to exorcism. 4 days scudding,
but now the sea is calm again. Misfortune
follows in our wake like sharks (our grinning
tutelary gods). Which one of us
has killed an albatross? A plague among
our blacks—Ophthalmia: blindness—& we
have jettisoned the blind to no avail.
It spreads, the terrifying sickness spreads.
Its claws have scratched sight from the Capt.'s eyes
& there is blindness is the fo'c'sle.
& we must sail 3 weeks before we come
to port."

What port awaits us, Davy Jones'
or home? I've heard of slavers drifting, drifting,
playthings of wind and storm and chance, their crews
gone blind, the jungle hatred
crawling up on deck.

Thou Who Walked on Galilee

"Deponent further sayeth *The Bella J*
left the Guinea Coast
with cargo of five hundred blacks and odd
for the barracoons of Florida:

"That there was hardly room 'tween-decks for half
the sweltering cattle stowed spoon-fashion there;
that some went mad of thirst and tore their flesh
and sucked the blood:

"That Crew and Captain lusted with the comeliest
of the savage girls kept naked in the cabins;
that there was one they called The Guinea Rose
and they cast lots and fought to lie with her:

"That when the Bo's'n piped all hands, the flames
spreading from starboard already were beyond
control, the negroes howling and their chains
entangled with the flames:

"That the burning blacks could not be reached,
that the Crew abandoned ship,
leaving their shrieking negresses behind,
that the Captain perished drunken with the wenches:

"Further Deponent sayeth not."

Pilot Oh Pilot Me

2

Aye, lad, and I have seen those factories,
Gambia, Rio Pongo, Calabar;
have watched the artful mongos baiting traps
of war wherein the victor and the vanquished

Were caught as prizes for our barracoons.
Have seen the nigger kings whose vanity
and greed turned wild black hides of Fellatah,
Mandingo, Ibo, Kru to gold for us.

And there was one—King Anthracite we named him—
fetish face beneath French parasols
of brass and orange velvet, impudent mouth
whose cups were carven skulls of enemies:

He'd honor us with drum and feast and conjo
and palm-oil-glistening wenches deft in love,
and for tin crowns that shone with paste,
red calico and German-silver trinkets

Would have the drums talk war and send
his warriors to burn the sleeping villages
and kill the sick and old and lead the young
in coffles to our factories.

Twenty years a trader, twenty years,
for there was wealth aplenty to be harvested
from those black fields, and I'd be trading still
but for the fevers melting down my bones.

3

Shuttles in the rocking loom of history,
the dark ships move, the dark ships move,
their bright ironical names
like jests of kindness on a murderer's mouth;
plough through thrashing glister toward
fata morgana's lucent melting shore,
weave toward New World littorals that are
mirage and myth and actual shore.

Voyage through death,
          voyage whose chartings are unlove.

A charnel stench, effluvium of living death
spreads outward from the hold,
where the living and the dead, the horribly dying,
lie interlocked, lie foul with blood and excrement.

   Deep in the festering hold thy father lies,
   the corpse of mercy rots with him,
   rats eat love's rotten gelid eyes.

But, oh, the living look at you
with human eyes whose suffering accuses you,
whose hatred reaches through the swill of dark
to strike you like a leper's claw.

You cannot stare that hatred down
or chain the fear that stalks the watches
and breathes on you its fetid scorching breath;
cannot kill the deep immortal human wish,
the timeless will.

"But for the storm that flung up barriers
of wind and wave, *The Amistad*, señores,
would have reached the port of Principe in two,
three days at most; but for the storm we should
have been prepared for what befell.
Swift as the puma's leap it came. There was
that interval of moonless calm filled only
with the water's and the rigging's usual sounds,
then sudden movement, blows and snarling cries
and they had fallen on us with machete
and marlinspike. It was as though the very
air, the night itself were striking us.
Exhausted by the rigors of the storm,
we were no match for them. Our men went down
before the murderous Africans. Our loyal
Celestino ran from below with gun
and lantern and I saw, before the cane-
knife's wounding flash, Cinquez,
that surly brute who calls himself a prince,
directing, urging on the ghastly work.
He hacked the poor mulatto down, and then
he turned on me. The decks were slippery
when daylight finally came. It sickens me
to think of what I saw, of how these apes
threw overboard the butchered bodies of
our men, true Christians all, like so much jetsam.
Enough, enough. The rest is quickly told:

Cinquez was forced to spare the two of us
you see to steer the ship to Africa,
and we like phantoms doomed to rove the sea
voyaged east by day and west by night,
deceiving them, hoping for rescue,
prisoners on our own vessel, till
at length we drifted to the shores of this
your land, America, where we were freed
from our unspeakable misery. Now we
demand, good sirs, the extradition of
Cinquez and his accomplices to La
Havana. And it distresses us to know
there are so many here who seem inclined
to justify the mutiny of these blacks.
We find it paradoxical indeed
that you whose wealth, whose tree of liberty
are rooted in the labor of your slaves
should suffer the august John Quincy Adams
to speak with so much passion of the right
of chattel slaves to kill their lawful masters
and with his Roman rhetoric weave a hero's
garland for Cinquez. I tell you that
we are determined to return to Cuba
with our slaves and there see justice done. Cinquez—
or let us say 'the Prince'—Cinquez shall die."

The deep immortal human wish,
the timeless will:

    Cinquez its deathless primaveral image,
    life that transfigures many lives.

  Voyage through death
              to life upon these shores.

William Melvin Kelley

*The African**

Like I said, nobody's claiming this story is all truth. It
must-a started out that way, but somebody along the way or
a whole parcel of somebodies must-a figured they could im-
prove on the truth. And they did. It's a damn sight better story
for being half lies. Can't a story be good without some lies.
You take the story of Samson. Might not all be true as you
read it in the Bible; folks must-a figured if you got a man just
a little bit stronger than most, it couldn't do no real harm if
you make him a whole lot stronger. So that's probably what
folks hereabouts did; take the African, who must-a been pretty
big and strong to start and make him even bigger and stronger.

I reckon they wanted to make certain we'd remember him.
But when you think on it, there's no reason why we'd ever forget the African, even though this all happened a long time ago,
because just like Tucker Caliban, the African was working for
the Willsons, who was the most important folks around these
parts. Only folks liked those Willsons a hell of a lot more in
them days than we do now. They weren't so uppity as our Willsons.

But we're not talking about the Willsons of nowadays; we're
talking about the African, who was owned by the General's
father, Dewitt Willson, even though Dewitt never got no work
out of him. But he owned him all the same.

Now the first time New Marsails (it was still New MAR-
SEILLES then, after the French city) ever saw the African was

* From A *Different Drummer*, 1962. The title of this selection
was supplied by the editor.

29

in the morning, just after the slave ship he was riding pulled into the harbor. In them days, a boat coming was always a big occasion and folks used to walk down to the dock to greet it; it wasn't a far piece since the town wasn't no bigger than Sutton is today.

The slaver came up, her sails all plump, and tied up, and let fall her gangplank. And the ship's owner, who was also the leading slave auctioneer in New Marsails—he talked so good and so fast he could sell a one-armed, one-legged, half-witted Negro for a premium price—he ambled up the gangplank. I'm told he was a spindly fellow, with no muscles whatever. He had hard-bargain-driving eyes and a nose all round and puffy and pocked like a rotten orange, and he always wore a blue old-time suit with lace at the collar, and a sort of derby of green felt. And following him, exactly three paces behind, was a Negro. Some folks said this was the auctioneer's son by a colored woman. I don't know that for certain, but I DO know this here Negro looked, walked, and talked just like his master. He had that same build, and the same crafty eyes, and dressed just like him too—green derby and all—so that the two of them looked like a print and a negative of the same photograph, since the Negro was brown and had kinky hair. This Negro was the auctioneer's bookkeeper and overseer and anything else you can think of. So then these two went up on deck, and while the Negro stood by, the auctioneer shook hands with the captain, who was standing on deck watching his men do their chores. You understand, they spoke different in them days, so I can't be certain exactly what they said, but I reckon it was something like: "How do. How was the trip?"

Already some folks standing on the dock could see the captain looked kind of sick. "Fine, excepting we had one real ornery son of a bitch. Had to chain him up, alone, away by himself."

"Let's have a look at him," said the auctioneer. The Negro behind him nodded, which he did every time the auctioneer spoke, so that he looked like he was a ventriloquist, and the auctioneer was his dummy, either that way or the other way around.

"Not yet. God damn! I'll bring him up after the rest of them niggers is OFF the boat. Then we can ALL hold him down. Damn!" He put his hand up to his brow, and that's when folks with good eyes could see the oily blue mark on his head like somebody spat axle grease on him and he hadn't had time yet to wipe it off. "God damn!" he said again.

Well, of course folks was getting real anxious, not just out of common interest like usual, but to see this son of a bitch that was causing all the trouble.

Dewitt Willson was there too. He hadn't come to see the boat, or even to buy slaves. He was there to pick up a grandfather clock. He was building himself a new house outside of Sutton and he'd ordered this clock from Europe and he wanted it to come as fast as possible, and the fastest way was for it to come by slaver. He'd heard how carrying things on a slaver was seven kinds of bad luck, but still, because he was so anxious to get the clock, he let them send it that way. The clock rode in the captain's cabin and was all padded up with cotton, and boxed in, and crated around, and wadded secure. And he'd come to get it, bringing in a wagon to carry it out to his house and surprise his wife with it.

Dewitt and everybody was waiting, but first the crew went down and cracked their whips and herded this long line of Negroes out of the hold. The women had breasts hanging most down to their waists, and some carried black babies. The men, their faces was all twisted up sullen as the inside of lemons. Most all the slaves was bone-naked and they stood on the deck, blinking; none of them had seen the sun in a long time. The auctioneer and his Negro walked up and down the row, as always, inspecting teeth, feeling muscles, looking over the goods, you might say. Then the auctioneer said, "Well, let's bring up this troublemaker, what say."

"No, sir!" yelled the captain.

"Why not?"

"I told you. I don't want him brung up until the rest of these niggers is off the boat."

"Yes, surely," said the auctioneer, but looked sort of blank. And so did his Negro.

The captain rubbed that shining grease-spot wound. "Don't you understand? He's their chief. If he says the word we'll have more trouble here than God has followers. I had enough already!" And he rubbed that spot again.

The crewmen pushed them Negroes down the gangplank and the folks on the dock stepped out of the way and watched them go by. Them Negroes even SMELLED angry, having been crammed together, each of them with no more room to himself than a baby in a crib. They was dirty, and mad, and ready for a fight. So the captain sent down some crewmen with rifles to keep them company. And the other crewmen, twenty or thirty there was, they just stood on deck fidgeting and shuffling. Folks on the dock knew right off what was the matter: them crewmen was afraid. You could see it in their eyes. All them grown men scared of whatever was down in the hold of that boat chained to the wall.

The captain looked sort of scared himself and fingered his wound and sighed and said to his mate: "I reckon you might as well go down there and get him." And to the twenty or thirty men standing around: "You go down there with him—all of you. Maybe you can manage."

Folks held their breath like youngsters at a circus waiting for a high-wire fellow to make it to his nest, because even if an old deaf-blind lady had-a been standing on that dock, she would-a known there was something down in the hold that was getting ready to make an appearance. Everybody got quiet and over the waves slapping against the hull they could hear all them crewmen tramping downstairs, the whole swarm of them in heavy brogans, taking their time about informing that thing in the hold it was wanted on deck.

Then, out of the bottom of the ship, way off in some dark place, came this roar, louder'n a cornered bear or maybe two bears mating. It was so loud the sides of the boat bulged out. They all knew it was from one throat since there wasn't no blending, just one loud sound. And then, right in front of their eyes, in the side of the boat, way down near the water line, they saw a hole tear open, and splinters fly, splashing like when you toss a handful of pebbles into a pond. There was a lot of muffled fighting, pushing, and hollering going on, and after a while this fellow staggered on deck with blood dripping from his head. "God damn—if he ain't pulled his chain outen the wall of the boat," he says. And everybody stared at that hold again, and didn't take note that the crewman had just passed on from a cracked skull.

Well sir, you can believe that folks got into close knots for protection in case that thing in the bottom of the ship should somehow get loose and start a-raging through the peaceful town of New Marsails. Then it got sort of quiet again, even on the inside of the ship, and folks leaned forward, listening. They heard chains dragging and then they saw the African for the first time.

To begin with, they seen his head coming up out of the gang-way, and then his shoulders, so broad he had to climb those stairs sideways; then his body began, and long after it should-a stopped it was still coming. Then he was full out, skin-naked except for a rag around his parts, standing at least two heads taller than any man on the deck. He was black and glistened like the captain's grease-spot wound. His head was as large as one of them kettles you see in a cannibal movie and looked as heavy. There was so many chains hung on him he looked like a fully trimmed Christmas tree. But it was his eyes they kept looking at; sunk deep in his head they was, making it look like a gigantic black skull.

There was something under his arm. At first they thought it was a tumor or growth and didn't pay it no mind, and it wasn't until it moved all by itself and they noticed it had eyes that they saw it was a baby. Yes sir, a baby tucked under his arm like a black lunch box, just peeping out at everybody.

So now they'd seen the African, and they stepped back a little as if the distance between him and them wasn't at all far enough, as if he could reach out over the railing of the ship, and down at them and pop off their heads with a flick of his fingers. But he was quiet now, not blinking in the sun like them others, just basking like it was his very own and he'd ordered it to come out and shine on him.

Dewitt Willson just stared. It was hard to tell what he was

thinking but some folks said they heard him saying slowly to himself over and over again: "I'll own him. He'll work for me. I'll break him. I have to break him." They said he just stared and talked to himself.

And the auctioneer's Negro, he just stared too. But he wasn't mumbling or talking. Folks said he just looked like he was pricing something—looking at the African from head to toe and adding totals: so much for the head and the brain; so much for the build and the muscles; so much for the eyes—making notes on a piece of paper with a crayon.

The captain had yelled down to his men to get them Negroes over to the auction place, a mound of dirt in the center of New Marsails in what is now Auction Square. Some men cleared a way and some others came down off the boat and started pushing the line of chained Negroes. Then came all the people on the dock who was going over to the Square to see what the going price for a good slave was on that day, like folks read the stock market reports nowadays, and more important, to see how much the African would sell for. And after they'd gone away some, came the African and his escort, twenty men at least, each holding a chain so he looked like a Maypole with all the men around him in a circle staying a good healthy distance out of his reach.

When they got to the Square they pulled them other Negroes way off to one side and the African and his attendants went right up on the hill. Then the auctioneer, with his Negro behind him those same three steps, started his selling:

"Now folks, you see here before you about the most magnificent piece of property any man'd ever want to own. Note the height, the breadth, the weight; note the extraordinary muscular development, the regal bearing. This is a chief so he's got to have great leadership ability. He's gentle with children as you may be able to see there under his arm. True, he's capable of destruction, but I maintain this is merely a sign of his ability to get a job done. I don't think you need any proof of all I say; just to look at him is proof enough. Why, if I didn't own him already, and if I had a farm or a plantation, I'd sell half my land

and all my slaves just to scrape up enough money to buy him to work the other half. But I DO own him, and I don't have any land. That's my problem. I can't use him; I don't need him; I got to get rid of him. And that's where you come in, friends. One of you has to take him off my hands. I'll pay you for that kindness. Yes, sir! Don't let anybody tell you I'm not grateful for the good turns my friends do for me. What I'll do is this: I'll toss right in this deal, at two for the price of one, that little baby he's got under his arm."

(Now some folks said they found out later the auctioneer HAD to make that deal, since it was the captain who'd tried in the first place to get that baby from the African, and that's how come he'd got his head smashed. So I reckon the auctioneer couldn't very well sell them two as separated items without having to kill one to get the other.)

"Now, you know that's a bargain," he was going on to say, "because that baby will grow up to be just like his daddy. So now just picture it: when this here man gets too old to work, you'll have his spitting image all set to take over for him.

"I reckon you must know I'm not very sharp when it comes to prices and costs, but I'd say right off this here worker shouldn't go for less than five hundred dollars. What say, Mister Willson, you figure he's worth that much?"

Dewitt Willson didn't answer, didn't say nothing, just reached into his pocket and pulled out one thousand cash, as calm as you'd pick lint off a suit, walked halfway up the hill and handed that money to the auctioneer.

The auctioneer rapped his green derby against his knee. "Sold!"

Nobody, not even folks what claims to-a seen it, is really certain about what happened next. It must-a been them crewmen, who was still holding all them chains, relaxed when they saw all that money, because the African spun around once and nobody was holding nothing except maybe a fist full of blood and skin where them chains had rushed through like a buzz saw. And now the African was holding ALL them chains, had gathered them up like a woman grabs up her skirts climbing into an

auto, and right off he started for the auctioneer like he understood what that man was saying and doing, which could not-a
been since he was African and likely spoke that gibberish them
Africans use. But leastways, he DID go after the auctioneer and
some folks swears, though not all, that, using his chains, he
sliced his head off—derby and all—and that the head sailed like
a cannon ball through the air a quarter mile, bounced another
quarter mile and still had up enough steam to cripple a horse
some fellow was riding into New Marsails. Fellow came into
town babbling about having to shoot his horse after its leg got
splintered by a flying head wearing a green derby.

Some strange things happened just then. The auctioneer's
Negro, who'd taken a step or two back when the African got
loose and didn't seem to take notice of the headless auctioneer
except to make certain he didn't have no blood splattered on
him to ruin his clothes, he ran up to the African, who was just
standing near the body which hadn't even had time to fall yet,
and grabbed his arm and pointed and started yelling: "This
way! This way!"

I reckon the African didn't really understand but he knew
the Negro was trying to help him and started out in the direction the Negro was pointing, and the Negro followed him just
like he'd followed the auctioneer, a distance of three steps back,
and the African ran down off the hill though he must-a been
carrying close to three hundred pounds of chains on him, swinging them, breaking seven or eight arms and a leg, carving himself and the Negro a path through the townspeople of New
Marsails. Some men raised rifles and took aim, and maybe
could-a hit them (not saying, mind you, they could-a stopped
the African), but Dewitt Willson ran up on the hill like a crazy
man, and got between the men and the African and Negro,
screaming all the while: "Don't shoot my property! I'll sue!
That's my property!" And by that time the African was out of
range and heading south into the swamps at the end of town.
So the men and Dewitt got horses and more rifles and after a
while set out after him.

The African was traveling pretty fast (he must-a been carrying not only his baby and the chains but the Negro too because

I don't see how that small Negro could-a kept up), and Dewitt and the men might-a never trailed him except that he went straight through the woods and swamps and left this trail of torn-up bushes, grass, and small trees where them chains had caught on things and he'd pulled them right out of the ground, heading straight for the sea. They just set out on this trail, wide enough for two horses to go abreast, as straight as a plumb line, and followed it through the swamp, right down to the sand and into the water. That's where it stopped.

The men figured the African must-a just tried to swim back home (some said he could-a made it—chains, baby and all) and that auctioneer's Negro must-a lit out on his own, and now they was sort of tired and wanted to go home and forget about it, but Dewitt was sure the African wasn't gone, not swimming, and was coming back, and got the men to look up and down the beach for some sign. They did, and half mile down the beach they found two sets of tracks going into the woods.

Right about now it got hard for Dewitt Willson to get men to help him chase his property. First of all, it was getting dark. Second of all, there wasn't no wide trail like before because the African must-a been holding them chains off the ground so they wouldn't catch on anything, like a little girl holds up her skirts around her waist when she goes wading. So the men just naturally cooled down when it came to tracking a wild man through the woods at night when, at best, it would be hard to see him and when you couldn't be sure where he was, and he could pay you a visit and slice off your head even before you knew he was calling. So they camped on the beach, and some men went for supplies and at daybreak they took out after him again.

But that one night was all the time the African and the auctioneer's Negro needed and it was going to be harder than ever to catch him now because when they came into a clearing about a mile into the woods, shining in the sun was a pile of broken stones, and links, and bracelets where the African had spent the night cleaning them off himself. So now he was loose, free of his chains, and was somewhere in the area. He was so big and so fast you didn't dare make a guess at WHERE he might be, since folks began to realize he could-a been anywhere within a distance of a hundred miles. But Dewitt, with fewer men now, kept going and tracked his property for two weeks, halfway to where Willson City is now, and back, which is a total of two hundred miles, and all along the Gulf Coast almost to Mississippi and the other way into Alabama, and finally, those men still with Dewitt noticed he was looking sort of funny. He didn't sleep at all, or eat, spent twenty-four hours a day on his horse and was talking to himself, saying: "I'll catch you . . . I'll catch you . . . I'll catch you." And then, nearly a month after the African got away, in which time Dewitt hadn't been home at all, while the men watched, he keeled off his horse and didn't wake up until they'd taken him home in a litter to his plantation and he'd slept in a featherbed for another week. His wife told folks he kept right on talking to himself and when he did wake up, he came up screaming: "But I am. I'm worth a thousand too! I am!"

Now the African changed his tactics.

One afternoon Dewitt and his wife was sitting on their front porch. Dewitt was trying to get back his strength by sipping something cool and taking in the sun. And up the front lawn, dressed in African clothes of bright colors, with a spear and a shield, comes the African, bearing down on the house like he was a train and it was a tunnel and he was going right through —which he did, on out the back door, across the back lawn to the slave quarters, where he freed every last one of Dewitt's Negroes and led them off into the dark of the woods before Dewitt could even set down his glass and get up out of his chair.

Well, if that wasn't enough, the next night almost the same thing happened to a fellow east of New Marsails. He came into town and told everybody about it: "I was sleeping peaceful when I heared this noise outside down by the slave cabins. God damn, when I rushed to the window if I didn't see all my niggers heading into the woods behind a man who was as big anyways as a black horse on its hind legs. And there was another one too," the fellow went on, "never more than a few steps behind the big one, waving his arms and telling MY niggers what to do and where to go."

Even though he was still ailing, Dewitt Willson came into

town and stood up in front of a big meeting they was holding to try and solve the problem and said: "Now I swear to you, I'm not going home until I can take the African or what's left of him with me. And let everybody know this: white or black, anybody who can give me news that'll help me catch the African will be walking around the next day with a thousand of my dollars in his pocket." And that news spread like the smell of cooking cabbage, spread all up and down the region so that years after, if you'd gone into Tennessee and mentioned you was from down this way, somebody'd ask: "Say, who DID get Dewitt Willson's thousand?"

Dewitt Willson kept his word; he set out after the African again. He tracked and trailed him for another month all over the state. Sometimes they'd come pretty close to getting him too, but not quite close enough. They'd come on him and his band, which they managed to thin out and keep down to twelve or so what with killing and capturings, and have a battle, but the African'd always wriggle out some way. One time they thought they had him trapped with his back to the river and he just turned around, dove in and swam it underwater. And you know some fellows can't even throw a stone that far. They could never get their hands on that auctioneer's Negro neither. He was always around, holding the baby while the African fought, looking at what went on out of them money-filled eyes which gleamed under that green derby. Yes sir, he still had the derby, though nothing else, was dressed now like the African in one of them long, multicolored sheets.

Dewitt was changing again, doing the same things he'd done before he collapsed, not talking to anybody, not even to himself now, moody and silent all the time. And so it went on, the African raiding and freeing slaves, Dewitt Willson catching up with the band and taking most of the slaves back and killing more, keeping the African's men down to twelve or thirteen, and the African and the auctioneer's Negro never getting caught.

Then one night they was camped a little north of New Marsails. Everybody was asleep except Dewitt, who was sitting on his horse looking into the fire. He heard a voice behind him, what seemed like it could-a been the voice of the auctioneer's ghost, but wasn't. "You want the African? I'll take you to him."

Dewitt turned around and saw the auctioneer's Negro standing there, wearing his sheet and his derby; he'd got into camp without being heard or seen.

"Where is he?" Dewitt asked.

"I'll take you to him. I'll go up to him and slap him on the cheek if you want it that way," said the Negro.

So Dewitt went. He said later he wasn't sure he'd done the right thing following that Negro because it could-a been an ambush or a trap. But he said, too, he didn't think the African'd do something like that. Some of the men with him said Dewitt was crazy enough by that time to do anything to catch the African, would-a gone anywhere with anyone to get him.

So Dewitt roused his men, and they rode out after the Negro. They didn't have to go more than a mile before they came into the African's camp. There was no fire and the Negroes, maybe twelve, was lying on the bare ground with no cover, sleeping. Right in the middle of the clearing, his back against a huge rock, the black baby across his knees, sat the African. He had a cloth over his head and set up in front of him was a pile of stones, which he seemed to be a-mumbling at.

Dewitt Willson couldn't figure out why no one'd warned the African, how come he'd been able to sneak up on him, and leaned down to the Negro and said: "Why aren't there no guards? He knew I was right close by. Why aren't there no guards?"

The Negro smiled up at him. "There WAS one guard. Me."

"Why'd you do this? Why'd you turn on him?"

The Negro smiled again. "I'm an American; I'm no savage. And besides, a man's got to follow where his pocket takes him, doesn't he?"

Dewitt Willson nodded. Some folks said he almost turned around and went back to his own camp and wanted to forget all about catching his property this way and then come back in the morning when the African would be gone and chase him until he caught him fair and square, because it seems like after all those weeks of chasing the African through the woods, after all that time of following his trail and thinking maybe he'd get him this time and finding he didn't any more have him than a dwarf has a chance of being a professional basketball player, after all the sweating and riding and bad food and hard sleeping, he'd come to respect this man, and I reckon, he must-a been a little sad that when he finally caught up with his property it was because some fellow the African'd trusted would turncoat and lead the white men into camp. But the other men didn't feel that way. They wanted the African any way they could get him because he'd been making fools of them and they knew it and they wanted an end to that.

So the white men circled the camp and when they had it surrounded, Dewitt Willson called out for the Negroes to give up. The white men lit torches so the African could see he was ringed by fire, horses, and men with rifles. The Negroes jumped to their feet and right away saw it wasn't no use, since all they had was African weapons, and they threw them down on the ground. But the African bolted up on top of the rock straddling the baby and made a full circle taking stock of what he was up against because he was alone and he knew it, since by then all the Negroes had scattered into the bushes or were standing around like they'd never seen him before and didn't know him from a third-century Roman Catholic Pope.

There he stood on the rock, alone, glistening in the fire, almost naked, his eyes just hollows of black. Then he stepped down. Someone raised a rifle.

"Wait!" Dewitt shouted. "See if we can take him alive. Don't you understand? That's the point. Take him alive!" He was standing up in his stirrups waving his arms for attention in the firelight.

Some fellow took this to mean that he should be a hero, and thinking he could run down the African, raced his horse straight at him, but the African just grabbed the fellow off the horse's back like you might catch a ring on a carousel and popped his back over his knee like a dry wishbone and tossed him aside.

"If you shoot, aim for his limbs," Dewitt was yelling.

Someone from the other side of the circle fired, and they

could see the bullet go right through the African's hand and dig into the ground near Dewitt's horse, but the African didn't seem to connect the report with any pain he might-a felt in his hand, didn't even wince or move. Someone else shot him just above the knee and blood ran down his leg like a ribbon.

Keeping his back to the rock, where the baby was sleeping, he made a full, slow circle, eying them all, eying the auctioneer's Negro too, who was standing next to Dewitt, but not stopping at him, or showing any anger or bitterness, stopping only when he came to Dewitt Willson and staring at him. They stared at each other, not like they was trying to stare each other down, more like they was discussing something without using words. And finally it seemed like they came to an agreement because the African bowed slightly like a fighter bows at the beginning of a match, and Dewitt Willson raised his rifle, sighted the African's upturned face, and shot him cleanly just above the bridge of his wide nose.

It hit him all right, but the African just stood there, and then finally sunk to his knees, and then forward on his hands. He seemed to be melting away, and then suddenly, he looked up with shock on his face, like he'd just remembered something and had to do it before he passed on, and gave a loud wail, and started crawling toward the sleeping baby, his eyes filled with blood, and a good-sized rock in his fist. He raised the rock above the baby, but Dewitt Willson shattered the back of his head before he could smash it down. And so the African died.

None of the men moved. They sat, disappointed, on their horses because they, each of them, had wanted to go back and say they'd gotten the bullet into the African what had killed him.

Dewitt Willson climbed down off his horse, walked to the baby, which was still sleeping, not knowing his daddy was dead, not knowing, I reckon, his daddy'd ever been alive. Coming back to his horse, Dewitt tripped over that pile of stones the African'd been talking to. They was all very flat stones, and Dewitt Willson stared down at them for a long time, and after a while he bent over, picked up the smallest one, a white one, and put it in his pocket.

Charles W. Chesnutt

Po' Sandy

On the northeast corner of my vineyard in central North Carolina, and fronting on the Lumberton plank-road, there stood a small frame house, of the simplest construction. It was built of pine lumber, and contained but one room, to which one window gave light and one door admission. Its weather-beaten sides revealed a virgin innocence of paint. Against one end of the house, and occupying half its width, there stood a huge brick chimney: the crumbling mortar had left large cracks between the bricks; the bricks themselves had begun to scale off in large flakes, leaving the chimney sprinkled with unsightly blotches. These evidences of decay were but partially concealed by a creeping vine, which extended its slender branches hither and thither in an ambitious but futile attempt to cover the whole chimney. The wooden shutter, which had once protected the unglazed window, had fallen from its hinges, and lay rotting in the rank grass and jimson-weeds beneath. This building, I learned when I bought the place, had been used as a schoolhouse for several years prior to the breaking out of the war, since which time it had remained unoccupied, save when some stray cow or vagrant hog had sought shelter within its walls from the chill rains and nipping winds of winter.

One day my wife requested me to build her a new kitchen. The house erected by us, when we first came to live upon the vineyard, contained a very conveniently arranged kitchen; but for some occult reason my wife wanted a kitchen in the back yard, apart from the dwelling-house, after the usual Southern fashion. Of course I had to build it.

To save expense, I decided to tear down the old school-house, and use the lumber, which was in a good state of preservation, in the construction of the new kitchen. Before demolishing the old house, however, I made an estimate of the amount of material contained in it, and found that I would have to buy several hundred feet of lumber additional, in order to build the new kitchen according to my wife's plan.

One morning old Julius McAdoo, our colored coachman, harnessed the gray mare to the rockaway, and drove my wife and me over to the sawmill from which I meant to order the new lumber. We drove down the long lane which led from our house to the plank-road; following the plank-road for about a mile, we turned into a road running through the forest and across the swamp to the sawmill beyond. Our carriage jolted over the half-rotted corduroy road which traversed the swamp, and then climbed the long hill leading to the sawmill. When we reached the mill, the foreman had gone over to a neighboring farmhouse, probably to smoke or gossip, and we were compelled to await his return before we could transact our business. We remained seated in the carriage, a few rods from the mill, and watched the leisurely movements of the mill-hands. We had not waited long before a huge pine log was placed in position, the machinery of the mill was set in motion, and the circular saw began to eat its way through the log, with a loud whir which resounded throughout the vicinity of the mill. The sound rose and fell in a sort of rhythmic cadence, which, heard from where we sat, was not unpleasing, and not loud enough to prevent conversation. When the saw started on its second journey through the log, Julius observed, in a lugubrious tone, and with a perceptible shudder:—

"Ugh! but dat des do cuddle my blood!"

"What's the matter, Uncle Julius?" inquired my wife, who is of a very sympathetic turn of mind. "Does the noise affect your nerves?"

"No, Mis' Annie," replied the old man, with emotion, "I ain' narvous; but dat saw, a-cuttin' en grindin' thoo dat stick er timber, en moanin', en groanin', en sweekin', kyars my

'memb'ance back ter ole times, en 'min's me er po' Sandy."
The pathetic intonation with which he lengthened out the "po'
Sandy" touched a responsive chord in our own hearts.

"And who was poor Sandy?" asked my wife, who takes a deep
interest in the stories of plantation life which she hears from
the lips of the older colored people. Some of these stories are
quaintly humorous; others wildly extravagant, revealing the Ori-
ental cast of the negro's imagination; while others, poured freely
into the sympathetic ear of a Northern-bred woman, disclose
many a tragic incident of the darker side of slavery.

"Sandy," said Julius, in reply to my wife's question, "was a
nigger w'at useter b'long ter ole Mars Marrabo McSwayne.
Mars Marrabo's place wuz on de yuther side'n de swamp, right
nex' ter yo' place. Sandy wus a monst'us good nigger, en could
do so many things erbout a plantation, en alluz 'ten' ter his
wuk so well, dat w'en Mars Marrabo's chilluns growed up en
married off, dey all un 'em wanted day daddy fer ter gin 'em
Sandy fer a weddin' present. But Mars Marrabo knowed de res'
wouldn' be satisfied ef he gin Sandy ter a'er one un 'em; so
w'en dey wuz all done married, he fix it by 'lowin' one er his
chilluns ter take Sandy fer a mont' er so, en den ernudder for a
mont' er so, en so on dat erway tel dey had all had 'im de same
lenk er time; en den dey would all take him roun' ag'in, 'cep'n'
oncet in a w'ile w'en Mars Marrabo would len' 'im ter some er
his yuther kinfolks 'roun' de country, w'en dey wuz short er
han's; tel bimeby it go so Sandy did n' hardly knowed whar he
wuz gwine ter stay fum one week's een' ter de yuther.

"One time w'en Sandy wuz lent out ez yushal, a spekilater
come erlong wid a lot er niggers, en Mars Marrabo swap'
Sandy's wife off fer a noo 'oman. W'en Sandy come back, Mars
Marrabo gin 'im a dollar, en 'lowed he wuz monst'us sorry fer
ter break up de fambly, but de spekilater had gin 'im big boot,
en times wuz hard en money skase, en so he wuz bleedst ter
make de trade. Sandy tuk on some 'bout losin' his wife, but he
soon seed dey want no use cryin' ober split merlasses; en bein'
ez he lacked de looks er de noo 'oman, he tuk up wid her atter
she'd be'n on de plantation a mont' er so.

"Sandy en his noo wife got on mighty well tergedder, en de niggers all 'mence' ter talk about how lovin' dey wuz. W'en Tenie wuz tuk sick oncet, Sandy useter set up all night wid 'er, en den go ter wuk in de mawnin' des lack he had his reg'lar sleep; en Tenie would 'a' done anythin' in de worl' for her Sandy.

"Sandy en Tenie had n' be'n libbin' tergedder fer mo d'n two mont's befo' Mars Marrabo's old uncle, w'at libbed down in Robeson County, sent up ter fin' out ef Mars Marrabo could n' len' 'im er hire 'im a good han' fer a mont' er so. Sandy's marster wuz one er dese yer easy-gwine folks w'at wanter please eve'ybody, en he says yas, he could len' 'im Sandy. En Mars Marrabo tol' Sandy fer ter git ready ter go down ter Robeson nex' day, fer ter stay a mont' er so.

"It wuz monst'us hard on Sandy fer ter take 'im 'way fum Tenie. It wuz so fur down ter Robeson dat he did n' hab no chance er comin' back ter see her tel de time wuz up; he would n' 'a' mine comin' ten er fifteen mile at night ter see Tenie, but Mars Marrabo's uncle's plantation wuz mo' d'n forty mile off. Sandy wuz mighty sad en cas' down atter w'at Mars Marrabo tol' 'im, en he says ter Tenie, sezee:—

" 'I'm gettin' monst'us ti'ed er dish yer gwine roun' so much. Here I is lent ter Mars Jeems dis mont', en I got ter do so-en-so; en ter Mars Archie de nex' mont', en I got ter do so-en-so; den I got ter go ter Miss Jinnie's: en hit's Sandy dis en Sandy dat, en Sandy yer en Sandy dere, tel it 'pears ter me I ain' got no home, ner no marster, ner no mistiss, ner no nuffin. I can't eben keep a wife: my yuther ole 'oman wuz sol' away widout my gittin' a chance fer ter tell her good-by; en now I got ter go off en leab you, Tenie, en I dunno whe'r I'm eber gwine ter see you ag'in er no. I wisht I wuz a tree, er a stump, er a rock, er sump'n w'at could stay on de plantation fer a w'ile.'

"Atter Sandy got thoo talkin', Tenie did n' say naer word, but des sot dere by de fier, studyin' en studyin'. Bimeby she up'n' says:—

" 'Sandy, is I eber tol' you I wuz a conjuh 'oman?'

"Co'se Sandy had n' nebber dremp' er nuffin lack dat, en he

made a great 'miration w'en he hear w'at Tenie say. Bimeby Tenie went on:—

" 'I ain' goophered nobody, ner done no cunjuh wuk, fer fifteen year er mo'; en w'en I got religion I made up my mine I would n' wuk no mo' goopher. But dey is some things I doan b'lieve it's no sin fer ter do; en ef you doan wanter be sent roun' fum pillar ter pos', en ef you doan wanter go down ter Robeson, I kin fix things so you won't haf ter. Ef you'll des say de word, I kin turn you ter w'ateber you wanter be, en you kin stay right whar you wanter, ez long ez you mineter.'

"Sandy say he doan keer; he's willin' fer ter do anythin' fer ter stay close ter Tenie. Den Tenie ax 'im ef he doan wanter be turnt inter a rabbit.

"Sandy say, 'No, de dogs mought git atter me.'

" 'Shill I turn you ter a wolf?' sez Tenie.

" 'No, eve'ybody's skeered er a wolf, en I doan want nobody ter be skeered er me.'

" 'Shill I turn you ter a mawkin'-bird?'

" 'No, a hawk mought ketch me. I wanter be turnt inter sump'n w'at 'll stay in one place.'

" 'I kin turn you ter a tree,' sez Tenie. 'You won't hab no mouf ner years, but I kin turn you back oncet in a w'ile, so you kin git sump'n ter eat, en hear w'at's gwine on.'

"Well, Sandy say dat 'll do. En so Tenie tuk 'im down by de aidge er de swamp, not fur fum de quarters, en turnt 'im inter a big pine-tree, en sot 'im out 'mongs' some yuther trees. En de nex' mawnin', ez some er de fiel' han's wuz gwine long dere, dey seed a tree w'at dey did n' 'member er habbin' seed befo'; it wuz monst'us quare, en dey wuz bleedst ter 'low dat dey had n' 'membered right, er e'se one er de saplin's had be'n growin' monst'us fas'.

"W'en Mars Marrabo 'skiver' dat Sandy wuz gone, he 'lowed Sandy had runned away. He got de dogs out, but de las' place dey could track Sandy ter wuz de foot er dat pine-tree. En dere de dogs stood en barked, en bayed, en pawed at de tree, en tried ter climb up on it; en w'en dey wuz tuk roun' thoo de swamp ter look for de scent, dey broke loose en made fer dat tree ag'in. It wuz de beatenis' thing de w'ite folks eber hearn of, en Mars Marrabo 'lowed dat Sandy must 'a' clim' up on de tree en jump' off on a mule er sump'n, en rid fur ernuff fer ter spile de scent. Mars Marrabo wanted ter 'cuse some er de yuther niggers er heppin' Sandy off, but dey all 'nied it ter de las'; en eve'ybody knowed Tenie sot too much sto' by Sandy fer ter he'p 'im run away whar she could n' nebber see 'im no mo'.

"W'en Sandy had be'n gone long ernuff fer folks ter think he done got clean away, Tenie useter go down ter de woods at night en turn 'im back, en den dey 'd slip up ter de cabin en set by de fire en talk. But dey ha' ter be monst'us keerful, er e'se somebody would 'a' seed 'em, en dat would 'a' spile' de whole thing; so Tenie alluz turnt Sandy back in de mawnin' early, befo' anybody wuz a-stirrin'.

"But Sandy did n' git erlong widout his trials en tribberlations. One day a woodpecker come erlong en 'mence' ter peck at de tree; en de nex' time Sandy wuz turnt back he had a little roun' hole in his arm, des lack a sharp stick be'n stuck in it. Atter dat Tenie sot a sparrer-hawk fer ter watch de tree; en w'en de woodpecker come erlong nex' mawnin' fer ter finish his nes', he got gobble' up mos' 'fo' he stuck his bill in de bark.

"Nudder time, Mars Marrabo sent a nigger out in de woods fer ter chop tuppentime boxes. De man chop a box in dish yer tree, en hack' de bark up two er th'ee feet, fer ter let de tuppentime run. De nex' time Sandy wuz turnt back he had a big skyar on his lef' leg, des lack it be'n skunt; en it tuk Tenie nigh 'bout all night fer ter fix a mixtry ter kyo it up. Atter dat, Tenie sot a hawnet fer ter watch de tree; en w'en de nigger come back ag'in fer ter cut ernudder box on de yuther side'n de tree, de hawnet stung 'im so hard dat de ax slip en cut his foot nigh 'bout off.

"W'en Tenie see so many things happenin' ter de tree, she 'cluded she 'd ha' ter turn Sandy ter sump'n e'se; en atter studyin' de matter ober, en talkin' wid Sandy one ebenin', she made up her mine fer ter fix up a goopher mixtry w'at would turn herse'f en Sandy ter foxes, er sump'n, so dey could run away en go some'rs whar dey could be free en lib lack w'ite folks.

"But dey ain' no tellin' w'at's gwine ter happen in dis worl'.

Tenie had got de night sot fer her en Sandy ter run away, w'en dat ve'y day one er Mars Marrabo's sons rid up ter de big house in his buggy, en say his wife wuz monst'us sick, en he want his mammy ter len' 'im a 'oman fer ter nuss his wife. Tenie's mistiss say sen' Tenie; she wuz a good nuss. Young mars wuz in a tarrible hurry fer ter git back home. Tenie wuz washin' at de big house dat day, en her mistiss say she should go right 'long wid her young marster. Tenie tried ter make some 'scuse fer ter git away en hide 'tel night, w'en she would have eve'ything fix' up fer her en Sandy; she say she wanter go ter her cabin fer ter git her bonnet. Her mistiss say it doan matter 'bout de bonnet; her head-hankcher wuz good ernuff. Den Tenie say she wanter git her bes' frock; her mistiss say no, she doan need no mo' frock, en w'en dat one got dirty she could git a clean one whar she wuz gwine. So Tenie had ter git in de buggy en go 'long wid young Mars Dunkin ter his plantation, w'ich wuz mo' d'n twenty mile away; en dey wa'n't no chance er her seein' Sandy no mo' 'tel she come back home. De po' gal felt monst'us bad 'bout de way things wuz gwine on, en she knowed Sandy mus' be a wond'rin' why she did n' come en turn 'im back no mo'.

"W'iles Tenie wuz away nussin' young Mars Dunkin's wife, Mars Marrabo tuk a notion fer ter buil' 'im a noo kitchen; en bein' ez he had lots er timber on his place, he begun ter look 'roun' fer a tree ter hab de lumber sawed out'n. En I dunno how it come to be so, but he happen fer ter hit on de ve'y tree w'at Sandy wuz turnt inter. Tenie wuz gone, en dey wa'n't nobody ner nuffin fer ter watch de tree.

"De two men w'at cut de tree down say dey nebber had sech a time wid a tree befo': dey axes would glansh off, en did n' 'pear ter make no progress thoo de wood; en of all de creakin', en shakin', en wobblin' you eber see, dat tree done it w'en it commence' ter fall. It wuz de beatenis' thing!

"W'en dey got de tree all trim' up, dey chain it up ter a timber waggin, en start fer de sawmill. But dey had a hard time gittin' de log dere: fus' dey got stuck in de mud w'en dey wuz gwine crosst de swamp, en it wuz two er th'ee hours befo' dey could git out. W'en dey start' on ag'in, de chain kep' a-comin' loose, en dey had ter keep a-stoppin' en a-stoppin' fer ter hitch de log up ag'in. W'en dey commence' ter climb de hill ter de sawmill, de log broke loose, en roll down de hill en in 'mongs' de trees, en hit tuk nigh 'bout half a day mo' ter git it haul' up ter de sawmill.

"De nex' mawnin' atter de day de tree wuz haul' ter de sawmill, Tenie come home. W'en she got back ter her cabin, de fus' thing she done wuz ter run down ter de woods en see how Sandy wuz gettin' on. W'en she seed de stump standin' dere, wid de sap runnin' out'n it, en de limbs layin' scattered roun', she nigh 'bout went out'n her min'. She run ter her cabin, en got her goopher mixtry, en den follered de track er de timber waggin ter de sawmill. She knowed Sandy could n' lib mo' d'n a minute er so ef she turnt him back, fer he wuz all chop' up so he 'd 'a' be'n bleedst ter die. But she wanted ter turn 'im back long ernuff fer ter 'splain ter 'im dat she had n' went off a-purpose, en lef' 'im ter be chop' down en sawed up. She did n' want Sandy ter die wid no hard feelin's to'ds her.

"De han's at de sawmill had des got de big log on de kerridge, en wuz startin' up de saw, w'en dey seed a 'oman runnin' up de hill, all out er bref, cryin' en gwine on des lack she wuz plumb 'stracted. It wuz Tenie; she come right inter de mill, en th'owed herse'f on de log, right in front er de saw, a-hollerin' en cryin' ter her Sandy ter fergib her, en not ter think hard er her, fer it wa'n't no fault er hern. Den Tenie 'membered de tree did n' hab no years, en she wuz gittin' ready fer ter wuk her goopher mixtry so ez ter turn Sandy back, w'en de mill-hands kotch holt er her en tied her arms wid a rope, en fasten' her to one er de posts in de sawmill; en den dey started de saw up ag'in, en cut de log up inter bo'ds en scantlin's right befo' her eyes. But it wuz mighty hard wuk; fer of all de sweekin', en moanin', en groanin', dat log done it w'iles de saw wuz a-cuttin' thoo it. De saw wuz one er dese yer ole-timey, up-en-down saws, en hit tuk longer dem days ter saw a log 'en it do now. Dey greased de saw, but dat did n' stop de fuss; hit kep' right on, tel fin'ly dey got de log all sawed up.

"W'en de oberseah w'at run de sawmill come fum breakfas', de han's up en tell him 'bout de crazy 'oman—ez dey s'posed she wuz—w'at had come runnin' in de sawmill, a-hollerin' en gwine on, en tried ter th'ow herse'f befo' de saw. En de ober-seah sent two er th'ee er de han's fer ter take Tenie back ter her marster's plantation.

"Tenie 'peared ter be out'n her min' fer a long time, en her marster ha' ter lock her up in de smoke-'ouse 'tel she got ober her spells. Mars Marrabo wuz monst'us mad, en hit would 'a' made yo' flesh crawl fer ter hear him cuss, 'caze he say de speki-later w'at he got Tenie fum had fooled 'im by wukkin' a crazy 'oman off on him. W'iles Tenie wuz lock up in de smoke-'ouse, Mars Marrabo tuk 'n' haul de lumber fum de sawmill, en put up his noo kitchen.

"W'en Tenie got quiet' down, so she could be 'lowed ter go 'roun' de plantation, she up'n' tole her marster all erbout Sandy en de pine-tree; en w'en Mars Marrabo hearn it, he 'lowed she wuz de wuss 'stracted nigger he eber hearn of. He did n' know w'at ter do wid Tenie: fus' he thought he'd put her in de po'-house; but fin'ly, seein' ez she did n' do no harm ter nobody ner nuffin, but des went 'roun' moanin', en groanin', en shakin' her head, he 'cluded ter let her stay on de plantation en nuss de little nigger chilluns w'en dey mammies wuz ter wuk in de cotton-fiel'.

"De noo kitchen Mars Marrabo buil' wuz n' much use, fer it had n' be'n put up long befo' de niggers 'mence' ter notice quare things erbout it. Dey could hear sump'n moanin' en groanin' 'bout de kitchen in de night-time, en w'en de win' would blow dey could hear sump'n a-hollerin' en sweekin' lack it wuz in great pain en sufferin'. En it got so atter a w'ile dat it wuz all Mars Marrabo's wife could do ter git a 'oman ter stay in de kitchen in de daytime long ernuff ter do de cookin'; en dey wa'n't naer nigger on de plantation w'at would n' rudder take forty dan ter go 'bout dat kitchen atter dark,—dat is, 'cep'n' Tenie; she did n' 'pear ter min' de ha'nts. She useter slip 'roun' at night, en set on de kitchen steps, en lean up agin de do'-jamb, en run on ter herse'f wid some kine er foolishness w'at nobody could n' make out; fer Mars Marrabo had th'eaten' ter sen' her off'n de plantation ef she say anything ter any er de yuther niggers 'bout de pine-tree. But somehow er 'nudder de niggers foun' out all erbout it, en dey all knowed de kitchen wuz

ha'nted by Sandy's sperrit. En bimeby hit got so Mars Marrabo's wife herse'f wuz skeered ter go out in de yard atter dark.

"W'en it come ter dat, Mars Marrabo tuk en to' de kitchen
down, en use' de lumber fer ter buil' dat ole school'ouse w'at
you er talkin' 'bout pullin' down. De school'ouse wuz n' use'
'cep'n' in de daytime, en on dark nights folks gwine 'long de
road would hear quare soun's en see quare things. Po' ole Tenie
useter go down dere at night, en wander 'round' de school'ouse;
en de niggers all 'lowed she went fer ter talk wid Sandy's sperrit.
En one winter mawnin', w'en one er de boys went ter school
early fer ter start de fire, w'at should he fin' but po' ole Tenie,
layin' on de flo', stiff, en col', en dead. Dere did n' 'pear ter be
nuffin pertickler de matter wid her,—she had des grieve' herse'f
ter def fer her Sandy. Mars Marrabo did n' shed no tears. He
thought Tenie wuz crazy, en dey wa'n't no tellin' w'at she
mought do nex'; en dey ain' much room in dis worl' fer crazy
w'ite folks, let 'lone a crazy nigger.

"Hit wa'n't long atter dat befo' Mars Marrabo sol' a piece er
his track er lan' ter Mars Dugal' McAdoo,—*my* ole marster,—
en dat's how de ole school'ouse happen to be on yo' place.
W'en de wah broke out, de school stop', en de ole school'ouse
be'n stannin' empty ever sence,—dat is, 'cep'n' fer de ha'nts. En
folks sez dat de ole school'ouse, er any yuther house w'at got
any er dat lumber in it w'at wuz sawed out'n de tree w'at Sandy
wuz turnt inter, is gwine ter be ha'nted tel de las' piece er plank
is rotted en crumble' inter dus'.'"

Annie had listened to this gruesome narrative with strained
attention.

"What a system it was," she exclaimed, when Julius had finished, "under which such things were possible!"

"What things?" I asked, in amazement. "Are you seriously
considering the possibility of a man's being turned into a tree?"

"Oh, no," she replied quickly, "not that"; and then she murmured absently, and with a dim look in her fine eyes, "Poor
Tenie!"

We ordered the lumber, and returned home. That night,
after we had gone to bed, and my wife had to all appearances

been sound asleep for half an hour, she startled me out of an incipient doze by exclaiming suddenly,—

"John, I don't believe I want my new kitchen built out of the lumber in that old schoolhouse."

"You wouldn't for a moment allow yourself," I replied, with some asperity, "to be influenced by that absurdly impossible yarn which Julius was spinning to-day?"

"I know the story is absurd," she replied dreamily, "and I am not so silly as to believe it. But I don't think I should ever be able to take any pleasure in that kitchen if it were built out of that lumber. Besides, I think the kitchen would look better and last longer if the lumber were all new."

Of course she had her way. I bought the new lumber, though not without grumbling. A week or two later I was called away from home on business. On my return, after an absence of several days, my wife remarked to me,—

"John, there has been a split in the Sandy Run Colored Baptist Church, on the temperance question. About half the members have come out from the main body, and set up for themselves. Uncle Julius is one of the seceders, and he came to me yesterday and asked if they might not hold their meetings in the old schoolhouse for the present."

"I hope you didn't let the old rascal have it," I returned, with some warmth. I had just received a bill for the new lumber I had bought.

"Well," she replied, "I couldn't refuse him the use of the house for so good a purpose."

"And I'll venture to say," I continued, "that you subscribed something toward the support of the new church?"

She did not attempt to deny it.

"What are they going to do about the ghost?" I asked, somewhat curious to know how Julius would get around this obstacle.

"Oh," replied Annie, "Uncle Julius says that ghosts never disturb religious worship, but that if Sandy's spirit *should* happen to stray into meeting by mistake, no doubt the preaching would do it good."

Heywood Ford *

The Red-Bone Hound

White folks, . . . I's gonna tell you a story 'bout a mean over-seer and what happened to him during the slavery days. It all commenced when a nigger named Jake Williams got a whupping for staying out after the time on his pass done give out. All the niggers on the place hated the overseer worse than pizen, 'cause he was so mean and used to try to think up things to whup us for.

One morning the slaves was lined up ready to eat their breakfast, and Jake Williams was a-petting his old red-bone hound. 'Bout that time the overseer come up and seed Jake a-petting his hound, and he say: "Nigger, you ain't got time to be a-fooling 'long that dog. Now make him git." Jake tried to make the dog go home, but the dog didn't want to leave Jake. Then the overseer pick up a rock and slam the dog in the back. The dog, he then went a-howling off.

That night Jake, he come to my cabin and he say to me: "Heywood, I is gonna run away to a free state. I ain't a-gonna put up with this treatment no longer. I can' stand much more." I gives him my hand, and I say: "Jake, I hopes you gits there. Maybe I'll see you again sometime."

"Heywood," he says, "I wish you'd look after my hound Belle. Feed her and keep her the best you can. She a mighty good possum and coon dog. I hates to part with her, but I knows that you is the best person I could leave her with." And

---

* Ford, a former slave, gave this story to an interviewer from the Slave Narrative Collection of the Federal Writers' Project in the 1930's.

with that Jake slip out the door, and I seed him a-walking toward the swamp down the long furrows of corn.

It didn't take that overseer long to find out that Jake done
run away, and when he did, he got out the bloodhounds and
started off after him. It wa'n't long afore Jake heard them
hounds a-howling in the distance. Jake, he was too tired to go
any further. He circled round and doubled on his tracks so as to
confuse the hounds and then he clumb a tree. 'Twa'n't long
afore he seed the light of the overseer coming through the
woods, and the dogs was a-gitting closer and closer. Finally they
smelled the tree that Jake was in, and they started barking
round it. The overseer lift his lighted pine knot in the air so's
he could see Jake. He say, "Nigger, come on down from there.
You done wasted 'nough of our time." But Jake, he never
move nor make a sound, and all the time the dogs kept a-
howling and the overseer kept a-swearing. "Come on down," he
say again. "Iffen you don't I's coming up and knock you outen
the tree with a stick." Jake, still he never moved, and the overseer began to climb the tree. When he got where he could almost reach Jake, he swung that stick, and it come down on
Jake's leg and hurt him terrible. Jake, he raised his foot and
kicked the overseer right in the mouth, and that white man
went a-tumbling to the ground. When he hit the earth, them
hounds pounced on him. Jake, he then lowered hisself to the
bottom limbs so's he could see what had happened. He saw the
dogs a-tearing at the man and he holler: "Hold him, Belle! Hold
him, gal!" The leader of that pack of hounds, white folks,
wa'n't no bloodhound. She was a plain old red-bone possum
and coon dog, and the rest done just like she done, tearing at
the overseer's throat. All the while, Jake he a-hollering from the
tree for the dogs to git him. 'Twa'n't long afore them dogs tore
that man all to pieces. He died right under that maple tree that
he run Jake up. Jake, he and that coon hound struck off
through the woods. The rest of the pack come home.

I seed Jake after us niggers was freed. That's how come I
knowed all about it. It musta been six years after they killed the
overseer. It was in Kentucky that I run across Jake. He was a-sit-

ting on some steps of a nigger cabin. A hound dog was a-sitting at his side. I tells him how glad I is to see him, and then I look at the dog. "That ain't Belle?" I says. "Naw," Jake answers, "this her puppy." Then he told me the whole story. I always did want to know what happened to 'em.

Jean Toomer

Portrait in Georgia

Hair—braided chestnut,
  coiled like a lyncher's rope,
Eyes—fagots,
Lips—old scars, or the first red blisters,
Breath—the last sweet scent of cane,
And her slim body, white as the ash
  of black flesh after flame.

Diane Oliver

Neighbors

The bus turning the corner of Patterson and Talford Avenue was dull this time of evening. Of the four passengers standing in the rear, she did not recognize any of her friends. Most of the people tucked neatly in the double seats were women, maids and cooks on their way from work or secretaries who had worked late and were riding from the office building at the mill. The cotton mill was out from town, near the house where she worked. She noticed that a few men were riding too. They were obviously just working men, except for one gentleman dressed very neatly in a dark grey suit and carrying what she imagined was a push-button umbrella.

He looked to her as though he usually drove a car to work. She immediately decided that the car probably wouldn't start this morning so he had to catch the bus to and from work. She was standing in the rear of the bus, peering at the passengers, her arms barely reaching the over-head railing, trying not to wobble with every lurch. But every corner the bus turned pushed her head toward a window. And her hair was coming down too, wisps of black curls swung between her eyes. She looked at the people around her. Some of them were white, but most of them were her color. Looking at the passengers at least kept her from thinking of tomorrow. But really she would be glad when it came, then everything would be over.

She took a firmer grip on the green leather seat and wished she had on her glasses. The man with the umbrella was two people ahead of her on the other side of the bus, so she could see him between other people very clearly. She watched as he

58

unfolded the evening newspaper, craning her neck to see what was on the front page. She stood, impatiently trying to read the headlines, when she realized he was staring up at her rather curiously. Biting her lips she turned her head and stared out of the window until the downtown section was in sight.

She would have to wait until she was home to see if they were in the newspaper again. Sometimes she felt that if another person snapped a picture of them she would burst out screaming. Last Monday reporters were already inside the pre-school clinic when she took Tommy for his last polio shot. She didn't understand how anyone could be so heartless to a child. The flashbulb went off right when the needle went in and all the picture showed was Tommy's open mouth.

The bus pulling up to the curb jerked to a stop, startling her and confusing her thoughts. Clutching in her hand the paper bag that contained her uniform, she pushed her way toward the door. By standing in the back of the bus, she was one of the first people to step to the ground. Outside the bus, the evening air felt humid and uncomfortable and her dress kept sticking to her. She looked up and remembered that the weatherman had forecast rain. Just their luck—why, she wondered, would it have to rain on top of everything else?

As she walked along, the main street seemed unnaturally quiet but she decided her imagination was merely playing tricks. Besides, most of the stores had been closed since five o'clock.

She stopped to look at a reversible raincoat in Ivey's window, but although she had a full time job now, she couldn't keep her mind on clothes. She was about to continue walking when she heard a horn blowing. Looking around, half-scared but also curious, she saw a man beckoning to her in a grey car. He was nobody she knew but since a nicely dressed woman was with him in the front seat, she walked to the car.

"You're Jim Mitchell's girl, aren't you?" he questioned. "You Ellie or the other one?"

She nodded yes, wondering who he was and how much he had been drinking.

"Now honey," he said leaning over the woman, "you don't know me but your father does and you tell him that if anything happens to that boy of his tomorrow we're ready to set things straight." He looked her straight in the eye and she promised to take home the message.

Just as the man was about to step on the gas, the woman reached out and touched her arm. "You hurry up home, honey, it's about dark out here."

Before she could find out their names, the Chevrolet had disappeared around a corner. Ellie wished someone would magically appear and tell her everything that had happened since August. Then maybe she could figure out what was real and what she had been imagining for the past couple of days.

She walked past the main shopping district up to Tanner's where Saraline was standing in the window peeling oranges. Everything in the shop was painted orange and green and Ellie couldn't help thinking that poor Saraline looked out of place. She stopped to wave to her friend who pointed the knife to her watch and then to her boyfriend standing in the rear of the shop. Ellie nodded that she understood. She knew Sara wanted her to tell her grandfather that she had to work late again. Neither one of them could figure out why he didn't like Charlie. Saraline had finished high school three years ahead of her and it was time for her to be getting married. Ellie watched as her friend stopped peeling the orange long enough to cross her fingers. She nodded again but she was afraid all the crossed fingers in the world wouldn't stop the trouble tomorrow.

She stopped at the traffic light and spoke to a shrivelled woman hunched against the side of a building. Scuffing the bottom of her sneakers on the curb she waited for the woman to open her mouth and grin as she usually did. The kids used to bait her to talk, and since she didn't have but one tooth in her whole head they called her Doughnut Puncher. But the woman was still, the way everything else had been all week.

From where Ellie stood, across the street from the Sears and Roebuck parking lot, she could see their house, all of the houses on the single street white people called Welfare Row. Those newspaper men always made her angry. All of their articles showed how rough the people were on their street. And the reporters never said her family wasn't on welfare, the papers always said the family lived on that street. She paused to look across the street at a group of kids pouncing on one rubber ball. There were always white kids around their neighborhood mixed up in the games, but playing with them was almost an unwritten rule. When everybody started going to school nobody played together any more.

She crossed at the corner ignoring the cars at the stop light and the closer she got to her street the more she realized that the newspaper was right. The houses were ugly, there were not even any trees, just patches of scraggly bushes and grasses. As she cut across the sticky asphalt pavement covered with cars she was conscious of the parking lot floodlights casting a strange glow on her street. She stared from habit at the house on the end of the block and except for the way the paint was peeling they all looked alike to her. Now at twilight the flaking grey paint had a luminous glow and as she walked down the dirt sidewalk she noticed Mr. Paul's pipe smoke added to the hazy atmosphere. Mr. Paul would be sitting in that same spot waiting until Saraline came home. Ellie slowed her pace to speak to the elderly man sitting on the porch.

"Evening, Mr. Paul," she said. Her voice sounded clear and out of place on the vacant street.

"Eh, who's that?" Mr. Paul leaned over the rail. "What you say, girl?"

"How are you?" she hollered louder. "Sara said she'd be late tonight, she has to work." She waited for the words to sink in.

His head had dropped and his eyes were facing his lap. She could see that he was disappointed. "Couldn't help it," he said finally. "Reckon they needed her again." Then as if he suddenly remembered he turned toward her.

"You people be ready down there? Still gonna let him go tomorrow?"

She looked at Mr. Paul between the missing rails on his porch, seeing how his rolled up trousers seemed to fit exactly in the vacant banister space.

"Last I heard this morning we're still letting him go," she said.

Mr. Paul had shifted his weight back to the chair. "Don't reckon they'll hurt him," he mumbled, scratching the side of his face. "Hope he don't mind being spit on though. Spitting ain't like cutting. They can spit on him and nobody'll ever know who did it," he said, ending his words with a quiet chuckle.

Ellie stood on the sidewalk grinding her heel in the dirt waiting for the old man to finish talking. She was glad somebody found something funny to laugh at. Finally he shut up.

"Goodbye, Mr. Paul," she waved. Her voice sounded loud to her own ears. But she knew the way her head ached intensified noises. She walked home faster, hoping they had some aspirin in the house and that those men would leave earlier tonight.

From the front of her house she could tell that the men were still there. The living room light shone behind the yellow shades, coming through brighter in the patched places. She thought about moving the geranium pot from the porch to catch the rain but changed her mind. She kicked a beer can under a car parked in the street and stopped to look at her reflection on the car door. The tiny flowers of her printed dress made her look as if she had a strange tropical disease. She spotted another can and kicked it out of the way of the car, thinking that one of these days some kid was going to fall and hurt himself. What she wanted to do she knew was kick the car out of the way. Both the station wagon and the Ford had been parked in front of her house all week, waiting. Everybody was just sitting around waiting.

Suddenly she laughed aloud. Reverend Davis' car was big and black and shiny just like, but no, the smile disappeared from her face, her mother didn't like for them to say things about other people's color. She looked around to see who else came, and saw Mr. Moore's old beat up blue car. Somebody had torn away half of his NAACP sign. Sometimes she really felt sorry for the man. No matter how hard he glued on his stickers somebody always yanked them off again.

Ellie didn't recognize the third car but it had an Alabama license plate. She turned around and looked up and down the street, hating to go inside. There were no lights on their street, but in the distance she could see the bright lights of the parking lot. Slowly she did an about face and climbed the steps.

She wondered when her mama was going to remember to get a yellow bulb for the porch. Although the lights hadn't been turned on, usually June bugs and mosquitoes swarmed all around the porch. By the time she was inside the house she always felt like they were crawling in her hair. She pulled on the screen and saw that Mama finally had made Hezekiah patch up the holes. The globs of white adhesive tape scattered over the screen door looked just like misshapen butterflies.

She listened to her father's voice and could tell by the tone that the men were discussing something important again. She rattled the door once more but nobody came.

"Will somebody please let me in?" Her voice carried through the screen to the knot of men sitting in the corner.

"The door's open," her father yelled. "Come on in."

"The door is not open," she said evenly. "You know we stopped leaving it open." She was feeling tired again and her voice had fallen an octave lower.

"Yeah, I forgot, I forgot," he mumbled walking to the door.

She watched her father almost stumble across a chair to let her in. He was shorter than the light bulb and the light seemed to beam down on him, emphasizing the wrinkles around his eyes. She could tell from the way he pushed open the screen that he hadn't had much sleep either. She'd overheard him telling Mama that the people down at the shop seemed to be piling on the work harder just because of this thing. And he couldn't do anything or say anything to his boss because they probably wanted to fire him.

"Where's Mama?" she whispered. He nodded toward the back.

"Good evening, everybody," she said looking at the three

men who had not looked up since she entered the room. One of the men half stood, but his attention was geared back to something another man was saying. They were sitting on the sofa in their shirt sleeves and there was a pitcher of ice water on the window sill.

"Your mother probably needs some help," her father said. She looked past him trying to figure out who the white man was sitting on the end. His face looked familiar and she tried to remember where she had seen him before. The men were paying no attention to her. She bent to see what they were studying and saw a large sheet of white drawing paper. She could see blocks and lines and the man sitting in the middle was marking a trail with the eraser edge of the pencil.

The quiet stillness of the room was making her head ache more. She pushed her way through the red embroidered curtains that led to the kitchen.

"I'm home, Mama," she said, standing in front of the back door facing the big yellow sun Hezekiah and Tommy had painted on the wall above the iron stove. Immediately she felt a warmth permeating her skin. "Where is everybody?" she asked, sitting at the table where her mother was peeling potatoes.

"Mrs. McAllister is keeping Helen and Teenie," her mother said. "Your brother is staying over with Harry tonight." With each name she uttered, a slice of potato peeling tumbled to the newspaper on the table. "Tommy's in the bedroom reading that Uncle Wiggily book."

Ellie looked up at her mother but her eyes were straight ahead. She knew that Tommy only read the Uncle Wiggily book by himself when he was unhappy. She got up and walked to the kitchen cabinet.

"The other knives dirty?" she asked.

"No," her mother said, "look in the next drawer."

Ellie pulled open the drawer, flicking scraps of white paint with her fingernail. She reached for the knife and at the same time a pile of envelopes caught her eye.

"Any more come today?" she asked, pulling out the knife and slipping the envelopes under the dish towels.

"Yes, seven more came today," her mother accentuated each

word carefully. "Your father has them with him in the other room."

"Same thing?" she asked picking up a potato and wishing she could think of some way to change the subject.

The white people had been threatening them for the past three weeks. Some of the letters were aimed at the family, but most of them were directed to Tommy himself. About once a week in the same handwriting somebody wrote that he'd better not eat lunch at school because they were going to poison him.

They had been getting those letters ever since the school board made Tommy's name public. She sliced the potato and dropped the pieces in the pan of cold water. Out of all those people he had been the only one the board had accepted for transfer to the elementary school. The other children, the members said, didn't live in the district. As she cut the eyes out of another potato she thought about the first letter they had received and how her father just set fire to it in the ashtray. But then Mr. Belk said they'd better save the rest, in case anything happened, they might need the evidence for court.

She peeped up again at her mother, "Who's that white man in there with Daddy?"

"One of Lawyer Belk's friends," she answered. "He's pastor of the church that's always on television Sunday morning. Mr. Belk seems to think that having him around will do some good." Ellie saw that her voice was shaking just like her hand as she reached for the last potato. Both of them could hear Tommy in the next room mumbling to himself. She was afraid to look at her mother.

Suddenly Ellie was aware that her mother's hands were trembling violently. "He's so little," she whispered and suddenly the knife slipped out of her hands and she was crying and breathing at the same time.

Ellie didn't know what to do but after a few seconds she cleared away the peelings and put the knives in the sink. "Why don't you lie down?" she suggested. "I'll clean up and get Tommy in bed." Without saying anything her mother rose and walked to her bedroom.

Ellie wiped off the table and draped the dishcloth over the

sink. She stood back and looked at the rusting pipes powdered with a whitish film. One of these days they would have to paint the place. She tiptoed past her mother who looked as if she had fallen asleep from exhaustion.

"Tommy," she called softly, "come in and get ready for bed."

Tommy sitting in the middle of the floor did not answer. He was sitting the way she imagined he would be, cross-legged, pulling his ear lobe as he turned the ragged pages of *Uncle Wiggily at the Zoo*.

"What you doing, Tommy?" she said squatting on the floor beside him. He smiled and pointed at the picture of the ducks.

"School starts tomorrow," she said, turning a page with him. "Don't you think it's time to go to bed?"

"Oh Ellie, do I have to go now?" She looked down at the serious brown eyes and the closely cropped head. For a minute she wondered if he questioned having to go to bed now or to school tomorrow.

"Well," she said, "aren't you about through with the book?" He shook his head. "Come on," she pulled him up, "you're a sleepy head." Still he shook his head.

"When Helen and Teenie coming home?"

"Tomorrow after you come home from school they'll be here."

She lifted him from the floor thinking how small he looked to be facing all those people tomorrow.

"Look," he said breaking away from her hand and pointing to a blue shirt and pair of cotton twill pants, "Mama got them for me to wear tomorrow."

While she ran water in the tub, she heard him crawl on top of the bed. He was quiet and she knew he was untying his sneakers.

"Put your shoes out," she called through the door, "and maybe Daddy will polish them."

"Is Daddy still in there with those men? Mama made me be quiet so I wouldn't bother them."

He padded into the bathroom with bare feet and crawled into the water. As she scrubbed him they played Ask Me A

Question, their own version of Twenty Questions. She had just dried him and was about to have him step into his pajamas when he asked: "Are they gonna get me tomorrow?"

"Who's going to get you?" She looked into his eyes and began rubbing him furiously with the towel.

"I don't know," he answered. "Somebody I guess."

"Nobody's going to get you," she said, "who wants a little boy who gets bubblegum in his hair anyway—but us?" He grinned but as she hugged him she thought how much he looked like his father. They walked to the bed to say his prayers and while they were kneeling she heard the first drops of rain. By the time she covered him up and tucked the spread off the floor the rain had changed to a steady downpour.

When Tommy had gone to bed her mother got up again and began ironing clothes in the kitchen. Something, she said, to keep her thoughts busy. While her mother folded and sorted the clothes Ellie drew up a chair from the kitchen table. They sat in the kitchen for a while listening to the voices of the men in the next room. Her mother's quiet speech broke the stillness in the room.

"I'd rather," she said making sweeping motions with the iron, "that you stayed home from work tomorrow and went with your father to take Tommy. I don't think I'll be up to those people."

Ellie nodded. "I don't mind," she said, tracing circles on the oil cloth covered table.

"Your father's going," her mother continued. "Belk and Reverend Davis are too. I think that white man in there will probably go."

"They may not need me," Ellie answered.

"Tommy will," her mother said, folding the last dish towel and storing it in the cabinet.

"Mama, I think he's scared," the girl turned toward the woman. "He was so quiet while I was washing him."

"I know," she answered sitting down heavily. "He's been that way all day." Her brown wavy hair glowed in the dim lighting of the kitchen. "I told him he wasn't going to school with Jakie and Bob any more but I said he was going to meet some other children just as nice."

Ellie saw that her mother was twisting her wedding band around and around on her finger.

"I've already told Mrs. Ingraham that I wouldn't be able to come out tomorrow." Ellie paused. "She didn't say very much. She didn't even say anything about his pictures in the newspaper. Mr. Ingraham said we were getting right crazy but even he didn't say anything else."

She stopped to look at the clock sitting near the sink. "It's almost time for the cruise cars to begin," she said. Her mother followed Ellie's eyes to the sink. The policemen circling their block every twenty minutes was supposed to make them feel safe, but hearing the cars come so regularly and that light flashing through the shade above her bed only made her nervous.

She stopped talking to push a wrinkle out of the shiny red cloth, dragging her finger along the table edges. "How long before those men going to leave?" she asked her mother. Just as she spoke she heard one of the men say something about getting some sleep. "I didn't mean to run them away," she said smiling. Her mother half-smiled too. They listened for the sound of motors and tires and waited for her father to shut the front door.

In a few seconds her father's head pushed through the curtain. "Want me to turn down your bed now, Ellie?" She felt uncomfortable staring up at him, the whole family looked drained of all energy.

"That's all right," she answered. "I'll sleep in Helen and Teenie's bed tonight."

"How's Tommy?" he asked looking toward the bedroom. He came in and sat down at the table with them.

They were silent before he spoke. "I keep wondering if we should send him." He lit a match and watched the flame disappear into the ashtray, then he looked into his wife's eyes. "There's no telling what these fool white folks will do."

Her mother reached over and patted his hand. "We're doing what we have to do, I guess," she said. "Sometimes though I wish the others weren't so much older than him."

"But it seems so unfair," Ellie broke in, "sending him there all by himself like that. Everybody keeps asking me why the MacAdams didn't apply for their children."

"Eloise." Her father's voice sounded curt. "We aren't answering for the MacAdams, we're trying to do what's right for your brother. He's not old enough to have his own say so. You and the others could decide for yourselves, but we're the ones that have to do for him."

She didn't say anything but watched him pull a handful of envelopes out of his pocket and tuck them in the cabinet drawer. She knew that if anyone had told him in August that Tommy would be the only one going to Jefferson Davis they would not have let him go.

"Those the new ones?" she asked. "What they say?"

"Let's not talk about the letters," her father said. "Let's go to bed."

Outside they heard the rain become heavier. Since early evening she had become accustomed to the sound. Now it blended in with the rest of the noises that had accumulated in the back of her mind since the whole thing began.

As her mother folded the ironing board they heard the quiet wheels of the police car. Ellie noticed that the clock said twelve-ten and she wondered why they were early. Her mother pulled the iron cord from the switch and they stood silently waiting for the police car to turn around and pass the house again, as if the car's passing were a final blessing for the night.

Suddenly she was aware of a noise that sounded as if everything had broken loose in her head at once, a loudness that almost shook the foundation of the house. At the same time the lights went out and instinctively her father knocked them to the floor. They could hear the tinkling of glass near the front of the house and Tommy began screaming.

"Tommy, get down," her father yelled.

She hoped he would remember to roll under the bed the way they had practiced. She was aware of objects falling and breaking as she lay perfectly still. Her breath was coming in jerks and then there was a second noise, a smaller explosion but still drowning out Tommy's cries.

"Stay still," her father commanded. "I'm going to check on Tommy. They may throw another one."

She watched him crawl across the floor, pushing a broken flower vase and an iron skillet out of his way. All of the sounds, Tommy's crying, the breaking glass, everything was echoing in her ears. She felt as if they had been crouching on the floor for hours but when she heard the police car door slam, the luminous hands of the clock said only twelve-fifteen.

She heard other cars drive up and pairs of heavy feet trample on the porch. "You folks all right in there?"

She could visualize the hands pulling open the door, because she knew the voice. Sergeant Kearns had been responsible for patrolling the house during the past three weeks. She heard him click the light switch in the living room but the darkness remained intense.

Her father deposited Tommy in his wife's lap and went to what was left of the door. In the next fifteen minutes policemen were everywhere. While she rummaged around underneath the cabinet for a candle, her mother tried to hush up Tommy. His cheek was cut where he had scratched himself on the springs of the bed. Her mother motioned for her to dampen a cloth and put some petroleum jelly on it to keep him quiet. She tried to put him to bed again but he would not go, even when she promised to stay with him for the rest of the night. And so she sat in the kitchen rocking the little boy back and forth on her lap.

Ellie wandered around the kitchen but the light from the single candle put an eerie glow on the walls making her nervous. She began picking up pans, stepping over pieces of broken crockery and glassware. She did not want to go into the living room yet, but if she listened closely, snatches of the policemen's conversation came through the curtain.

She heard one man say that the bomb landed near the edge of the yard, that was why it had only gotten the front porch. She knew from their talk that the living room window was shattered completely. Suddenly Ellie sat down. The picture of the living room window kept flashing in her mind and a wave of feeling invaded her body making her shake as if she had lost all muscular control. She slept on the couch, right under that window.

She looked at her mother to see if she too had realized, but her mother was looking down at Tommy and trying to get him to close his eyes. Ellie stood up and crept toward the living room trying to prepare herself for what she would see. Even that minute of determination could not make her control the horror that she felt. There were jagged holes all along the front of the house and the sofa was covered with glass and paint. She started to pick up the picture that had toppled from the book shelf, then she just stepped over the broken frame.

Outside her father was talking and, curious to see who else was with him, she walked across the splinters to the yard. She could see pieces of the geranium pot and the red blossoms turned face down. There were no lights in the other houses on the street. Across from their house she could see forms standing in the door and shadows being pushed back and forth. "I guess the MacAdams are glad they just didn't get involved." No one heard her speak, and no one came over to see if they could help; she knew why and did not really blame them. They were afraid their house could be next.

Most of the policemen had gone now and only one car was left to flash the revolving red light in the rain. She heard the tall skinny man tell her father they would be parked outside for the rest of the night. As she watched the reflection of the police cars returning to the station, feeling sick on her stomach, she wondered now why they bothered.

Ellie went back inside the house and closed the curtain behind her. There was nothing anyone could do now, not even to the house. Everything was scattered all over the floor and poor Tommy still would not go to sleep. She wondered what would happen when the news spread through their section of town, and at once remembered the man in the grey Chevrolet. It would serve them right if her father's friends got one of them.

Ellie pulled up an overturned chair and sat down across from her mother who was crooning to Tommy. What Mr. Paul said was right, white people just couldn't be trusted. Her family had expected anything but even though they had practiced ducking, they didn't really expect anybody to try tearing down the house. But the funny thing was the house belonged to one of them. Maybe it was a good thing her family were just renters.

Exhausted, Ellie put her head down on the table. She didn't know what they were going to do about tomorrow, in the day time they didn't need electricity. She was too tired to think any more about Tommy, yet she could not go to sleep. So, she sat at the table trying to sit still, but every few minutes she would involuntarily twitch. She tried to steady her hands, all the time listening to her mother's sing-songy voice and waiting for her father to come back inside the house.

She didn't know how long she lay hunched against the kitchen table, but when she looked up, her wrists bore the imprints of her hair. She unfolded her arms gingerly, feeling the blood rush to her fingertips. Her father sat in the chair opposite her, staring at the vacant space between them. She heard her mother creep away from the table, taking Tommy to his room.

Ellie looked out the window. The darkness was turning to gray and the hurt feeling was disappearing. As she sat there she could begin to look at the kitchen matter-of-factly. Although the hands of the clock were just a little past five-thirty, she knew somebody was going to have to start clearing up and cook breakfast.

She stood and tipped across the kitchen to her parents' bedroom. "Mama," she whispered, standing near the door of Tommy's room. At the sound of her voice, Tommy made a funny throaty noise in his sleep. Her mother motioned for her to go out and be quiet. Ellie knew then that Tommy had just fallen asleep. She crept back to the kitchen and began picking up the dishes that could be salvaged, being careful not to go into the living room.

She walked around her father, leaving the broken glass underneath the kitchen table. "You want some coffee?" she asked.

He nodded silently, in strange contrast she thought to the water faucet that turned with a loud gurgling noise. While she let the water run to get hot she measured out the instant coffee in one of the plastic cups. Next door she could hear people moving around in the Williams' kitchen, but they too seemed much quieter than usual.

"You reckon everybody knows by now?" she asked, stirring the coffee and putting the saucer in front of him.

"Everybody will know by the time the city paper comes out," he said. "Somebody was here last night from the *Observer*. Guess it'll make front page."

She leaned against the cabinet for support watching him trace endless circles in the brown liquid with the spoon. "Sergeant Kearns says they'll have almost the whole force out there tomorrow," he said.

"Today," she whispered.

Her father looked at the clock and then turned his head.

"When's your mother coming back in here?" he asked, finally picking up the cup and drinking the coffee.

"Tommy's just off to sleep," she answered. "I guess she'll be in here when he's asleep for good."

She looked out the window of the back door at the row of tall hedges that had separated their neighborhood from the white people for as long as she remembered. While she stood there she heard her mother walk into the room. To her ears the steps seemed much slower than usual. She heard her mother stop in front of her father's chair.

"Jim," she said, sounding very timid, "what we going to do?" Yet as Ellie turned toward her she noticed her mother's face was strangely calm as she looked down on her husband.

Ellie continued standing by the door listening to them talk. Nobody asked the question to which they all wanted an answer.

"I keep thinking," her father said finally, "that the policemen will be with him all day. They couldn't hurt him inside the school building without getting some of their own kind."

"But he'll be in there all by himself," her mother said softly. "A hundred policemen can't be a little boy's only friends."

She watched her father wrap his calloused hands, still splotched with machine oil, around the salt shaker on the table.

"I keep trying," he said to her, "to tell myself that some-body's got to be the first one and then I just think how quiet he's been all week."

Ellie listened to the quiet voices that seemed to be a room apart from her. In the back of her mind she could hear phrases of a hymn her grandmother used to sing, something about trou-ble, her being born for trouble.

"Jim, I cannot let my baby go." Her mother's words, al-though quiet, were carefully pronounced.

"Maybe," her father answered, "it's not in our hands. Rever-end Davis and I were talking day before yesterday how God tested the Israelites, maybe he's just trying us."

"God expects you to take care of your own," his wife inter-rupted. Ellie sensed a trace of bitterness in her mother's voice.

"Tommy's not going to understand why he can't go to school," her father replied. "He's going to wonder why, and how are we going to tell him we're afraid of them?" Her fa-ther's hands clutched the coffee cup. "He's going to be fighting them the rest of his life. He's got to start sometime."

"But he's not on their level. Tommy's too little to go around hating people. One of the others, they're bigger, they under-stand about things."

Ellie still leaning against the door saw that the sun covered part of the sky behind the hedges and the light slipping through the kitchen window seemed to reflect the shiny red of the table cloth.

"He's our child," she heard her mother say. "Whatever we do, we're going to be the cause." Her father had pushed the cup away from him and sat with his hands covering part of his face. Outside Ellie could hear a horn blowing.

"God knows we tried but I guess there's just no use." Her father's voice forced her attention back to the two people sit-ting in front of her. "Maybe when things come back to normal, we'll try again."

He covered his wife's chunky fingers with the palm of his hand and her mother seemed to be enveloped in silence. The three of them remained quiet, each involved in his own thoughts, but related,Ellie knew, to the same thing. She was the first to break the silence.

"Mama," she called after a long pause, "do you want me to start setting the table for breakfast?"

Her mother nodded.

Ellie turned the clock so she could see it from the sink while she washed the dishes that had been scattered over the floor.

"You going to wake up Tommy or you want me to?"

"No," her mother said, still holding her father's hand, "let him sleep. When you wash your face, you go up the street and call Hezekiah. Tell him to keep up with the children after school. I want to do something to this house before they come home."

She stopped talking and looked around the kitchen, finally turning to her husband. "He's probably kicked the spread off by now," she said. Ellie watched her father, who without saying anything walked toward the bedroom.

She watched her mother lift herself from the chair and automatically push in the stuffing underneath the cracked plastic cover. Her face looked set, as it always did when she was trying hard to keep her composure.

"He'll need something hot when he wakes up. Hand me the oatmeal," she commanded, reaching on top of the icebox for matches to light the kitchen stove.

Albert Murray

Stonewall Jackson's Waterloo

Sometimes a thin gray, ghost-whispering midwinter drizzle would begin while you were still at school and not only would it settle in for the rest of the afternoon but it would still be falling after dark as if it would continue throughout the night. That, as Miss Lexine Metcalf for one never failed to remind you, was always the coziest time to get your homework done, even when it was arithmetic. But as nobody ever needed to tell me or anybody else I knew, it was also one of the very best of all good times to be where grown folks were talking, especially when there were people visiting because somebody was there from out of town and you could stay up beyond your usual time to be in bed. Not even the barbershop was better than that.

Their chairs always formed the same family-style semicircle before the huge open hearth, and from my place in the chimney corner you could see the play of the firelight against their faces and watch the shadows spreading up the newspaper wallpaper walls to the ceiling. They would be talking and, aware of the roof-sanding night weather outside, I would be listening, and above them on the mantelpiece was the old-fashioned pendulum clock, which was Papa's heirloom from that old Manor of antebellum columns and calico kitchens in which his mulatto grandmother had herself been an inherited slave until Sherman's March to the Sea.

Sometimes it was obvious enough that they were only telling the most outrageous lies they could either fabricate or remember, and sometimes you could be every bit as certain that their

only purpose was to spell out as precisely as possible the incon-
testable facts. Uncle Jerome would always be there, clearing his
throat even when he was not going to say anything, squinting
his eyes and making a face and clearing and swallowing because
he was a preacher. Because although he had been a longshoreman for the last twenty-five years and a farmer for thirty years
before that, he was also supposed to have The Call, although he
had never been called by any congregation to pastor any church.

Sometimes Mister Dock (for dockhand) Donahue would be
there too, but they wouldn't be drinking wine if he were there;
because stevedore that he was, he said that wine was for
women, children, and Christmas morning; and he would get up
and get the longshoreman's knapsack he always carried and
bring out a jug of corn whiskey, and Papa Whit would look at
Mama and get just about tickled to death. They would be passing it around, pouring against the light of the fire, and there
would be that smell then, which also went with cigar ashes and
freshly opened Prince Albert tobacco cans.

I always said Papoo to Papa Whit (*who was not really my
flesh-and-blood father, whom I have never seen, just as Mama
was not my flesh-and-blood mother*), who used to call me his
little gingerbrown Papoose-boy, which may have been why I
called him Papoo, who himself was as white as any out-and-out
white man I have ever seen in my life. Who not only was said
to be more than half white but was also said quite accurately to
be acknowledged by most of his white relatives much more
readily than he himself was ever willing to acknowledge any of
them. I myself once overheard Mama telling Aunt Cat Calla-
han that the main reason they moved down into Mobile
County when the war boom came was to get away from Papa's
white kinfolks in the country; and another time I heard her telling Miss Sadie Womack about how red Papa's ears used to get
when the white people back in the country used to see him
driving her into town in the buckboard and pretend that they
thought she was one of his black field hands.

Papa himself never talked about white people as such. But
sometimes when they were talking about hard times, somebody

would get him to tell about how he used to go off somewhere and pass for white to get a job; and that was something to hear about too; and one time when I was telling Little Buddy about it, he said, "Everybody say don't care how much of his skin and his keen nose and his flat ass Mister Whit might have got from the white folks, he got his mother wit from the getting place. That's why you don't never hear nobody calling him no shit-colored half-peckerwood, even behind his back."

There was also that time downtown by the marine store, on Government Street, and that was a white man. He and Papa knew each other and they were laughing and talking and I was having a good time looking in store windows, and I went looking all the way up to the sporting-goods store and when I came back they were talking about a job; and the man said something about something both of them had been doing somewhere, and that brought up something else *and I heard the man say that Papa was a fool for being a durned ole niggie when he could be a wyat man, and Papa just shook his head and said, you don't understand, Pete.*

Soldier Boy Crawford was the one who would always take over when they started talking about the war, because he was an old foot trooper and sometimes he still wore his Army coat, and sometimes in the winter he would wear his wrap-around leggings too, and he also had a steel helmet that looked like a washbasin, and he had a German Luger and some hand grenades and a bayonet and a knapsack and a gas mask too (because he said that he for one was never going to let them catch him with his pants down if he could help it). He had been to France to help them stop old Kaiser Bill. He would tell about the ocean and the torpedoes and the submarines and then about the French places he had been to, and sometimes he would mix in a lot of French words with what he was saying. He would tell all about the kind of farming country they had over there, especially the wine-making country. He would also tell about the mountain country and the churches and then he would tell all about Paris, which he said was the best town in the world, and he used to always say a man is a man over there, and somebody else would say a man ain't nothing but a man no-wheres.

Old Soldier Boy Crawford was also the one who used to tell me and old Little Buddy about some of the things old Luzana Cholly used to do during the war, because old Luzana himself never did talk about that, not even when you asked him about it. Sometimes he would say he was going to save it and tell us about it when we were old enough to understand it, and sometimes he would answer one or two questions about something like how far Big Bertha could shoot, and how the Chau-Chau automatic rifle worked and things like that. But he never did sit down and tell about the actual fighting like old Soldier Boy Crawford did. They used to always say that once old Soldier Boy Crawford got worked up you couldn't stop him from fighting the whole war all over again.

The rain that was falling then would be crackling down on the shingles of the gabled roof of that house, and the fire in the hearth would sparkle as Papa poked it, and I would be in my same chair in my same place in the corner, and sometimes they would be telling about some of the same old notorious rounders and roustabouts that the guitar players and the piano players made up songs about. Especially if Mr. Dock Donahue was there, because he was the one who could always remember something else about old John Henry, who went with blue steel sparks, and old John Hardy, who went with greased lightning. He held the floor all night one night just describing how old Stagolee shot and killed Billy Lyons, and they gave it to him again the next night and he told about what happened at that famous trial.

He was also the one who used to tell about how old Robert Charles declared war on the city of New Orleans and fought the whole police force all by himself with his own special homemade bullets. But the best of all the old so-called outlaws he used to tell about was always the one from Alabama named Railroad Bill, who was so mean when somebody crossed him, and so tricky, that most people believed that there was something supernatural about him. He was the one that no jail could hold overnight and no bloodhounds could track beyond a certain point. Because he worked a mojo on them that nobody ever heard of before or since. And the last time he broke jail, they had the best bloodhounds in the whole state there to track him. But the next morning they found them all tied together in a fence corner near the edge of the swamp, not even barking anymore, just whining; and when they got them untangled they were ruined forever, couldn't scent a polecat and wouldn't even run a rabbit. And nobody ever saw or came near hide nor hair of old Railroad Bill from that time on.

But naturally the white folks claimed they caught him and lynched him. But Negroes knew better than that. The white folks were always claiming something like that. They claimed that they had caught old Pancho Villa and hung him for what he had done out in New Mexico; and they claimed that they had hemmed up old Robert Charles in a steeple and burned him alive; and they also claimed that Jess Willard had salivated old Jack Johnson down in Havana that time! Well, they could go around bragging about how the great white hope had put the big black menace back in his place and proved white supremacy all they wanted to, but everybody knew that Jack Johnson, who was married to a white woman, had to trade his world championship in for his American citizenship, and thirty thousand dollars, to get back in the U.S.A. and there was a picture in every barbershop which showed him letting himself be counted out, lying shading his eyes from the Cuban sun, lying with his legs propped like somebody lying on the front porch; and as for Jess Willard, everybody knew he couldn't even stand up to Jack Dempsey, who was the same Jack Dempsey who brought back old John L. Sullivan's color line because he didn't ever intend to get caught in the same ring with the likes of Jack Johnson, Sam Langford, or even the likes of old cream-colored Harry Wills, not even with a submachine gun. Everybody knew that.

The white folks claimed that they had finally caught up with old Railroad Bill at some crossroads store somewhere and had slipped up on him while he was sitting in the middle of the floor sopping molasses with his gun lying off to one side, and they swore that they had blown the back of his head off with a double-barrel charge of Triple-O buckshot. But in the first place Railroad Bill didn't eat molasses, and in the second place he didn't have to break into any store to get something to eat. Because folks kept him in plenty of rations everywhere he went by putting out buckets of it in certain special places for him mostly along the Railroad, which was what his name was all about; and in the third place he must have broken into more than fifty stores by that time and he just plain didn't rob a store in the broad daylight, not and then sit down in the middle of the floor and eat right there—and in the fourth place there were at least a dozen other mobs in at least a dozen other places all claiming that they had been the ones who laid him low, each one of them telling a completely different tale about how and when and where it all happened. Some claimed that they had hung him upside down on the drawbridge and then riddled him and left what was left of him there for the buzzards. But they never settled on one bridge.

I didn't know very much then, but I knew enough to realize that when something happened it was always a part of something that had been going on before, and I wasn't surprised at all that time looking at Uncle Walt sitting by the fire in Papa's clothes telling about finding a way through Tombigbee Swamp, not afraid but careful, talking about how he was going to make it on across the Mason-Dixie, and I didn't really know anything at all about whatever it was he had done or hadn't done, and I still don't know what it was: but I knew that whatever it was it was trouble, and I said, *It's like once upon a time back then.* Because Mama had said it, who knew it from her grandfather, who was Uncle Walt's grandfather too, who knew it from his father when there was no hope of foot rest this side of Canada, which was also called Canaan, which was the Promised Land, and I also knew that all of that was about something called the Underground Railroad, which ran from the house of bondage to the land of Jubilo.

They were always talking about freedom and citizenship. And that was something else that Uncle Jerome used to start preaching about. He had all kinds of sermons ready for times like that. Sometimes he would be talking about the Children of Israel, and sometimes it would be the walls of Jericho, and sometimes it would be the Big Handwriting on the wall which was also the BIG HAND writing on the wall which was also the Big Hand writing on the WAR. That was when he used to say that the color of freedom was blue. The Union Army came dressed in blue. The big hand that signed the freedom papers signed them in blue ink which was also blood. The very sky itself was blue, limitless (*and gentlemen sir, before I'd be a slave, I'll be buried in my grave. And I said my name is Jack the Rabbit and my home is in the briarpatch*).

Sometimes he would also say that the freedom road was a road through the wilderness and sometimes it wasn't any road at all because there never was any royal road to freedom for anybody (*so don't you let nobody turn you around, and don't you let nobody know too much about your business either, and I said call me Jack the Bear on my way somewhere*).

Then it would be Education again. They didn't ever get tired of talking about that, the old folks telling about how they learned to spell and write back in the old days when they used to use slate tablets and the old Blue Back Webster. The old days when they used to have to hold school whenever and wherever they could. Whenever they could spare the time from working the crops and wherever the teacher could find a place to shelter them. Whenever there was a teacher.

Then later on I was the one they meant when they said the young generation was the hope and glory. Because I had come that far in school then. And sometimes it was Geography and sometimes it was History, and sometimes I had to tell about it, and sometimes I had to get the book and read it to them. Especially when it was about the Revolutionary War. Sometimes I had to read about Columbus too, and sometimes it would also be the explorers and the early settlers. But most of the time what they wanted to hear about was how the original thirteen colonies became the first thirteen states and who said what and who did what during that time and how the Constitution was made and who the first Presidents were and what they did.

That was also when I used to love to recite the Declaration of Independence, and the Gettysburg Address for them; and I could also recite the Preamble to the Constitution and part of the Emancipation Proclamation; and I could also quote from the famous speeches of Patrick Henry and James Otis and Citizen Tom Paine; and I knew all kinds of sayings from *Poor Richard's Almanac.*

"That boy can just about preach that thing right now," Mister Jeff Jefferson said one night after I had recited the William Lloyd Garrison and Frederick Douglass parts from the National Negro History Week pageant.

"That boy can talk straight out of the dictionary when he want to," Mister Big Martin said looking at me but talking to everybody.

"It just do you good to hear that kind of talk."

"White folks need to hear some talk like that."

"The white folks the very one said all that, Jeff."

"What kind of white folks talking like that?"

"Histry book white folks."

"What kind of histry book white folks?"

"White folks in that same book that child reading."

"I ain't never heard no white folks believing nothing like that, in all of my born days."

"White folks printed that book, didn't they?"

"I don't care who printed that book, that's freedom talk."

"Well, the histry book white folks got up the Constitution, didn't they?"

"Yeah, and there was some histry book black folks in there somewhere too, you can just about bet on that. There was a jet black roustabout right in there with old Christopher Columbus, and the very first one to try to climb that Bunker Hill was a mean black son of a gun from Boston. Ain't nothing never happened and wasn't some kind of a black hand mixed up in it somewhere. You just look at it close enough. The very first ones to come up with iron was them royal black Ethiopians."

"You right about that," Mister Big Martin said. "Ain't nobody going to dispute you about that."

"I know I'm right," Mister Jeff said, "and I still say these white folks need to hear some of that kind of gospel. These ain't no histry book white folks around here and this ain't no histry. This ain't nothing but just a plain old everyday mess!"

"Trying to keep the black man down."

"All white folks ain't like that, Phil."

"Yeah, but them that is."

"And some of us too Jesus," Minnie Stovall said. "Lord the truth is the light, and some of us just ain't ready yet."

"Amen," Mister Big Martin said.

"Amen?" Mister Phil Motley said. "What you mean Amen?"

"That's what I want to know," Mister Jeff Jefferson said.

"I mean the truth is the light just like Minnie say."

"Well, ain't none of these peckerwoods around here ready for nothing neither, but just look at them. That's some truth for the light too."

"Yeah but I still say some of us still ain't learned how to stick together yet."

"Now Big'un, you know good and well that can get to be a horse of another color," Mister Dock Donahue said. "I for one don't never intend to be sticking with any and every body coming along because he say he one of us. You know better than that."

"That why I say some of us Jesus," Miss Minnie Stovall said.

"That's all right about all that," Mister Big Martin said. "I'm talking about when you talking about going up against that stone wall. I want us to be ready. I'm talking about Stonewall Jackson. I'm talking about Jericho."

"Well, we talking about the same thing then," Mister Phil Motley said.

"That's all right about your Stonewall Jackson too," Mister Jeff Jefferson said, "and your Vardaman and your Pitchfork Ben and all the rest of them. This child right here is getting old Stonewall Jackson's water ready."

They were all laughing then. Because everybody in Gasoline Point knew how Shorty Hollingsworth had met his Waterloo and got the name Hot Water Shorty. His wife had come up behind him and dashed a pot of scalding lye water down the seat of his pants while he was sitting on the front steps cleaning his shotgun and bragging about what he was going to do if she didn't have his supper on the table in the next five minutes. He had yelled, dropped his shotgun, and lit out across the barbwire fence and hadn't stopped until he was chin-deep in Three Mile Creek. He had a new name from then on, and he also had a new reputation: he could outrun a striped-assed ape.

Uncle Jerome said I was learning about verbs and adverbs and proverbs; and he preached his sermon on the dictionary that time, and he had his own special introduction to the principles of grammar: "A noun is someone or something; a pronoun is anything or anybody; a verb is tells and does and is; an adverb is anyhow, anywhere, anytime; an adjective is number and nature; a preposition is relationship; and conjunction is membership; and interjection is the spirit of energy."

Another time when Aunt Sue was visiting us from Atmore, old Mayfield Turner was there, Old Sawmill Turner, the log-carriage expert. Mama said he had been trying to marry Aunt Sue for more than seventeen years, which meant that he had started before she married her first husband (she was visiting us because she had just separated from her fourth husband). Old Sawmill was wearing his blue pinstripe, tailor-made suit and his Edwin Clapp shoes and smelling like the barbershop and sitting cross-legged like Henry Ford; and every time he took a puff on his White Owl, he flashed his diamond ring like E. Berry Wall. Sometimes when they were talking about him behind his back they used to give him names like John D. Rockefeller Turner and J. P. Morgan Turner and Jay Gould Turner because he also sported pearl-gray kidskin gloves, and he was always talking about stocks and bonds and worrying about the National Debt.

I was reading about Valley Forge that night, and I knew he was there just as I knew that Mister Lige and Miss Emma Tolliver and Bro Mark Simpkins and his wife, Miss Willeen, were all there, because they were always the first ones to come by to see Aunt Sue when she was in town. But at first the only ones that I was really conscious of were Miss Lula Crayton and Miss Ida Jefferson, because every time I paused Miss Lula Crayton kept saying, Tribulation tribulation trials and tribulation, and Miss Ida Jefferson would respond one time as if she were hearing some new gossip, and the next time as if I were reading the Bible itself. Saying, "Honey don't tell me." Saying, "Lord have mercy Jesus."

Then I happened to glance up and see old Sawmill again, and he had stopped puffing on his cigar. He was leaning forward with his hand under his chin, his eyes closed, his lips moving, repeating everything I was reading, word for word. He had forgotten all about Aunt Sue, for the time being at least. I was reading about how the Redcoats were wining and dining and dancing warm in Philadelphia while the ragtag bobtail Continental Army was starving and freezing in makeshift huts and hovels, and about how General George Washington himself had to get out and personally whip slackers and stragglers and would-be deserters back into the ranks with the flat of his sword. All of which was what Give me liberty or give me death really meant, which was why whenever you talked about following in the footsteps of our great American forefathers you were also talking about the bloody tracks the half-barefooted troops left in the snow that fateful winter.

Every time I glanced up I could see old Sawmill Turner still leaning forward toward me, his lips still moving, the tip of his cigar gone to ash. Then when I came to the end of the chapter and closed the book, he stood up and stepped out into the center of the semicircle as Uncle Jerome always did. "I'm a histry scholar myself," he said. "I been a histry scholar ever since I first saw the Post Office when I was a little boy back in Lowdness County." Then he ran his hand down into his pocket and pulled out a fat roll of brand-new greenbacks, which he held against his chest like a deck of gambling cards. He peeled off a crisp one-dollar bill and held it up and said, "Old George Washington is number one because he was first in war and first in peace and first in the hearts of his countrymen. He got it started."

"And old Tom Jefferson." (Off came a two-dollar bill.) "He was a educated man and he knowed exactly what to do with his book learning. And old Abe Lincoln . . ." (he held up a five-dollar bill) "came along later on and had to save the Union. Old Alexander Hamilton didn't get to be the President, but he was in there amongst them when they started talking about how they were going to handle the money, and here he is." (He pulled off a ten-dollar bill.) "And here's old razor-back Andy Jackson." (Off came a twenty-dollar bill.) "He was against the red man but when he was up there making things better for all them old poor butt hillbillies he was laying the landmark for the black man without even knowing it. And then you come on up to old Ulysses S. Grant." (He held up a fifty-dollar bill without even pausing.) "He was the one old Abe Lincoln himself had to send for when the going got tight, and later on they made him the eighteenth President."

He held up the fifty-dollar bill long enough for everybody to see that it really was a fifty-dollar bill and then he held up a hundred-dollar bill and said, "Old Ben Franklin didn't ever even want to be the President. But old Ben Franklin left just as big a mark in histry as any of them. They didn't put him up there on no one-hundred-dollar for nothing. Old Ben Franklin was one of the smartest men they had back in them days, and everybody gave him his due respect. Old Ben Franklin gave them a lot of good points about how to put them clauses in the Constitution. He was just about the first one they thought about when they had to send somebody across the water to do some official business for the government with them fast-talking Frenchmen. And talking about being cunning, old Ben Franklin was the one that took a kite and Cocola bottle and stole naked lightning."

He came and stood in front of my chair then. "This boy is

worth more than one hundred shares of gilt-edged preferred, and the good part about it is we all going to be drawing down interest on him." Then he handed me a five-dollar bill as crisp as the one he had held up before, and told me to buy myself a fountain pen; and he told Mama he was going to be the one to stake me to all the ink and paper I needed as long as I stayed in school. All I had to do was just show him my report card every term.

All I could do was say thank you, and I promised I would always do my best. And Miss Lula Crayton said Amen. And Miss Ida Jefferson said, "God bless the Lamb and God bless you Mayfield Turner." Then before anybody else could say anything he excused himself, and Aunt Sue walked him to the door and he put on his alpaca topcoat, his black Homburg hat and his Wall Street gloves and was gone.

All Mama could do was wipe her eyes, and all Papa could do was look at the floor and shake his head and smile. But Uncle Jerome was on his feet again, saying he was talking about the word made manifest for manifest destiny; and I knew he was going to take over where Sawmill Turner had left off and preach a whole sermon with me in it that night. And so did everybody else, and they were looking at me as if I really had become the Lamb or something. So I looked at the mantelpiece, and I heard the Mother Goose clock and outside there was the Valley Forge bitter wind in the turret-tall chinaberry tree.

I was still sitting by the reading lamp, and he came and put his hand on my shoulder. Then I had to stand up and go to the hearth and when he said, "Say not I am a child, gentlemen sir, as I am a witness," and they said amen to him, they were also saying amen to me, and amen to the Declaration of Independence, and amen to the Gettysburg Address and the Emancipation Proclamation and amen to the Constitution of the United States of America.

III Migration

The vast migrations of Negroes from the rural South to the cities of the North, Midwest and Far West just prior to World War I and shortly after World War II were events of far-reaching historic importance. The consequent revolutionary changes in the life of American cities and the national, social, political and economic problems attendant on these migrations are only now beginning to be understood. For the Southern black, recently released from the trauma of slavery and conditioned to a peasant existence, the new upheavals once more sorely tested his endurance. The confusion, suffering and humor of his movements are recorded in his many folk songs and blues, some of which are reproduced here. There were undoubtedly a variety of reasons for his leaving the South—among them the boll weevil, the mechanization of agriculture, the lure of Northern industry (see Attaway) and the flight from oppression as in Richard Wright's "Big Boy Leaves Home." But whatever the specific causes, they represent in their totality a restless search for freedom and equality—a quest in the American tradition.

Ramblin' Thomas

Poor Boy Blues

Poor boy, poor boy, poor boy, long ways from home.

I was down in Louisiana doin' as I please,
Now I'm in Texas I got to work or leave.
Poor boy, poor boy, poor boy, long ways from home.

'If your home is in Louisiana, what you doin' over here?'
Says, 'My home ain't in Texas and I sure don't care.'
Poor boy, poor boy, poor boy, long ways from home.

I don't care if the boat don't never land,
I'd like to stay on water long as any man.
Poor boy, poor boy, poor boy, long ways from home.

When my boat comes a-rockin' feels like a drunken man,
Says, 'My home's on the water and I sure don't like land.'
Poor boy, poor boy, poor boy, long ways from home.

William Attaway

*The Green Men**

They hunched against one another, whispering and wondering, and big drops of rain, grayed with slag and soot, rolled on the long wooden bunkhouse. Passing the makings back and forth, they burned cigarettes until their tongues felt like flannel in their jaws. There was a crap game going on in the bunkhouse, but the newcomers didn't have any money to put on the wood. There was nothing for them to do that first day, except smoke and keep walking the rows of bunks. Windows stretched in the long wooden walls around them. And outside they could see the things that they would see for a long time to come.

A giant might have planted his foot on the heel of a great shovel and split the bare hills. Half buried in the earth where the great shovel had trenched were the mills. The mills were as big as creation when the new men had ridden by on the freight. From the bunkhouse they were just so much scrap iron, scattered carelessly, smoking lazily. In back of them ran a dirty-as-a-catfish-hole river with a beautiful name: the Monongahela. Its banks were lined with mountains of red ore, yellow limestone and black coke. None of this was good to the eyes of men accustomed to the pattern of fields.

Most of the crap shooters had been in the valley a long time. Some of them took time from the game to come back and talk with the green men.

"See them towers? That's where I works. The iron blast. Don't take the blast if you kin help it. It ain't the work—it's

* From *Blood on the Forge* (1941). The title of this selection was supplied by the editor.

93

the head blower. Goddamn tough mick. Why, I seen the time when the keeper on my furnace mess up the blast, and the furnace freeze before you know it. That head blower don't stop to find who the fault go to. Naw, he run up and right quick lays out three men with a sow. One of the hunkies yanks a knife on him, but that hunky gits laid out too. I reckon somebody woulda got that mick 'fore this. Only a man ain't much fer a fight when he's makin' four hundred tons of fast iron from one sun to the other."

The men from the hills were not listening. They were not talking. Their attitude spoke. Like a refrain:

We have been tricked away from our poor, good-as-bad-ground-and-bad-white-men-will-let-'em-be hills. What men in their right minds would leave off tending green growing things to tend iron monsters?

"Lots of green guys git knocked out by the heat—'specially hunkies. They don't talk nothin' but gobbler talk. Don't understand nothin' else neither. Foreman tell one old feller who was workin' right next to me to put leather over his chest. Foreman might jest as well been whistlin', 'cause when the heat come down there that hunky lays with a chest like a scrambled egg."

Yes, them red-clay hills was what we call stripped ground, but there was growing things everywhere and crab-apple trees bunched—stunted but beautiful in the sun.

"Them old fellers hadn't oughta be put on a furnace. Course, a green man got to expect to git pitted up some. Lots o' young'uns got lead in their pants, and they gits tagged when the flame come jumpin' for their shovel. There always burns, too, when the furnace gits tapped and the slag spills over into the pit. But the quicker a man learn to move around on his feet the longer he stays livin'."

A man don't git to know what the place where he's born looks like until he goes someplace else. Then he begins to see with his mind things that his eyes had never been able to see. To us niggers who are seeing the red-clay hills with our minds this Allegheny County is an ugly, smoking hell out of a backwoods preacher's sermon.

"Mebbe they start you new boys out on the skull buster. That's a good way to get broke in. But jest keep minded that you got to be keerful o' that old devil, skull buster. Kill many a green man. How? Well, magnet lift the steel ball thirty feet up and drop her. Steel ball weigh nigh eight tons. That eight tons bust the hell out of old scrap metal. Got to be keerful not to git some of it in your skull. Yessir, many a green man long gone 'cause he couldn't keep old skull buster from aimin' at his head."

What's the good in strainin' our eyes out these windows? We can't see where nothin' grows around here but rusty iron towers and brick stacks, walled up like somebody's liable to try and steal them. Where are the trees? They so far away on the tops of the low mountains that they look like the fringe on a black wear-me-to-a-wake dress held upside down against the sky.

"Skull buster don't git as many as whores git. Roll mill help the gals out. Feller sees all that hot steel shooting along the runout tables, all them red-and-white tongues licking 'twixt them rollers. Feller go hog wild fer any gal what 'll take his money. She don't have to work him up none—he's hot from that bakin' steel."

The sun on the red hillsides baked a man, but it was only a short walk to the bottoms and the mud that oozed up between his toes like a cool drink to hot black feet, steppin' easy, mindful of the cottonmouth.

"On the floor, under the Bessemers, you ain't got time to think what a gal's got 'tween her legs. . . ."

Melody and Chinatown went out into the wet. The door closed behind them. The rain had lessened to a drizzle. They could hear the clank of the mills over the steady swish of the rain. Melody led the way. He turned from the river and walked toward the town.

"Boy, this here North don't seem like nothin' to me," complained Chinatown. "All this smoke and stuff in the air! How a man gonna breathe?"

The drizzle stopped. Thin clouds rolled. Melody looked up. "Sun liable to break through soon."

"Won't make no difference to us if the sun don't shine."
"How come?"
"There won't be no crop to make or take out."
"Sun make you feel better," said Melody.
"Couldn't shine through the smoke, nohow. Long time ago a fella told me a nigger need sun so's he kin keep black."

Melody kicked Chinatown with his knee. Chinatown kicked back. Soon they were kicking and dodging around the ash piles. They were laughing when they came to the weedy field at the edge of town. Both men stopped. The laughter died.

Quivering above the high weeds were the freckled white legs of a girl. She struggled with a small form—a little boy who wanted to be turned loose. Other children were peeping through the wet grass. They began to chant, "Shame, shame! Mary and her brother—shame!"

Chinatown and Melody wheeled and hurried away. They had no need to speak to each other. In both of them was the fear brought from Kentucky: that girl might scream. Back in the hills young Charley had been lynched because a girl screamed.

Breathing hard, they followed the path until it became a dirt street. In front of them was a long line of women waiting in front of a pump shed. A few boys crouched underneath one corner of the shelter, held by a game with a jackknife.

"Look—more hunkies!" breathed Chinatown.

"Keep shut," warned Melody.

The pump at the edge of town watered about fifty families. Every Saturday the women were here in line. This day they carried bathing water home. The rain had soaked into their shawl head coverings. They stood patiently.

Then one of the boys spied the two strangers. He was on his feet in a second.

"Ya-a-a . . ."

A rock whizzed between Melody and Chinatown. The two men halted, confused. In the eyes of all the Slavs was a hatred and contempt different from anything they had ever experienced in Kentucky. Another rock went past. Chinatown started to back away.

"We ain't done nothin'," cried Melody. He took a step toward the pump shed. The women covered their faces with their shawls.

"We ain't done nothin'," he cried again.

His words were lost in the shrill child voices: "Ya-a-a . . . ya-a-a . . . ya-a-a . . ."

Melody backed after his half brother. A little distance away they turned and trotted riverward.

"So this how the North different from the South," panted Chinatown.

"Musta mistook us for somebody," said Melody.

"When white folks git mad all niggers look alike," said Chinatown.

"Musta mistook us," insisted Melody.

It should have been easy for them to find the bunkhouse. The river was a sure landmark. But, in turning in among a series of knolls, they lost direction and found themselves back at the town. Before them a dirt road ran between rows of frame shacks. A large pile of garbage blocked the far end of the road.

"Oughta be somebody we kin ask where the bunkhouse," said Chinatown.

"Well, I ain't knockin' on nobody's door to ask nothing."

"All we got to do is start back to the river."

"Which way the river?" puzzled Melody, craning his neck around.

The light rain had started again. A mist had arisen through the rain. The low mountains were no longer visible. The mills along the water were blotted out. Their sound seemed to come from all directions.

"Maybe if I climbs that garbage . . ."

Chinatown started at a run down the road. At the top of the garbage pile he got his bearings. To the west the gray was tinged with faint streaks of orange.

"Over yonder apiece," he yelled, pointing westward.

At the cry, white faces appeared in the doorway opposite him. Nothing was said. Little faces grimaced between the overalled legs of the bearded father. With a movement of her hands beneath an apron, the mother fanned the breadth of her hips at him. An old Slav bent like a burned weed out of the window. Great handle-bar mustaches dripped below his chin. With eyes a snow-washed blue, he looked contempt at Chinatown. Then he wrinkled his nose and spat.

Chinatown slid down the pile of wet garbage. Hardly daring to hurry, he walked the middle of the road to the place where Melody waited.

"These here folks ain't mistook nobody."

They made quick tracks in the mud to the west.

At the river they did not stop to rest or look around. They wanted the shelter of the bunkhouse. This new place was full of hatreds that they did not understand. Melody led the way down-river. They had been going ten minutes when he stopped. There was no sign of the bunkhouse. Nothing but the river looked familiar.

"You reckon we been goin' wrong?" asked Chinatown.

"Got to be one way or the other," said Melody. He turned and looked behind him.

A fat-cheeked black girl moved along the river-front road. Bright red lipstick had turned to purple on her lips. A man's hat was pulled down over her ears. She wore an old overall coat over a stained satin dress.

Melody stared at her. She drew the coat tight around her hips and began to swagger. He was drawn by her eyes. They were cold pieces of wet glass.

"Wish I knowed what the way to Kentucky," Chinatown was moaning. He turned and saw the woman. "Man! Man! Kentucky kin wait."

The girl passed them. Her swimming eyes invited. They caught a heavy scent of perfume. Under the perfume was a rot stink. The stink sickened them. They were unnerved.

"Howdy, boys. Green, huh?"

They whirled and faced a small, dark man. He shifted from one foot to the other. His movements were like a squirrel's.

"Howdy," said Chinatown.

"How come you know we green?" asked Melody.

"They give all green niggers the same clothes," said the man.

"Oh . . ." Melody's gaze followed the woman.

"Beside, only a green man stop to look at that there gal."

They questioned him with their eyes.

"Her left breast 'bout rotted off." The man laughed. "You kin smell it a mile away."

"What you know!" Chinatown laughed.

Melody was stunned. He could not get the wet eyes out of his mind. All he could think to say was, "We lost from the bunkhouse."

"You been goin' wrong," said the man. "Back the other way a piece."

"Obliged," said Melody.

"I got to pass by there. Point it out."

"Obliged."

They walked along together.

"You work around here?" Chinatown asked.

"Blast. Boss of stove gang," said the man.

"Oh," said Chinatown. He looked at the old overalls.

"Sparks," explained the little man. "They'll git you too."

"Oh."

A group of Slav workmen came out of a gate in front of one of the mills. They moved with a slow stiffness, hardly shaking their drooping mustaches. There was dignity in the way they walked.

"Uh-uh," groaned Chinatown.

The workmen paused at the gate. One of them turned and waved at the little black man.

"Hallo, Bo."

The little man waved back. That greeting was the easy familiarity of men who had known each other over a period of years.

Chinatown voiced what was in his mind: "That there's the first white guy we seen don't hate niggers."

Bo asked, "You been havin' trouble?"

"Everybody treat us like poison," said Chinatown.

"Everythin' be smooth in a coupla weeks," said Bo. "Always hate new niggers round here."

"How come?"

"Well, company bring them in when there strike talk. Keep the old men in line."

"Oh . . ." said Chinatown. They walked a little. "There strike talk now?"

Bo looked him in the eye. "Looka here, boy. I don't know nothin' but my job."

"Yessir," said Chinatown.

"Don't mean nothin' by talkin' short," said Bo, "only it ain't a good thing for a feller to go spoutin' off."

"That's like Kentucky," said Chinatown.

Within sight of the bunkhouse, Bo stopped in the open to let water.

"Good idea," he said. "The outhouse always full of flies. Smells because nobody sprinkle ashes like they supposed to." He laughed. "Sometime a lizard use your behind for a bridge when you on the hole."

The men from the hills had always let water in the open. It made a feller feel free—space around him and the warm water running in the weeds. Nothing overhead but what God first put there. This touch of the past relaxed them. Their recent experiences became the unreality. This was the reality. They felt for a minute like Bo was an old friend.

"Well, so long," said Bo. "Be keerful. They puts green men on the hot jobs afore they know enough to keep alive."

They stood and watched him cut across the weedy ground to the cinder path leading to the lunch car.

Richard Wright

Big Boy Leaves Home

I

Yo mama don wear no drawers . . .

Clearly, the voice rose out of the woods, and died away. Like an echo another voice caught it up:

Ah seens when she pulled em off . . .

Another, shrill, cracking, adolescent:

N she washed 'em in alcohol . . .

Then a quartet of voices, blending in harmony, floated high above the tree tops:

N she hung 'em out in the hall . . .

Laughing easily, four black boys came out of the woods into cleared pasture. They walked lollingly in bare feet, beating tangled vines and bushes with long sticks.

"Ah wished Ah knowed some mo lines t tha song."

"Me too."

"Yeah, when yuh gits t where she hangs em out in the hall huh has t stop."

"Shucks, whut goes wid *hall?*"

"*Call.*"

"*Fall.*"

"*Wall.*"

"*Quall.*"

They threw themselves on the grass, laughing.

"Big Boy?"

"Huh?"

"Yuh know one thing?"

"Whut?"

"Yuh sho is crazy!"

"Crazy?"

"Yeah, yuh crazys a bed-bug!"

"Crazy bout whut?"

"Man, whoever hearda *quall?*"

"Yuh said yuh wanted something t go wid *hall*, didn't yuh?"

"Yeah, but whats a *quall?*"

"Nigger, a *qualls* a *quall*."

They laughed easily, catching and pulling long green blades of grass with their toes.

"Waal, ef a *qualls* a *quall*, what IS a *quall?*"

"Oh, Ah know."

"Whut?"

"The ol song goes something like this:

Yo mama don wear no drawers,
  Ah seens when she pulled em off,
N she washed em in alcohol,
  N she hung em out in the hall,
N then she put em back on her Quall!"

They laughed again. Their shoulders were flat to the earth, their knees propped up, and their faces square to the sun.

"Big Boy, yuhs CRAZY!"

"Don ax me nothin else."

"Nigger, yuhs CRAZY!"

They fell silent, smiling, drooping the lids of their eyes softly against the sunlight.

"Man, don the groun feel warm?"

"Jus lika bed."

"Jeesus, Ah could stay here ferever."

"Me too."

"Ah kin feel the ol sun goin all thu me."

"Feels like mah bones is warm."

In the distance a train whistled mournfully.

"There goes number fo!"

"Hittin on all six!"
"Highballin it down the line!"
"Boun fer up Noth, Lawd, bound fer up Noth!"
They began to chant, pounding bare heels in the grass.

Dis train boun fo Glory \
Dis train, Oh Hallelujah
Dis train bound fo Glory
Dis train, Oh Hallelujah
Dis train bound fo Glory
Ef yuh ride no need fer fret er worry
Dis train, Oh Hallelujah
Dis train . . .

Dis train don carry no gambler
Dis train, Oh Hallelujah
Dis train don carry no gambler
Dis train, Oh Hallelujah
Dis train don carry no gambler
No fo day creeper er midnight rambler
Dis train, Oh Hallelujah
Dis train . . .

When the song ended they burst out laughing, thinking of a
train bound for Glory.
"Gee, thas a good ol song!"
"Huuuuummmmmmmmmmman . . ."
"Whut?"
"Geeee whiiiiiz . . ."
"Whut?"
"Somebody don let win! Das whut!"
Buck, Bobo and Lester jumped up. Big Boy stayed on the
ground, feigning sleep.
"Jeesus, that sho stinks!"
"Big Boy!"
Big Boy feigned to snore.
"Big Boy!"

Big Boy stirred as though in sleep.

"Big Boy!"

"Hunh?"

"Yuh rotten inside!"

"Rotten?"

"Lawd, cant yuh smell it?"

"Smell whut?"

"Nigger, yuh mus gotta bad col!"

"*Smell whut?*"

"NIGGER, YUH BROKE WIN!"

Big Boy laughed and fell back on the grass, closing his eyes.

"The hen whut cackles is the hen whut laid the egg."

"We ain no hens."

"Yuh cackled, didnt yuh?"

The three moved off with noses turned up.

"C mon!"

"Where yuh-all goin?"

"T the creek for a swim."

"Yeah, les swim."

"Naw buddy naw!" said Big Boy, slapping the air with a scornful palm.

"Aa, c mon! Don be a heel!"

"N git *lynched?* Hell naw!"

"He ain gonna see us."

"How yuh know?"

"Cause he ain."

"Yuh-all go on. Ahma stay righ here," said Big Boy.

"Hell, let im stay! C mon, les go," said Buck.

The three walked off, swishing at grass and bushes with sticks. Big Boy looked lazily at their backs.

"Hey!"

Walking on, they glanced over their shoulders.

"Hey, niggers!"

"C mon!"

Big Boy grunted, picked up his tick, pulled to his feet, and stumbled off.

"Wait!"

"C mon!"

He ran, caught up with them, leaped upon their backs, bearing them to the ground.

"Nigger, whut yuh think we is, hosses?"

"How come yuh awways hoppin on us?"

"Lissen, wes gonna doubl-team on yuh one of these days n beat yo ol ass good."

Big Boy smiled.

"Sho nough?"

"Yeah, don yuh like it?"

"We gonna beat yuh sos yuh cant walk!"

"N dare yuh t do nothing erbout it!"

Big Boy bared his teeth.

"C mon! Try it now!"

The three circled around him.

"Say, Buck, yuh grab his feets!"

"N yuh git his head, Lester!"

"No Bobo, yuh git behin n grab his arms!"

Keeping more than arm's length, they circled round and round Big Boy.

"C mon!" said Big Boy, feinting at one and then the other.

Round and round they circled, but could not seem to get any closer. Big Boy stopped and braced his hands on his hips.

"Is all three of yuh-all scareda me?"

"Les git im some other time," said Bobo, grinning.

"Yeah, we kin ketch yuh when yuh ain thinkin," said Lester.

"We kin trick yuh," said Buck.

They laughed and walked together.

Big Boy belched.

"Ahm hongry," he said.

"Me too."

"Ah wished Ah hada big hot pota belly-busters!"

"Cooked wid some good ol salty ribs . . ."

"N some good ol egg cornbread . . ."

"N some buttermilk . . ."

"N some hot peach cobbler swimmin in juice . . ."

"Nigger, Hush!"

They began to chant, emphasizing the rhythm by cutting at grass with sticks.

Bye n bye
Ah wanna piece of pie
Pies too sweet
Ah wanna piece of meat
Meats too red
Ah wanna piece of bread
Breads too brown
Ah wanna go t town
Towns too far
Ah wanna ketch a car
Cars too fas
Ah fall n break mah ass
Ahll understan it better bye n bye . . .

They climbed over a barbed-wire fence and entered a stretch of thick woods. Big Boy was whistling softly, his eyes half-closed.

"LES GIT IM!"

Buck, Lester, and Bobo whirled, grabbed Big Boy about the neck, arms, and legs, bearing him to the ground. He grunted and kicked wildly as he went back into weeds.

"Hol im tight!"

"Git his arms! Git his arms!"

"Set on his legs so he cant kick!"

Big Boy puffed heavily, trying to get loose.

"WE GOT YUH NOW, GAWDDAMMIT, WE GOT YUH NOW!"

"Thas a Gawddam lie!" said Big Boy. He kicked, twisted, and clutched for a hold on one and then the other.

"Say, yuh-all hep me hol his arms!" said Bobo.

"Aw, we got this bastard now!" said Lester.

"Thas a Gawddam lie!" said Big Boy again.

"Say, yuh-all hep me hol his arms!" called Bobo.

Big Boy managed to encircle the neck of Bobo with his left

arm. He tightened his elbow scissors-like and hissed through his teeth:

"Yuh got me, ain yuh?"

"Hol im!"

"Les beat this bastard's ass!"

"Say, hep me hol his *arms!* Hes got aholda mah *neck!*" cried Bobo.

Big Boy squeezed Bobo's neck and twisted his head to the ground.

"Yuh got me, ain yuh?"

"Quit, Big Boy, yuh chokin me! Yuh hurtin mah neck!" cried Bobo.

"Turn me loose!" said Big Boy.

"Ah ain got yuh! Its the others whut got yuh!" pleaded Bobo.

"Tell them others t git t hell offa me or Ahma break yo neck," said Big Boy.

"Ssssay, yyyuh-al gggit ooooffa Bbig Boy. Hhes got me," gurgled Bobo.

"Cant yuh hol im?"

"Nnaw, hhes ggot mmah nneck . . ."

Big Boy squeezed tighter.

"N Ahma break it too les yuh tell em t git t hell offa me!"

"Ttturn mmmeee lllloose," panted Bobo, tears gushing.

"Cant yuh hol im, Bobo?" asked Buck.

"Nnaw, yuh-all tturn im lloose; hhhes got mah nnneck . . ."

"Grab his neck, Bobo . . ."

"Ah cant; yugurgur . . ."

To save Bobo, Lester and Buck got up and ran to a safe distance. Big Boy released Bobo, who staggered to his feet, slobbering and trying to stretch a crick out of his neck.

"Shucks, nigger, yuh almos broke mah neck," whimpered Bobo.

"Ahm gonna break yo ass nex time," said Big Boy.

"Ef Bobo coulda hel yuh we woulda had yuh," yelled Lester.

"Ah waznt gonna let im do that," said Big Boy.

They walked together again, swishing sticks.

"Yuh see," began Big Boy, "when a ganga guys jump on yuh, all yuh gotta do is put the heat on one of them n make im tell the other t let up, see?"

"Gee, thas a good idee!"

"Yeah, thas a good idee!"

"But yuh almost broke mah neck, man," said Bobo.

"Ahma smart nigger," said Big Boy, thrusting out his chest.

II

They came to the swimming hole.

"Ah ain goin in," said Bobo.

"Done get scared?" asked Big Boy.

"Naw, Ah ain scared . . ."

"How come yuh ain goin in?"

"Yuh know ol man Harvey don erllow no niggers t swim in this hole."

"N jus las year he took a shot at Bob fer swimmin in here," said Lester.

"Shucks, ol man Harvey ain studyin bout us niggers," said Big Boy.

"Hes at home thinking about his jelly-roll," said Buck.

They laughed.

"Buck, yo mins lowern a snakes belly," said Lester.

"Ol man Harveys too doggone ol t think erbout jelly-roll," said Big Boy.

"Hes dried up; all the saps done lef im," said Bobo.

"C mon, les go!" said Big Boy.

Bobo pointed.

"See tha sign over yonder?"

"Yeah."

"Whut it say?"

"NO TRESPASSIN," read Lester.

"Know whut tha mean?"

"Mean ain no dogs n niggers erllowed," said Buck.

"Waal, wes here now," said Big Boy. "Ef he ketched us even like this thered be trouble, so we just as waal go on in . . ."

"Ahm wid the nex one!"

"Ahll go ef anybody else goes!"

Big Boy looked carefully in all directions. Seeing nobody, he began jerking off his overalls.

"LAS ONE INS A OL DEAD DOG!"

"THAS YO MA!"

"THAS YO PA!"

"THAS BOTH YO MA N YO PA!"

They jerked off their clothes and threw them in a pile under a tree. Thirty seconds later they stood, black and naked, on the edge of the hole under a sloping embankment. Gingerly Big Boy touched the water with his foot.

"Man, this waters col," he said.

"Ahm gonna put mah cloes back on," said Bobo, withdrawing his foot.

Big Boy grabbed him about the waist.

"Like hell yuh is!"

"Git outta the way, nigger!" Bobo yelled.

"Throw im in!" said Lester.

"Duck im!"

Bobo crouched, spread his legs, and braced himself against Big Boy's body. Locked in each other's arms, they tussled on the edge of the hole, neither able to throw the other.

"C mon, les me n yuh push em in."

"O.K."

Laughing, Lester and Buck gave the two locked bodies a running push. Big Boy and Bobo splashed, sending up silver spray in the sunlight. When Big Boy's head came up he yelled:

"Yuh bastard!"

"That wuz yo ma yuh pushed!" said Bobo, shaking his head to clear the water from his eyes.

They did a surface dive, came up and struck out across the creek. The muddy water foamed. They swam back, waded into shallow water, breathing heavily and blinking eyes.

"C mon in!"

"Man, the waters fine!"

Lester and Buck hesitated.

"Les wet em," Big Boy whispered to Bobo.

Before Lester and Buck could back away, they were dripping wet from handsful of scooped water.

"Hey, quit!"

"Gawddam, nigger; that waters col!"

"C mon in!" called Big Boy.

"We just as waal go on in now," said Buck.

"Look n see ef anybodys comin."

Kneeling, they squinted among the trees.

"Ain nobody."

"C mon, les go."

They waded in slowly, pausing each few steps to catch their breath. A desperate water battle began. Closing eyes and backing away, they shunted water into one another's faces with the flat palms of hands.

"Hey, cut it out!"

"Yeah, Ahm bout drownin!"

They came together in water up to their navels, blowing and blinking. Big Boy ducked, upsetting Bobo.

"Look out, nigger!"

"Don holler so loud!"

"Yeah, they kin hear yo ol big mouth a mile erway."

"This waters too col fer me."

"Thas cause it rained yistiddy."

They swam across and back again.

"Ah wish we hada bigger place t swim in."

"The white folks got plenty swimmin pools n we ain got none."

"Ah useta swim in the ol Missippi when we lived in Vicksburg."

Big Boy put his head under the water and blew his breath. A sound came like that of a hippopotamus.

"C mon, les be hippos."

Each went to a corner of the creek and put his mouth just below the surface and blew like a hippopotamus. Tiring, they came and sat under the embankment.

"Look like Ah gotta chill."

"Me too."

"Les stay here n dry off."

"Jeesus, Ahm col!"

They kept still in the sun, suppressing shivers. After some of the water had dried off their bodies they began to talk through clattering teeth.

"Whut would yuh do ef ol man Harveyd come erlong right now?"

"Run like hell!"

"Man, Ahd run so fas hed thinka black streaka lightnin shot pass im."

"But spose he hada gun?"

"Aw, nigger, shut up!"

They were silent. They ran their hands over wet, trembling legs, brushing water away. Then their eyes watched the sun sparkling on the restless creek.

Far away a train whistled.

"There goes number seven!"

"Headin fer up Noth!"

"Blazin it down the line!"

"Lawd, Ahm goin Noth some day."

"Me too, man."

"They say colored folks up Noth is got ekual rights."

They grew pensive. A black winged butterfly hovered at the water's edge. A bee droned. From somewhere came the sweet scent of honeysuckles. Dimly they could hear sparrows twittering in the woods. They rolled from side to side, letting sunshine dry their skins and warm their blood. They plucked blades of grass and chewed them.

"Oh!"

They looked up, their lips parting.

"Oh!"

A white woman, poised on the edge of the opposite embankment, stood directly in front of them, her hat in her hand and her hair lit by the sun.

"Its a woman!" whispered Big Boy in an underbreath. "A *white* woman!"

They stared, their hands instinctively covering their groins.

Then they scrambled to their feet. The white woman backed slowly out of sight. They stood for a moment, looking at one another.

"Les git outta here!" Big Boy whispered.

"Wait till she goes erway."

"Les run, theyll ketch us here naked like this!"

"Mebbe theres a man wid her."

"C mon, les git our cloes," said Big Boy.

They waited a moment longer, listening.

"What t hell! Ahma git mah cloes," said Big Boy.

Grabbing at short tufts of grass, he climbed the embankment.

"Don run out there now!"

"C mon back, fool!"

Bobo hesitated. He looked at Big Boy, and then at Buck and Lester.

"Ahm goin wid Big Boy n git mah cloes," he said.

"Don run out there naked like tha, fool!" said Buck. "Yuh don know whos out there!"

Big Boy was climbing over the edge of the embankment.

"C mon," he whispered.

Bobo climbed after. Twenty-five feet away the woman stood. She had one hand over her mouth. Hanging by fingers, Buck and Lester peeped over the edge.

"C mon back; that womans scared," said Lester.

Big Boy stopped, puzzled. He looked at the woman. He looked at the bundle of clothes. Then he looked at Buck and Lester.

"C mon, les git our cloes!"

He made a step.

"Jim!" the woman screamed.

Big Boy stopped and looked around. His hands hung loosely at his side. The woman, her eyes wide, her hand over her mouth, backed away to the tree where their clothes lay in a heap.

"Big Boy, come back here n wait till shes gone!"

Bobo ran to Big Boy's side.

"Les go home! Theyll ketch us here," he urged.

Big Boy's throat felt tight.

"Lady, we wanna git our cloes," he said.

Buck and Lester climbed the embankment and stood indecisively. Big Boy ran toward the tree.

"Jim!" the woman screamed. "Jim! Jim!"

Black and naked, Big Boy stopped three feet from her.

"We wanna git our cloes," he said again, his words coming mechanically.

He made a motion.

"You go away! You go away! I tell you, you go away!"

Big Boy stopped again, afraid. Bobo ran and snatched the clothes. Buck and Lester tried to grab theirs out of his hands.

"You go away! You go away!" You go away!" the woman screamed.

"Les go!" said Bobo, running toward the woods.

CRACK!

Lester grunted, stiffened, and pitched forward. His forehead struck a toe of the woman's shoes.

Bobo stopped, clutching the clothes. Buck whirled. Big Boy stared at Lester, his lips moving.

"Hes gotta gun; hes gotta gun!" yelled Buck, running wildly.

CRACK!

Buck stopped at the edge of the embankment, his head jerked backward, his body arched stiffly to one side; he toppled headlong, sending up a shower of bright spray to the sunlight. The creek bubbled.

Big Boy and Bobo backed away, their eyes fastened fearfully on a white man who was running toward them. He had a rifle and wore an army officer's uniform. He ran to the woman's side and grabbed her hand.

"You hurt, Bertha, you hurt?"

She stared at him and did not answer.

The man turned quickly. His face was red. He raised the rifle and pointed it at Bobo. Bobo ran back, holding the clothes in front of his chest.

"Don shoot me, Mistah, don shoot me . . ."

Big Boy lunged for the rifle, grabbing the barrel.

"You black sonofabitch!"

Big Boy clung desperately.

"Let go, you black bastard!"

The barrel pointed skyward.

CRACK!

The white man, taller and heavier, flung Big Boy to the ground. Bobo dropped the clothes, ran up, and jumped onto the white man's back.

"You black sonsofbitches!"

The white man released the rifle, jerked Bobo to the ground, and began to batter the naked boy with his fists. Then Big Boy swung, striking the man in the mouth with the barrel. His teeth caved in, and he fell, dazed. Bobo was on his feet.

"C mon, Big Boy, les go!"

Breathing hard, the white man got up and faced Big Boy. His lips were trembling, his neck and chin wet with blood. He spoke quietly.

"Give me that gun, boy!"

Big Boy leveled the rifle and backed away.

The white man advanced.

"Boy, I say give me that gun!"

Bobo had the clothes in his arms.

"Run, Big Boy, run!"

The man came at Big Boy.

"Ahll kill yuh; Ahll kill yah!" said Big Boy.

His fingers fumbled for the trigger.

The man stopped, blinked, spat blood. His eyes were bewildered. His face whitened. Suddenly, he lunged for the rifle, his hands outstretched.

CRACK!

He fell forward on his face.

"Jim!"

Big Boy and Bobo turned in surprise to look at the woman.

"Jim!" she screamed again, and fell weakly at the foot of the tree.

Big Boy dropped the rifle, his eyes wide. He looked around. Bobo was crying and clutching the clothes.

"Big Boy, Big Boy . . ."

Big Boy looked at the rifle, started to pick it up, but didn't. He seemed at a loss. He looked at Lester, then at the white man; his eyes followed a thin stream of blood that seeped to the ground.

"Yuh done killed im," mumbled Bobo.

"Les go home!"

Naked, they turned and ran toward the wood. When they reached the barbed-wire fence they stopped.

"Les git our cloes on," said Big Boy.

They slipped quickly into overalls. Bobo held Lester's and Buck's clothes.

"Whut we gonna do wid these?"

Big Boy stared. His hands twitched.

"Leave em."

They climbed the fence and ran through the woods. Vines and leaves switched their faces. Once Bobo tripped and fell.

"C mon!" said Big Boy.

Bobo started crying, blood streaming from his scratches.

"Ahm scared!"

"C mon! Don cry! We wanna git home fo they ketches us!"

"Ahm scared!" said Bobo again, his eyes full of tears.

Big Boy grabbed his hand and dragged him along.

"C mon!"

III

They stopped when they got to the end of the woods. They could see the open road leading home, to ma and pa. But they hung back, afraid. The thick shadows cast from the trees were friendly and sheltering. But the wide glare of sun stretching out over the fields was pitiless. They crouched behind an old log.

"We gotta git home," said Big Boy.

"Theys gonna lynch us," said Bobo, half-questioningly.

Big Boy did not answer.

"Theys gonna lynch us," said Bobo again.

Big Boy shuddered.

"Hush!" he said. He did not want to think of it. He could not think of it; there was but one thought, and he clung to that one blindly. He had to get home, home to ma and pa.

Their heads jerked up. Their ears had caught the rhythmic jingle of a wagon. They fell to the ground and clung flat to the side of a log. Over the crest of the hill came the top of a hat. A white face. Then shoulders in a blue shirt. A wagon drawn by two horses pulled into full view.

Big Boy and Bobo held their breath, waiting. Their eyes followed the wagon till it was lost in dust around a bend of the road.

"We gotta git home," said Big Boy.

"Ahm scared," said Bobo.

"C mon! Les keep t the fields."

They ran till they came to the cornfields. Then they went slower, for last year's corn stubbles bruised their feet.

They came in sight of a brickyard.

"Wait a minute," gasped Big Boy.

They stopped.

"Ahm goin on t mah home n yuh better go on t yos."

Bobo's eyes grew round.

"Ahm scared!"

"Yuh better go on!"

"Lemme go wid yuh; theyll ketch me . . ."

"Ef yuh kin git home mebbe yo folks kin hep yuh to git erway."

Big Boy started off. Bobo grabbed him.

"Lemme go wid yuh!"

Big Boy shook free.

"Ef yuh stay here theys gonna lynch yuh!" he yelled, running.

After he had gone about twenty-five yards he turned and looked; Bobo was flying through the woods like the wind.

Big Boy slowed when he came to the railroad. He wondered if he ought to go through the streets or down the track. He decided on the tracks. He could dodge a train better than a mob.

He trotted along the ties, looking ahead and back. His cheek itched, and he felt it. His hand came away smeared with blood. He wiped it nervously on his overalls.

When he came to his back fence he heaved himself over. He landed among a flock of startled chickens. A bantam rooster tried to spur him. He slipped and fell in front of the kitchen steps, grunting heavily. The ground was slick with greasy dish-water.

Panting, he stumbled through the doorway.

"Lawd, Big Boy, whuts wrong wid yuh?"

His mother stood gaping in the middle of the floor. Big Boy flopped wordlessly onto a stool, almost toppling over. Pots simmered on the stove. The kitchen smelled of food cooking.

"Whuts the matter, Big Boy?"

Mutely, he looked at her. Then he burst into tears. She came and felt the scratches on his face.

"Whut happened t yuh, Big Boy? Somebody been botherin yuh?"

"They after me, Ma! They after me . . ."

"Who!"

"Ah . . . Ah . . . We . . ."

"Big Boy, whuts wrong wid yuh?"

"He killed Lester n Buck," he muttered simply.

"Killed!"

"Yessum."

"Lester n Buck!"

"Yessum, Ma!"

"Lawd Gawd in Heaven, have mercy on us all! This is mo trouble, mo trouble," she moaned, wringing her hands.

"N Ah killed im, Ma . . ."

She stared, trying to understand.

"What happened, Big Boy?"

"We tried t git our cloes from the tree . . ."

"Whut tree?"

"We wuz swimmin, Ma. N the white woman . . ."

"*White* woman? . . ."

"Yessum. She wuz at the swimmin hole . . ."

"Lawd have mercy! Ah knowed yuh boys wuz gonna keep on till yuh got into somethin like this!"

She ran into the hall.

"Lucy!"

"Mam?"

"C mere!"

"Mam?"

"C mere, Ah say!"

"Whutcha wan, Ma? Ahm sewin."

"Chile, will yuh c mere like Ah ast yuh?"

Lucy came to the door holding an unfinished apron in her hands. When she saw Big Boy's face she looked wildly at her mother.

"Whuts the matter?"

"Wheres Pa?"

"Hes out front, Ah reckon."

"Git im, quick!"

"Whuts the matter, Ma?"

"Go git yo Pa, Ah say!"

Lucy ran out. The mother sank into a chair, holding a dish rag. Suddenly, she sat up. "Big Boy, Ah thought yuh wuz at school?"

Big Boy looked at the floor.

"How come yuh didnt go to school?"

"We went t the woods."

She sighed.

"Ah done done all Ah kin fer yuh, Big Boy. Only Gawd kin help yuh now."

"Ma, don let em git me; don let em git me . . ."

His father came into the doorway. He stared at Big Boy, then at his wife.

"Whats Big Boy inter now?" he asked sternly.

"Saul, Big Boys done gone n got inter trouble wid the white folks."

The old man's mouth dropped, and he looked from one to the other.

"Saul, we gotta git im erway from here."

"Open yo mouth n talk! Whut yuh been doin?" The old man gripped Big Boy's shoulders and peered at the scratches on his face.

"Me n Lester n Buck n Bobo wuz out on ol man Harveys place swimmin . . ."

"Saul, its a *white* woman!"

Big Boy winced. The old man compressed his lips and stared at his wife. Lucy gaped at her brother as though she had never seen him before.

"Whut happened? Cany yuh all talk?" the old man thundered, with a certain helplessness in his voice.

"We wuz swimmin," Big Boy began, "n then a white woman comes up t the hole. We got up right erway to git our cloes sos we could git erway, n she started screamin. Our cloes wuz right by the tree where she wuz standin, n when we started t git em she jus screamed. We told her we wanted our cloes . . . Yuh see, Pa, she was standin' right *by* our cloes; n when we went to git em she jus screamed . . . Bobo got the cloes, n then he shot Lester . . ."

"*Who* shot Lester?"

"The white man."

"Whut white man?"

"Ah dunno, Pa. He wuz a soljer, n he had a rifle."

"A soljer?"

"Yessuh."

"A *soljer?*"

"Yessuh, Pa. A soljer."

The old man frowned.

"N then what yuh-all do?"

"Waal, Buck said, 'Hes gotta gun!' N we started runnin. N then he shot Buck, n he fell in the swimmin hole. We didn't see im no mo . . . He wuz close on us then. He looked at the white woman n then he started t shoot Bobo. Ah grabbed the gun, n we started fightin. Bobo jumped on his back. He started beatin Bobo. Then Ah hit im wid the gun. Then he started at me n Ah shot im. Then we run . . ."

"Who seen?"

"Nobody."

"Wheres Bobo?"

"He went home."

"Anybody run after yuh-all?"

"Nawsuh."

"Yuh see anybody?"

"Nawsuh. Nobody but a white man. But he didn't see us."

"How long fo yuh-all lef the swimmin hole?"

"Little while ergo."

The old man nervously brushed his hand across his eyes and walked to the door. His lips moved, but no words came.

"Saul, whut we gonna do?"

"Lucy," began the old man, "go t Brother Sanders n tell im Ah said c mere; n go t Brother Jenkins n tell im Ah said c mere; n go to Elder Peters n tell im Ah said c mere. N don say nothin to nobody but whut Ah tol yuh. N when yuh git thu come straight back. Now go!"

Lucy dropped her apron across the back of a chair and ran down the steps. The mother bent over, crying and praying. The old man walked slowly over to Big Boy.

"Big Boy?"

Big Boy swallowed.

"Ahm talkin t yuh!"

"Yessuh."

"How come yuh didnt go t school this mawnin?"

"We went t the woods."

"Didnt yo ma send yuh t school?"

"Yessuh."

"How come yuh didnt go?"

"We went t the woods."

"Don yuh know thas wrong?"

"Yessuh."

"How come yuh go?"

Big Boy looked at his fingers, knotted them, and squirmed in his seat.

"AHM TALKIN T YUH!"

His wife straightened up and said reprovingly:

"Saul!"

The old man desisted, yanking nervously at the shoulder straps of his overalls.

"How long wuz the woman there?"

"Not long."

"Wuz she young?"

"Yessuh. Lika gal."

"Did yuh-all say anythin t her?"

"Nawsuh. We jes said we wanted our cloes."

"N what she say?"

"Nothin, Pa. She jus backed erway t the tree n screamed."

The old man stared, his lips trying to form a question.

"Big Boy, did yuh-all bother her?"

"Nawsuh, Pa. We didn't *touch* her."

"How long fo the white man come up?"

"Right erway."

"Whut he say?"

"Nothin. He jus cussed us."

Abruptly the old man left the kitchen.

"Ma, cant Ah go fo they ketches me?"

"Sauls doin whut he kin."

"Ma, Ma, Ah don want em t ketch me . . ."

"Sauls doin whut he kin. Nobody but the good Lawd kin hep us now."

The old man came back with a shotgun and leaned it in a corner. Fascinatedly, Big Boy looked at it.

There was a knock at the front door.

"Liza, see whos there."

She went. They were silent, listening. They could hear her talking.

"Whos there?"

"Me."

"Who?"

"Me, Brother Sanders."

"C mon in. Sauls waitin fer yuh."

Sanders paused in the doorway, smiling.

"Yuh sent fer me, Brother Morrison?"

"Brother Sanders, wes in deep trouble here."

Sanders came all the way into the kitchen.

"Yeah?"

"Big Boy done gone n killed a white man."

Sanders stopped short, then came forward, his face thrust out, his mouth open. His lips moved several times before he could speak.

"A *white* man?"

"They gonna kill me; they gonna kill me!" Big Boy cried, running to the old man.

"Saul, cant we git im erway somewhere?"

"Here now, take it easy; take it easy," said Sanders, holding Big Boy's wrists.

"They gonna kill me; they gonna lynch me!"

Big Boy slipped to the floor. They lifted him to a stool. His mother held him closely, pressing his head to her bosom.

"Whut we gonna do?" asked Sanders.

"Ah done sent fer Brother Jenkins n Elder Peters."

Sanders leaned his shoulders against the wall. Then, as the full meaning of it came to him, he exclaimed:

"Theys gonna git a mob! . . ." His voice broke off and his eyes fell on the shotgun.

Feet came pounding on the steps. They turned toward the door. Lucy ran in crying. Jenkins followed. The old man met him in the middle of the room, taking his hand.

"Wes in bad trouble here, Brother Jenkins. Big Boy's done gone n killed a white man. Yuh-alls gotta hep me . . ."

Jenkins looked hard at Big Boy.

"Elder Peters says hes comin," said Lucy.

"When all this happen?" asked Jenkins.

"Near bout a hour ergo, now," said the old man.

"Whut we gonna do?" asked Jenkins.

"Ah wanna wait till Elder Peters come," said the old man helplessly.

"But we gotta work fas ef we gonna do anythin," said Sanders. "We'll git in trouble jus standin here like this."

Big Boy pulled away from his mother.

"Pa, lemma go now! Lemma go now!"

"Be still, Big Boy!"

"Where kin yuh go?"

"Ah could ketch a freight!"

"Thas *sho* death!" said Jenkins. "They'll be watchin em all!"

"Kin yuh-all hep me wid some money?" the old man asked.
They shook their heads.

"Saul, whut kin we do? Big Boy cant stay here."

There was another knock at the door.

The old man backed stealthily to the shotgun.

"Lucy, go!"

Lucy looked at him, hesitating.

"Ah better go," said Jenkins.

It was Elder Peters. He came in hurriedly.

"Good evenin, everybody!"

"How yuh, Elder?"

"Good evenin."

"How yuh today?"

Peters looked around the crowded kitchen.

"Whuts the matter?"

"Elder, wes in deep trouble," began the old man. "Big Boy n
some mo boys . . ."

". . . Lester n Buck n Bobo . . ."

". . . wuz over on ol man Harveys place swimmin . . ."

"N he don like us niggers *none*," said Peters emphatically.
He widened his legs and put his thumbs in the armholes of his
vest.

". . . n some white woman . . ."

"Yeah?" said Peters, coming closer.

". . . comes erlong n the boys tries t git their cloes where
they done lef em under a tree. Waal, she started screamin n all,
see? Reckon she thought the boys wuz after her. Then a white
man in a soljers suit shoots two of em . . ."

". . . Lester n Buck . . ."

"Huummm," said Peters. "Tha wuz old man Harveys son."

"Harveys son?"

"Yuh mean the one that wuz in the Army?"

"Yuh mean Jim?"

"Yeah," said Peters. "The papers said he wuz here fer a vacation from his regiment. N tha woman the boys saw wuz jus erbout his wife . . ."

They stared at Peters. Now that they knew what white person had been killed, their fears became definite.

"N whut else happened?"

"Big Boy shot the man . . ."

"Harveys *son?*"

"He had t, Elder. He wuz gonna shoot im ef he didnt . . ."

"Lawd!" said Peters. He looked around and put his hat back on.

"How long ergo wuz this?"

"Mighty near an hour, now, Ah reckon."

"Do the white folks know yit?"

"Don know, Elder."

"Yuh-all better git this boy outta here right now," said Peters. "Cause ef yuh don theres gonna be a lynchin . . ."

"Where kin Ah go, Elder?" Big Boy ran up to him.

They crowded around Peters. He stood with his legs wide apart, looking up at the ceiling.

"Mabbe we kin hide im in the church till he kin git erway," said Jenkins.

Peters' lips flexed.

"Naw, Brother, thall never do! Theyll git him there sho. N anyhow, ef they ketch im there itll ruin us all. We gotta git the boy outta town . . ."

Sanders went up to the old man.

"Lissen," he said in a whisper. "Mah son, Will, the one whut drives fer the Magnolia Express Comny, is takin a truck o goods t Chicawgo in the mawnin. If we kin hide Big Boy somewhere till then, we kin put him on the truck . . ."

"Pa, please, lemme go wid Will when he goes in the mawnin," Big Boy begged.

The old man stared at Sanders.

"Yuh reckon thas safe?"

"Its the only thing yuh *kin* do," said Peters.

"But where we gonna hide im till then?"

"Whut time yo boy leaving out in the mawnin?"

"At six."

They were quiet, thinking. The water kettle on the stove sang.

"Pa, Ah knows where Will passes erlong wid the truck out on Bullards Road. Ah kin hide in one of them ol kilns . . ."

"Where?"

"In one of them kilns we built . . ."

"But they'll git yuh there," wailed the mother.

"But there ain no place else fer im to go."

"Theres some holes big enough fer me t git in n stay till Will comes erlong," said Big Boy. "Please, Pa, lemme go fo they ketches me . . ."

"Let im go!"

"Please, Pa . . ."

The old man breathed heavily.

"Lucy, git his things!"

"Saul, theyll git im out there!" wailed the mother, grabbing Big Boy.

Peters pulled her away.

"Sister Morrison, ef yuh don let im go n git erway from here hes gonna be caught shos theres a Gawd in Heaven!"

Lucy came running with Big Boy's shoes and pulled them on his feet. The old man thrust a battered hat on his head. The mother went to the stove and dumped the skillet of corn pone into her apron. She wrapped it, and unbuttoning Big Boy's overalls, pushed it into his bosom.

"Heres something fer yuh t eat; n pray, Big Boy, cause thas all anybody kin do now . . ."

Big Boy pulled to the door, his mother clinging to him.

"Let im go, Sister Morrison!"

"Run fas, Big Boy!"

Big Boy raced across the yard, scattering the chickens. He paused at the fence and hollered back:

"Tell Bobo where Ahm hidin n tell im to c mon!"

IV

He made for the railroad, running straight toward the sunset. He held his left hand tightly over his heart, holding the hot pone of corn bread there. At times he stumbled over the ties, for his shoes were tight and hurt his feet. His throat burned from thirst; he had had no water since noon.

He veered off the track and trotted over the crest of a hill, following Bullard's Road. His feet slipped and slid in the dust. He kept his eyes straight ahead, fearing every clump of shrubbery, every tree. He wished it were night. If he could only get to the kilns without meeting anyone. Suddenly a thought came to him like a blow. He recalled hearing the old folks tell tales of blood-hounds, and fear made him run slower. None of them had thought of that. Spose blood-houns wuz put on his trail? Lawd! Spose a whole pack of em, foamin n howlin, tore im t pieces? He went limp and his feet dragged. Yeah, thas whut they wuz gonna send after im, blood-houns! N then thered be no way fer im t dodge! Why hadn't Pa let im take tha shotgun? He stopped. He oughta go back n git tha shotgun. And then when the mob came he would take some with him.

In the distance he heard the approach of a train. It jarred him back to a sharp sense of danger. He ran again, his big shoes sopping up and down in the dust. He was tired and his lungs were bursting from running. He wet his lips, wanting water. As he turned from the road across a plowed field he heard the train roaring at his heels. He ran faster, gripped in terror.

He was nearly there now. He could see the black clay on the sloping hillside. Once inside a kiln he would be safe. For a little while, at least. He thought of the shotgun again. If he only had something! Someone to talk to . . . Thas right! Bobo! Bobod be wid im. Hed almost fergot Bobo. Bobod bringa gun; he knowed he would. N tergether they could kill the whole mob. Then in the mawning theyd git inter Will's truck n go far erway, to Chicawgo . . .

He slowed to a walk, looking back and ahead. A light wind skipped over the grass. A beetle lit on his cheek and he brushed it off. Behind the dark pines hung a red sun. Two bats flapped against that sun. He shivered, for he was growing cold; the sweat on his body was drying.

He stopped at the foot of the hill, trying to choose between two patches of black kilns high above him. He went to the left, for there lay the ones he, Bobo, Lester, and Buck had dug only last week. He looked around again; the landscape was bare. He climbed the embankment and stood before a row of black pits sinking four and five feet deep into the earth. He went to the largest and peered in. He stiffened when his ears caught the sound of a whir. He ran back a few steps and poised on his toes. Six foot of snake slid out of the pit and went into coil. Big Boy looked around wildly for a stick. He ran down the slope, peering into the grass. He stumbled over a tree limb. He picked it up and tested it by striking it against the ground.

Warily, he crept back up the slope, his stick poised. When about seven feet from the snake he stopped and waved the stick. The coil grew tighter, the whir sounded louder, and a flat head reared to strike. He went to the right, and the flat head followed him, the blue-black tongue darting forth; he went to the left, and the flat head followed him there too.

He stopped, teeth clenched. He had to kill this snake. Jus had t kill im! This wuz the safest pit on the hillside. He waved the stick again, looking at the snake before, thinking of a mob behind. The flat head reared higher. With stick over shoulder, he jumped in, swinging. The stick sang through the air, catching the snake on the side of the head, sweeping him out of coil. There was a brown writhing mass. Then Big Boy was upon him, pounding blows home, one on top of the other. He fought viciously, his eyes red, his teeth bared in a snarl. He beat till the snake lay still; then he stomped it with his heel, grinding its head into the dirt.

He stopped, limp, wet. The corners of his lips were white with spittle. He spat and shuddered.

Cautiously, he went to the hole and peered. He longed for a

match. He imagined whole nests of them in there waiting. He put the stick into the hole and waved it around. Stooping, he peered again. It mus be awright. He looked over the hillside, his eyes coming back to the dead snake. Then he got to his knees and backed slowly into the hole.

When inside he felt there must be snakes about him, ready to strike. It seemed he could see and feel them there, waiting tensely in coil. In the dark he imagined long, white fangs ready to sink into his neck, his side, his legs. He wanted to come out, but kept still. Shucks, he told himself, ef there wuz any snakes in here they sho woulda done bit me by now. Some of his fear left, and he relaxed.

With elbows on ground and chin on palms, he settled. The clay was cold to his knees and thighs, but his bosom was kept warm by the hot pone of corn bread. His thirst returned and he longed for a drink. He was hungry, too. But he did not want to eat the corn pone. Naw, not now. Mabbe after erwhile, after Bobo came. Then theyd both eat the corn pone.

The view from his hole was fringed by the long tufts of grass. He could see all the way to Bullard's Road, and even beyond. The wind was blowing, and in the east the first touch of dusk was rising. Every now and then a bird floated past, a spot of wheeling black printed against the sky. Big Boy sighed, shifted his weight, and chewed at a blade of grass. A wasp droned. He heard number nine, far away and mournful.

The train made him remember how they had dug these kilns on long hot summer days, how they had made boilers out of big tin cans, filled them with water, fixed stoppers for steam, cemented them in holes with wet clay, and built fires under them. He recalled how they had danced and yelled when a stopper blew out of a boiler, letting out a big spout of steam and a shrill whistle. There were times when they had the whole hillside blazing and smoking. Yeah, yuh see, Big Boy wuz Casey Jones n wuz speedin it down the gleamin rails of the Southern Pacific. Bobo had number two on the Santa Fe. Buck wuz on the Illinoy Central. Lester the Nickle Plate. Lawd, how they shoveled the wood in! The boiling water would almost jar the cans loose from the clay. More and more pine-knots and dry

leaves would be piled under the cans. Flames would grow so tall they would have to shield their eyes. Sweat would poor off their faces. Then, suddenly, a peg would shoot high into the air, and
Pssseeeezzzzzzzzzzzzzzzz . . .

Big Boy sighed and stretched out his arm, quenching the flames and scattering the smoke. Why didnt Bobo c mon? He looked over the fields; there was nothing but dying sunlight. His mind drifted back to the kilns. He remembered the day when Buck, jealous of his winning, had tried to smash his kiln. Yeah, that ol sonofabitch! Naw, Lawd! He didnt go t say tha! Whut wu he thinkin erbout? Cussin the dead! Yeah, po ol Buck wuz dead now. N Lester too. Yeah, it wuz awright fer Buck t smash his kiln. Sho. N he wished he hadnt socked ol Buck so hard tha day. He wuz sorry fer Buck now. N he sho wished he hadnt cussed po ol Bucks ma, neither. Tha wuz sinful! Mabbe Gawd would git im fer that? But he didnt go t do it! Po Buck! Po Lester! Hed never treat anybody like tha ergin, never . . .

Dusk was slowly deepening. Somewhere, he could not tell exactly where, a cricket took up a fitful song. The air was growing soft and heavy. He looked over the fields, longing for Bobo . . .

He shifted his body to ease the cold damp of the ground, and thought back over the day. Yeah, hed been dam right erbout not wantin t go swimmin. N ef hed followed his right min hed neverve gone n got inter all this trouble. At first hed said naw. But shucks, somehow hed just went on wid the res. Yeah he shoulda went on t school tha mawnin, like Ma told im t do. But, hell, who wouldnt git tireda awways drivin a guy t school! Tha wuz the big trouble awways drivin a guy to school. He wouldnt be in all this trouble now if it wuznt fer that Gawddam school! Impatiently, he took the grass out of his mouth and threw it away, demolishing the little red school house . . .

Yeah, if they had all kept still n quiet when tha ol white woman showed-up, mabbe shedve went on off. But yuh never kin tell erbout these white folks. Mabbe she wouldntve went. Mabbe tha white man woulda killed all of em! All *fo* of em! Yeah, yuh never kin tell erbout white folks. Then, ergin, mabbe tha white woman woulda went on off n laffed. Yeah, mabbe that white man woulda said: *Yuh nigger bastards git t hell outta here! Yuh know Gawdam well yuh don berlong here!* N then they woulda grabbed their cloes n run like all hell . . . He blinked the white man away. Where wuz Bobo? Why didnt he hurry up n c mon?

He jerked another blade and chewed. Yeah, ef Pa had only let im have tha shotgun! He could stan off a whole mob wid a shotgun. He looked at the ground as he turned a shotgun over in his hands. Then he leveled it at an advancing white man. *Boooom!* The man curled up. Another came. He reloaded quickly, and let him have what the other had got. He too curled up. Then another came. He got the same medicine. Then the whole mob swirled around him, and he blazed away, getting as many as he could. They closed in; but, by Gawd, he had done his part, hadnt he? N the newspapersd say: NIGGER KILLS DOZEN OF MOB BEFO LYNCHED! Er mabbe theyd say: TRAPPED NIGGER SLAYS TWENTY BEFO KILLED! He smiled a little. Tha wouldnt be so bad, would it? Blinking the newspaper away, he looked over the fields. Where wuz Bobo? Why didnt he hurry up n c mon?

He shifted, trying to get a crick out of his legs. Shucks, he wuz gettin tireda this. N it wuz almos dark now. Yeah, there wuz a little bittie star way over yonder in the eas. Mabbe tha white man wuznt dead? Mabbe they wuznt even lookin fer im? Mabbe he could go back home now? Naw, better wait erwhile. Thad be bes. But, Lawd, ef he only had some water! He could hardly swallow, his throat was so dry. Gawddam them white folks! Thas all they wuz good fer, t run a nigger down lika rabbit! Yeah, they git yuh in a corner n then they let yuh have it. A thousan of em! He shivered, for the cold of the clay was chilling his bones. Lawd, spose they found im here in this hole? N wid nobody t help im? . . . But ain no use in thinkin erbout tha; wait till trouble come fo yuh start fightin it. But if tha mob came one by one hed wipe em all out. Clean up the whole bunch. He caught one by the neck and choked him long and hard, choked him till his tongue and eyes popped out. Then he jumped upon his chest and stomped him like he had stomped that snake. When he had finished with one, another came. He choked him too. Choked till he sank slowly to the ground, gasping . . .

"Hoalo!"

Big Boy snatched his fingers from the white man's neck and looked over the fields. He saw nobody. Had someone spied him? He was shure that somebody had hollered. His heart pounded. But, shucks, nobody couldnt see im here in this hole . . . But mabbe theyd seen im when he wuz comin n had laid low n wuz now closin in on im! Praps they wuz signalin fer the others? Yeah, they wuz creepin up on im! Mabbe he oughta git up n run . . . Oh! Mabbe tha wuz Bobo! Yeah, Bobo! He oughta clim out n see if Bobo wuz lookin fer im . . . He stiffened.

"Hoalo!"

"Hoalo!"

"Wheres yuh?"

"Over here on Bullards Road!"

"C mon over!"

"Awright!"

He heard footsteps. Then voices came again, low and far away this time.

"Seen anybody?"

"Naw. Yuh?"

"Naw."

"Yuh reckon they got erway?"

"Ah dunno. Its hard t tell."

"Gawddam them sonofabitchin niggers!"

"We ought kill ever black bastard in this country!"

"Waal, Jim got two of em, anyhow."

"But Bertha said there wuz *fo!*"

"Where in hell they hidin?"

"She said one of em wuz named Big Boy, or somethin like tha."

"We went t his shack lookin fer im."

"Yeah?"

"But we didnt fin im."

"These niggers stick tergether; they don never tell on each other."

"We looked all thu the shack n couldnt fin hide ner hair of im. Then we drove the ol woman n man out n set the shack on fire . . ."

"Jeesus! Ah wished Ah coulda been there!"

"Yuh shoulda heard the ol nigger woman howl . . ."

"Hoalo!"

"C mon over!"

Big Boy eased to the edge and peeped. He saw a white man with a gun slung over his shoulder running down the slope. Wuz they gonna search the hill? Lawd, there wuz no way fer im t git erway now; he wuz caught! He shoulda knowed theyd git im here. N he didnt hava thing, notta thing t fight wid. Yeah, soon as the blood-houns came theyd fin im. Lawd, have mercy! Theyd lynch im right here on the hill . . . Theyd git im n tie im t a stake n burn im erlive? Lawd! Nobody but the good Lawd could hep im now, nobody . . .

He heard more feet running. He nestled deeper. His chest ached. Nobody but the good Lawd could hep now. They wuz crowdn all round im n when they hada big crowd theyd close in on im. Then itd be over . . . The good Lawd would have t hep im, cause nobody could hep im now, nobody . . .

And then he went numb when he remembered Bobo. Spose Bobod come now? Hed be caught sho! Both of em would be caught! Theyd make Bobo tell where he wuz! Bobo oughta not try to come now. Somebody oughta tell im . . . But there wuz nobody; there wuz no way . . .

He eased slowly back to the opening. There was a large group of men. More were coming. Many had guns. Some had coils of rope slung over shoulders.

"Ah tell yuh they still here, somewhere . . ."

"But we looked all over!"

"What t hell! Wouldnt do t let em git erway!"

"Naw. Ef they git erway notta woman in this town would be safe."

"Say, whuts tha yuh got?"

"Er pillar."

"Fer whut?"

"Feathers, fool!"

"Chris! Thisll be hot if we kin ketch them niggers!"

"Ol Anderson said he wuz gonna bringa barella tar!"

"Ah got some gasolin in mah car if yuh need it."

Big Boy had no feelings now. He was waiting. He did not wonder if they were coming after him. He just waited. He did not wonder about Bobo. He rested his cheek against the cold clay, waiting.

A dog barked. He stiffened. It barked again. He balled himself into a knot at the bottom of the hole, waiting. Then he heard the patter of dog feet.

"Look!"

"Whuts he got?"

"Its a snake!"

"Yeah, the dogs foun a snake!"

"Gee, its a big one!"

"Shucks, Ah wish he could fin one of them sonofabitchin niggers!"

The voices sank to low murmurs. Then he heard number twelve, its bell tolling and whistle crying as it slid along the rails. He flattened himself against the clay. Someone was singing:

"We'll hang ever nigger t a sour apple tree . . ."

When the song ended there was hard laughter. From the other side of the hill he heard the dog barking furiously. He listened. There was more than one dog now. There were many and they were barking their throats out.

"Hush. Ah hear them dogs!"

"When theys barkin like tha theys foun somethin!"

"Here they come over the hill!"

"WE GOT IM! WE GOT IM!"

There came a roar. Tha must be Bobo; tha mus be Bobo . . . In spite of his fear, Big Boy looked. The road, and half of the hillside across the road, were covered with men. A few were at the top of the hill, stenciled against the sky. He could see dark forms moving up the slopes. They were yelling.

"By Gawd, we got im!"

"C mon!"

"Where is he?"

"Theyre bringin im over the hill!"

"Ah got a rope fer im!"

"Say, somebody go n git the others!"

"Where is he? Cant we see im, Mister?"

"They say Berthas comin, too."

"Jack! Jack! Don leave me! Ah wanna see im!"

"Theyre bringin im over the hill, sweetheart!"

"AH WANNA BE THE FIRS T PUT A ROPE ON THA BLACK BASTARDS NECK!"

"Les start the fire!"

"Heat the tar!"

"Ah got some chains t chain im."

"Bring im over this way!"

"Chris, Ah wished Ah hada drink . . ."

Big Boy saw men moving over the hill. Among them was a long dark spot. Tha mus be Bobo; tha must be Bobo theys carryin . . . Theyll git im here. He oughta git up n run. He clamped his teeth and ran his hand across his forehead, bringing it away wet. He tried to swallow, but could not; his throat was dry.

They had started the song again:

"We'll hang ever nigger t a sour apple tree . . ."

There were women singing now. Their voices made the song round and full. Song waves rolled over the top of pine trees. The sky sagged low, heavy with clouds. Wind was rising. Sometimes cricket cries cut surprisingly across the mob song. A dog had gone to the utmost top of the hill. At each lull of the song his howl floated full into the night.

Big Boy shrank when he saw the first flame light the hillside. Would they see im here? Then he remembered you could not see into the dark if you were standing in the light. As flames leaped higher he saw two men rolling a barrel up the slope.

"Say, gimme a han here, will yuh?"

"Awright, heave!"

"C mon! Straight up! Git t the other end!"

"Ah got the feathers here in this pillar!"

"BRING SOME MO WOOD!"

Big Boy could see the barrel surrounded by flames. The mob fell back, forming a dark circle. Theyd fin im here! He had a wild impulse to climb out and fly across the hills. But his legs would not move. He stared hard, trying to find Bobo. His eyes played over a long, dark spot near the fire. Fanned by wind, flames leaped higher. He jumped. That dark spot had moved. Lawd, thas Bobo; thas Bobo . . .

He smelt the scent of tar, faint at first, then stronger. The wind brought it full into his face, then blew it away. His eyes burned and he rubbed them with his knuckles. He sneezed.

"LES GIT SOURVINEERS!"

He saw the mob close in around the fire. Their faces were hard and sharp in the light of the flames. More men and women were coming over the hill. The long, dark spot was smudged out.

"Everybody git back!"

"Look! Hes gotta finger!"

"C MON! GIT THE GALS BACK FROM THE FIRE!"

"He's got one of his ears, see?"

"Whuts the matter!"

"A woman fell out! Fainted, Ah reckon . . ."

The stench of tar permeated the hillside. The sky was black and the wind was blowing hard.

"HURRY UP N BURN THE NIGGER FO IT RAINS!"

Big Boy saw the mob fall back, leaving a small knot of men around the fire. Then, for the first time, he had a full glimpse of Bobo. A black body flashed in the light. Bobo was struggling, twisting; they were binding his arms and legs.

When he saw them tilt the barrel he stiffened. A scream quivered. He knew the tar was on Bobo. The mob fell back. He saw a tar-drenched body glistening and turning.

"THE BASTARDS GOT IT!"

There was a sudden quiet. Then he shrank violently as the

wind carried, like a flurry of snow, a widening spiral of white
feathers into the night. The flames leaped tall as the trees. The
scream came again. Big Boy trembled and looked. The mob was
running down the slopes, leaving the fire clear. Then he saw a
writhing white mass cradled in yellow flame, and heard screams,
one on top of the other, each shriller and shorter than the last.
The mob was quiet now, standing still, looking up the slopes at
the writhing white mass gradually growing black, growing black
in a cradle of yellow flames.

"PO ON MO GAS!"

"Gimme a lif, will yuh!"

Two men were struggling, carrying between them a heavy
can. They set it down, tilted it, leaving it so that the gas would
trickle down to the hollowed earth around the fire.

Big Boy slid back into the hole, his face buried in clay. He
had no feelings now, no fears. He was numb, empty, as though
all blood had been drawn from him. Then his muscles flexed
taut when he heard a faint patter. A tiny stream of cold water
seeped to his knees, making him push back to a drier spot. He
looked up; rain was beating in the grass.

"It's rainin!"

"C mon, let git t town!"

" . . . don worry, when the fire git thu wid him hell be
gone . . ."

"Wait, Charles! Don leave me; its slippery here . . ."

"Ahll take some of yuh ladies back in mah car . . ."

Big Boy heard the dogs barking again, this time closer. Running feet pounded past. Cold water chilled his ankles. He could
hear raindrops steadily hissing.

Now a dog was barking at the mouth of the hole, barking furiously, sensing a presence there. He balled himself into a knot
and clung to the bottom, his knees and shins buried in water.
The bark came louder. He heard paws scraping and felt the hot
scent of dog breath on his face. Green eyes glowed and drew
nearer as the barking, muffled by the closeness of the hole, beat
upon his eardrums. Backing till his shoulders pressed against
the clay, he held his breath. He pushed out his hands, his fingers stiff. The dog yawped louder, advancing, his bark rising

sharp and thin. Big Boy rose to his knees, his hands before him. Then he flattened out still more against the bottom, breathing lungsful of hot dog scent, breathing it slowly, hard, but evenly. The dog came closer, bringing hotter dog scent. Big Boy could go back no more. His knees were slipping and slopping in the water. He braced himself, ready. Then, he never exactly knew how—he never knew whether he had lunged or the dog had lunged—they were together, rolling in the water. The green eyes were beneath him, between his legs. Dog nails bit into his arms. His knees slipped backward and he landed full on the dog; the dog's breath left in a heavy gasp. Instinctively, he fumbled for the throat as he felt the dog twisting between his knees. The dog snarled, long and low, as though gathering strength. Big Boy's hands traveled swiftly over the dog's back, groping for the throat. He felt dognails again and saw green eyes, but his fingers had found the throat. He choked, feeling his fingers sink; he choked, throwing back his head and stiffening his arms. He felt the dog's body heave, felt dognails digging into his loins. With strength flowing from fear, he closed his finers, pushing his full weight on the dog's throat. The dog heaved again, and lay still . . . Big Boy heard the sound of his own breathing filling the hole, and heard shouts and footsteps above him going past.

For a long time he held the dog, held it long after the last footstep had died out, long after the rain had stopped.

V

Morning found him still on his knees in a puddle of rainwater, staring at the stiff body of a dog. As the air brightened he came to himself slowly. He held still for a long time, as though waking from a dream, as though trying to remember.

The chug of a truck came over the hill. He tried to crawl to the opening. His knees were stiff and a thousand needle-like pains shot from the bottom of his feet to the calves of his legs. Giddiness made his eyes blur. He pulled up and looked. Through brackish light he saw Will's truck standing some twenty-five yards away, the engine running. Will stood on the running board, looking over the slopes of the hill.

Big Boy scuffled out, falling weakly in the wet grass. He tried to call to Will, but his dry throat would make no sound. He tried again.

"Will!"

Will heard, answering:

"Big Boy, c mon!"

He tried to run, and fell. Will came, meeting him in the tall grass.

"C mon," Will said, catching his arm.

They struggled to the truck.

"Hurry up!" said Will, pushing him onto the runningboard.

Will pushed back a square trapdoor which swung above the back of the driver's seat. Big Boy pulled through, landing with a thud on the bottom. On hands and knees he looked around in the semi-darkness.

"Wheres Bobo?"

Big Boy stared.

"Wheres Bobo?"

"They got im."

"When?"

"Las night."

"The mob?"

Big Boy pointed in the direction of a charred sapling on the slope of the opposite hill. Will looked. The trapdoor fell. The engine purred, the gears whined, and the truck lurched forward over the muddy road, sending Big Boy on his side.

For a while he lay as he had fallen, on his side, too weak to move. As he felt the truck swing around a curve he straightened up and rested his back against a stack of wooden boxes. Slowly, he began to make out objects in the darkness. Through two long cracks fell thin blades of daylight. The floor was of smooth steel, and cold to his thighs. Splinters and bits of sawdust danced with the rumble of the truck. Each time they swung around a curve he was pulled over the floor; he grabbed at corners of boxes to steady himself. Once he heard the crow of a rooster. It made him think of home, of ma and pa. He thought he remembered hearing somewhere that the house had burned, but could not remember where . . . It all seemed unreal now.

He was tired. He dozed, swaying with the lurch. Then he jumped awake. The truck was running smoothly, on gravel. Far away he heard two short blasts from the Buckeye Lumber Mill. Unconsciously, the thought sang through his mind: Its six erclock . . .

The trapdoor swung in. Will spoke through a corner of his mouth.

"How yuh comin?"

"Awright."

"How they git Bobo?"

"He wuz comin over the hill."

"Whut they do?"

"They burnt im . . . Will, Ah wan some water; mah throats like fire . . ."

"Well git some when we pas a fillin station."

Big Boy leaned back and dozed. He jerked awake when the truck stopped. He heard Will get out. He wanted to peep through the trapdoor, but was afraid. For a moment, the wild fear he had known in the hole came back. Spose theyd search n fin im? He quieted when he heard Will's footsteps on the runningboard. The trapdoor pushed in. Will's hat came through, dripping.

"Take it, quick!"

Big Boy grabbed, spilling water into his face. The truck lurched. He drank. Hard cold lumps of brick rolled into his hot stomach. A dull pain made him bend over. His intestines seemed to be drawing into a tight knot. After a bit it eased, and he sat up, breathing softly.

The truck swerved. He blinked his eyes. The blades of daylight had turned brightly golden. The sun had risen.

The truck sped over the asphalt miles, sped northward, jolting him, shaking out of his bosom the crumbs of corn bread, making them dance with the splinters and sawdust in the golden blades of sunshine.

He turned on his side and slept.

IV The City

The diffuse, impersonal and anarchic bustle of the city, and the often hostile welcome from competitive European immigrants recently arrived, deepened the anxieties of the black peasants who had been fleeing another kind of oppression in the South. In time, most Negro migrants made their adjustments—frequently bitterly, as in Wright's story "The Man Who Went to Chicago," or more cavalierly as in Gwendolyn Brooks's "The Sundays of Satin-Legs Smith." But for others, the tensions, the broken promises, the very conditions of life became intolerable. Langston Hughes's "Harlem" and Ralph Ellison's description of the 1943 Harlem riots from his novel Invisible Man are expressions of these new explosive forces in American life.

Richard Wright

The Man Who Went to Chicago

When I rose in the morning the temperature had dropped below zero. The house was as cold to me as the Southern streets had been in winter. I dressed, doubling my clothing. I ate in a restaurant, caught a streetcar, and rode south, rode until I could see no more black faces on the sidewalks. I had now crossed the boundary line of the Black Belt and had entered the territory where jobs were perhaps to be had from white folks. I walked the streets and looked into shop windows until I saw a sign in a delicatessen: PORTER WANTED.

I went in and a stout white woman came to me.

"Vat do you vant?" she asked.

The voice jarred me. She's Jewish, I thought, remembering with shame the obscenities I used to shout at Jewish storekeepers in Arkansas.

"I thought maybe you needed a porter," I said.

"Meester 'Offman, he eesn't here yet," she said. "Vill you vait?"

"Yes, ma'am."

"Seet down."

"No, ma'am, I'll wait outside."

"But eet's cold out zhere," she said.

"That's all right," I said.

She shrugged. I went to the sidewalk. I waited for half an hour in the bitter cold, regretting that I had not remained in the warm store, but unable to go back inside. A bald, stoutish white man went into the store and pulled off his coat. Yes, he was the boss man . . .

143

"Zo you vant a job?" he asked.

"Yes, sir," I answered, guessing at the meaning of his words.

"Vhere you vork before?"

"In Memphis, Tennessee."

"My brudder-in-law vorked in Tennessee vonce," he said.

I was hired. The work was easy, but I found to my dismay that I could not understand a third of what was said to me. My slow Southern ears were baffled by their clouded, thick accents. One morning Mrs. Hoffman asked me to go to a neighboring store—it was owned by a cousin of hers—and get a can of chicken *à la* king. I had never heard the phrase before and I asked her to repeat it.

"Don't you know nosing?" she demanded of me.

"If you would write it down for me, I'd know what to get," I ventured timidly.

"I can't vite!" she shouted in a sudden fury. "Vat kinda boy iss you?"

I memorized the separate sounds that she had uttered and went to the neighboring store.

"Mrs. Hoffman wants a can Cheek Keeng Awr Lar Keeng," I said slowly, hoping he would not think I was being offensive.

"All vite," he said, after staring at me a moment.

He put a can into a paper bag and gave it to me; outside in the street I opened the bag and read the label: Chicken *à la* King. I cursed, disgusted with myself. I knew those words. It had been her thick accent that had thrown me off. Yet I was not angry with her for speaking broken English; my English, too, was broken. But why could she not have taken more patience? Only one answer came to my mind. I was black and she did not care. Or so I thought . . . I was persisting in reading my present environment in the light of my old one. I reasoned thus: though English was my native tongue and America my native land, she, an alien, could operate a store and earn a living in a neighborhood where I could not even live. I reasoned further that she was aware of this and was trying to protect her position against me.

It was not until I had left the delicatessen job that I saw how grossly I had misread the motives and attitudes of Mr. Hoffman and his wife. I had not yet learned anything that would have helped me to thread my way through these perplexing racial relations. Accepting my environment at its face value, trapped by my own emotions, I kept asking myself what had black people done to bring this crazy world upon them?

The fact of the separation of white and black was clear to me; it was its effect upon the personalities of people that stumped and dismayed me. I did not feel that I was a threat to anybody; yet, as soon as I had grown old enough to think, I had learned that my entire personality, my aspirations, had long ago been discounted; that, in a measure, the very meaning of the words I spoke could not be fully understood.

And when I contemplated the area of No Man's Land into which the Negro mind in America had been shunted I wondered if there had ever been in all human history a more corroding and devastating attack upon the personalities of men than the idea of racial discrimination. In order to escape the racial attack that went to the roots of my life, I would have gladly accepted any way of life but the one in which I found myself. I would have agreed to live under a system of feudal oppression, not because I preferred feudalism but because I felt that feudalism made use of a limited part of a man, defined man, his rank, his function in society. I would have consented to live under the most rigid type of dictatorship, for I felt that dictatorships, too, defined the use of men, however degrading that use might be.

While working as a porter in Memphis I had often stood aghast as a friend of mine had offered himself to be kicked by the white men; but now, while working in Chicago, I was learning that perhaps even a kick was better than uncertainty . . . I had elected, in my fevered search for honorable adjustment to the American scene, not to submit and in doing so I had embraced the daily horror of anxiety, of tension, of eternal disquiet. I could now sympathize with—though I could never bring myself to approve—those tortured blacks who had given up and had gone to their white tormentors and had said: "Kick me, if that's all there is for me; kick me and let me feel at home, let me have peace!"

Color-hate defined the place of black life as below that of white life; and the black man, responding to the same dreams as the white man, strove to bury within his heart his awareness of this difference because it made him lonely and afraid. Hated by whites and being an organic part of the culture that hated him, the black man grew in turn to hate in himself that which others hated in him. But pride would make him hate his self-hate, for he would not want whites to know that he was so thoroughly conquered by them that his total life was conditioned by their attitude; but in the act of hiding his self-hate, he could not help but hate those who evoked his self-hate in him. So each part of his day would be consumed in a war with himself, a good part of his energy would be spent in keeping control of his unruly emotions, emotions which he had not wished to have, but could not help having. Held at bay by the hate of others, preoccupied with his own feelings, he was continuously at war with reality. He became inefficient, less able to see and judge the objective world. And when he reached that state, the white people looked at him and laughed and said:

"Look, didn't I tell you niggers were that way?"

To solve this tangle of balked emotion, I loaded the empty part of the ship of my personality with fantasies of ambition to keep it from toppling over into the sea of senselessness. Like any other American, I dreamed of going into business and making money; I dreamed of working for a firm that would allow me to advance until I reached an important position; I even dreamed of organizing secret groups of blacks to fight all whites . . . And if the blacks would not agree to organize, then they would have to be fought. I would end up again with self-hate, but it was now a self-hate that was projected outward upon other blacks. Yet I knew—with that part of my mind that the whites had given me—that none of my dreams were possible. Then I would hate myself for allowing my mind to dwell upon the unattainable. Thus the circle would complete itself.

Slowly I began to forge in the depths of my mind a mechanism that repressed all the dreams and desires that the Chicago streets, the newspapers, the movies were evoking in me. I was going through a second childhood; a new sense of the limit of the possible was being born in me. What could I dream of that had the barest possibility of coming true? I could think of nothing. And, slowly, it was upon exactly that nothingness that my mind began to dwell, that constant sense of wanting without having, of being hated without reason. A dim notion of what life meant to a Negro in America was coming to consciousness in me, not in terms of external events, lynchings, Jim Crowism, and the endless brutalities, but in terms of crossed-up feeling, of emotional tension. I sensed that Negro life was a sprawling land of unconscious suffering, and there were but few Negroes who knew the meaning of their lives, who could tell their story.

Word reached me that an examination for postal clerk was impending and at once I filed an application and waited. As the date for the examination drew near, I was faced with another problem. How could I get a free day without losing my job? In the South it would have been an unwise policy for a Negro to have gone to his white boss and asked for time to take an examination for another job. It would have implied that the Negro did not like to work for the white boss, that he felt he was not receiving just consideration and, inasmuch as most jobs that Negroes held in the South involved a personal, paternalistic relationship, he would have been risking an argument that might have led to violence.

I now began to speculate about what kind of man Mr. Hoffman was, and I found that I did not know him; that is, I did not know his basic attitude toward Negroes. If I asked him, would he be sympathetic enough to allow me time off with pay? I needed the money. Perhaps he would say: "Go home and stay home if you don't like this job!" I was not sure of him. I decided, therefore, that I had better not risk it. I would forfeit the money and stay away without telling him.

The examination was scheduled to take place on a Monday; I had been working steadily and I would be too tired to do my

best if I took the examination without benefit of rest. I decided
to stay away from the shop Saturday, Sunday, and Monday. But
what could I tell Mr. Hoffman? Yes, I would tell him that I
had been ill. No, that was too thin. I would tell him that my
mother had died in Memphis and that I had gone down to
bury her. That lie might work.

I took the examination and when I came to the store on
Tuesday, Mr. Hoffman was astonished, of course.

"I didn't sink you vould ever come back," he said.

"I'm awfully sorry, Mr. Hoffman."

"Vat happened?"

"My mother died in Memphis, and I had to go down and
bury her," I lied.

He looked at me, then shook his head.

"Rich, you lie," he said.

"I'm not lying," I lied stoutly.

"You vanted to do somesink, zo you zayed ervay," he said,
shrugging.

"No, sir. I'm telling you the truth;" I piled another lie upon
the first one.

"No. You lie. You disappoint me," he said.

"Well, all I can do is tell you the truth," I lied indignantly.

"Vy didn't you use the phone?"

"I didn't think of it," I told a fresh lie.

"Rich, if your mudder die, you vould tell me," he said.

"I didn't have time. Had to catch the train," I lied yet again.

"Vhere did you get the money?"

"My aunt gave it to me," I said, disgusted that I had to lie
and lie again.

"I don't vant a boy vat tells lies," he said.

"I don't lie," I lied passionately to protect my lies.

Mrs. Hoffman joined in and both of them hammered at me.

"Ve know. You come from ze Zouth. You feel you can't tell
us ze truth. But ve don't bother you. Ve don't feel like people
in ze Zouth. Ve treat you nice, don't ve?" they asked.

"Yes, ma'am," I mumbled.

"Zen vy lie?"

"I'm not lying," I lied with all my strength.

I became angry because I knew that they knew that I was lying. I had lied to protect myself, and then I had to lie to protect my lie. I had met so many white faces that would have violently disapproved of my taking the examination that I could not have risked telling Mr. Hoffman the truth. But how could I tell him that I had lied because I was so unsure of myself? Lying was bad, but revealing my own sense of insecurity would have been worse. It would have been shameful, and I did not like to feel ashamed.

Their attitudes had proved utterly amazing. They were taking time out from their duties in the store to talk to me, and I had never encountered anything like that from whites before. A Southern white man would have said: "Get to hell out of here!" or "All right, nigger. Get to work." But no white people had ever stood their ground and probed at me, questioned me at such length. It dawned upon me that they were trying to treat me as an equal, which made it even more impossible for me ever to tell them that I had lied, why I had lied. I felt that if I confessed I would be giving them a moral advantage over me that would have been unbearable.

"All vight, zay and vork," Mr. Hoffman said. "I know you're lying, but I don't care, Rich."

I wanted to quit. He had insulted me. But I liked him in spite of myself. Yes, I had done wrong; but how on earth could I have known the kind of people I was working for? Perhaps Mr. Hoffman would have gladly consented for me to take the examination; but my hopes had been far weaker than my powerful fears.

Working with them from day to day and knowing that they knew I had lied from fear crushed me. I knew that they pitied me and pitied the fear in me. I resolved to quit and risk hunger rather than stay with them. I left the job that following Saturday, not telling them that I would not be back, not possessing the heart to say good-by. I just wanted to go quickly and have them forget that I had ever worked for them.

After an idle week, I got a job as a dishwasher in a North Side café that had just opened. My boss, a white woman, directed me in unpacking barrels of dishes, setting up new tables, painting, and so on. I had charge of serving breakfast; in the late afternoon I carted trays of food to patrons in the hotel who did not want to come down to eat. My wages were fifteen dollars a week; the hours were long, but I ate my meals on the job.

The cook was an elderly Finnish woman with a sharp, bony face. There were several white waitresses. I was the only Negro in the café. The waitresses were a hard, brisk lot, and I was keenly aware of how their attitudes contrasted with those of Southern white girls. They had not been taught to keep a gulf between me and themselves; they were relatively free of the heritage of racial hate.

One morning as I was making coffee, Cora came forward with a tray loaded with food and squeezed against me to draw a cup of coffee.

"Pardon me, Richard," she said.

"Oh, that's all right," I said in an even tone.

But I was aware that she was a white girl and that her body was pressed closely against mine, an incident that had never happened to me before in my life, an incident charged with the memory of dread. But she was not conscious of my blackness or of what her actions would have meant in the South. And had I not been born in the South, her trivial act would have been as unnoticed by me as it was by her. As she stood close to me, I could not help thinking that if a Southern white girl had wanted to draw a cup of coffee, she would have commanded me to step aside so that she might not come in contact with me. The work of the hot and busy kitchen would have had to cease for the moment so that I could have taken my tainted body far enough away to allow the Southern white girl a chance to get a cup of coffee. There lay a deep, emotional safety in knowing that the white girl who was now leaning carelessly against me was not thinking of me, had no deep, vague, irrational fright that made her feel that I was a creature to be avoided at all costs.

One summer morning a white girl came late to work and rushed into the pantry where I was busy. She went into the women's room and changed her clothes; I heard the door open and a second later I was surprised to hear her voice:

"Richard, quick! Tie my apron!"

She was standing with her back to me and the strings of her apron dangled loose. There was a moment of indecision on my part, then I took the two loose strings and carried them around her body and brought them again to her back and tied them in a clumsy knot.

"Thanks a million," she said, grasping my hand for a split second, and was gone.

I continued my work, filled with all the possible meanings that that tiny, simple, human event could have meant to any Negro in the South where I had spent most of my hungry days.

I did not feel any admiration or any hate for the girls. My attitude was one of abiding and friendly wonder. For the most part I was silent with them, though I knew that I had a firmer grasp of life than most of them. As I worked I listened to their talk and perceived its puzzled, wandering superficial fumbling with the problems and facts of life. There were many things they wondered about that I could have explained to them, but I never dared.

During my lunch hour, which I spent on a bench in a near-by park, the waitresses would come and sit beside me, talking at random, laughing, joking, smoking cigarettes. I learned about their tawdry dreams, their simple hopes, their home lives, their fear of feeling anything deeply, their sex problems, their husbands. They were an eager, restless, talkative, ignorant bunch, but casually kind and impersonal for all that. They knew nothing of hate and fear, and strove instinctively to avoid all passion.

I often wondered what they were trying to get out of life, but I never stumbled upon a clue, and I doubt if they themselves had any notion. They lived on the surface of their days; their smiles were surface smiles, and their tears were surface tears. Negroes lived a truer and deeper life than they, but I wished that Negroes, too, could live as thoughtlessly, serenely, as they. The girls never talked of their feelings; none of them possessed the insight or the emotional equipment to understand themselves or others. How far apart in culture we stood! All my life I had done nothing but feel and cultivate my feelings; all their lives they had done nothing but strive for petty goals, the trivial material prizes of American life. We shared a common tongue, but my language was a different language from theirs.

It was in the psychological distance that separated the races that the deepest meaning of the problem of the Negro lay for me. For these poor, ignorant white girls to have understood my life would have meant nothing short of a vast revolution in theirs. And I was convinced that what they needed to make them complete and grown-up in their living was the inclusion in their personalities of a knowledge of lives such as I lived and suffered containedly.

As I, in memory, think back now upon those girls and their lives, I feel that for white America to understand the significance of the problem of the Negro will take a bigger and tougher America than any we have yet known. I feel that America's past is too shallow, her national character too superficially optimistic, her very morality too suffused with color hate for her to accomplish so vast and complex a task. Culturally the Negro represents a paradox: Though he is an organic part of the nation, he is excluded by the entire tide and direction of American culture. Frankly, it is felt to be right to exclude him, and it is felt to be wrong to admit him freely. Therefore if, within the confines of its present culture, the nation ever seeks to purge itself of its color hate, it will find itself at war with itself, convulsed by a spasm of emotional and moral confusion. If the nation ever finds itself examining its real relation to the Negro, it will find itself doing infinitely more than that; for the anti-Negro attitude of whites represents but a tiny part—though a symbolically significant one—of the moral attitude of the nation. Our too-young and too-new America, lusty because it is lonely, aggressive because it is afraid, insists upon seeing the world in terms of good and bad, the holy and the evil, the high and the low, the white and the black; our America is frightened by fact, by history, by processes, by necessity. It hugs the easy way of damning those whom it cannot understand, of excluding those who look different; and it salves its conscience with a self-draped cloak of righteousness. Am I damning my native land?

No; for I, too, share these faults of character! And I really do not think that America, adolescent and cocksure, a stranger to suffering and travail, an enemy of passion and sacrifice, is ready to probe into its most fundamental beliefs.

I knew that not race alone, not color alone, but the daily values that gave meaning to life stood between me and those white girls with whom I worked. Their constant outward-looking, their mania for radios, cars, and a thousand other trinkets, made them dream and fix their eyes upon the trash of life, made it impossible for them to learn a language that could have taught them to speak of what was in theirs or others' hearts. The words of their souls were the syllables of popular songs.

The essence of the irony of the plight of the Negro in America, to me, is that he is doomed to live in isolation, while those who condemn him seek the basest goals of any people on the face of the earth. Perhaps it would be possible for the Negro to become reconciled to his plight if he could be made to believe that his sufferings were for some remote, high, sacrificial end; but sharing the culture that condemns him, and seeing that a lust for trash is what blinds the nation to his claims, is what sets storms to rolling in his soul.

Though I had fled the pressure of the South, my outward conduct had not changed. I had been schooled to present an unalteringly smiling face and I continued to do so despite the fact that my environment allowed more open expression. I hid my feelings and avoided all relationships with whites that might cause me to reveal them.

Tillie, the Finnish cook, was a tall, ageless, red-faced, raw-boned woman with long snow-white hair, which she balled in a knot at the nape of her neck. She cooked expertly and was superbly efficient. One morning as I passed the sizzling stove, I thought I heard Tillie cough and spit, but I saw nothing; her face, obscured by steam, was bent over a big pot. My senses told me that Tillie had coughed and spat into that pot but my heart told me that no human being could possibly be so filthy. I decided to watch her. An hour or so later I heard Tillie clear her throat with a grunt, saw her cough and spit into the boiling soup. I held my breath; I did not want to believe what I had seen.

Should I tell the boss lady? Would she believe me? I watched Tillie for another day to make sure that she was spitting into the food. She was; there was no doubt of it. But who would believe me if I told them what was happening? I was the only black person in the café. Perhaps they would think that I hated the cook. I stopped eating my meals there and bided my time.

The business of the café was growing rapidly and a Negro girl was hired to make salads. I went to her at once.

"Look, can I trust you?" I asked.

"What are you talking about?" she asked.

"I want you to say nothing, but watch that cook."

"For what?"

"Now, don't get scared. Just watch the cook."

She looked at me as though she thought I was crazy; and, frankly, I felt that perhaps I ought not to say anything to anybody.

"What do you mean?" she demanded.

"All right," I said. "I'll tell you. That cook spits in the food."

"What are you saying?" she asked aloud.

"Keep quiet," I said.

"Spitting?" she asked me in a whisper. "Why would she do that?"

"I don't know. But watch her."

She walked away from me with a funny look in her eyes. But half an hour later she came rushing to me, looking ill, sinking into a chair.

"Oh, God, I feel awful!"

"Did you see it?"

"She *is* spitting in the food!"

"What ought we do?" I asked.

"Tell the lady," she said.

"She wouldn't believe me," I said.

She widened her eyes as she understood. We were black and the cook was white.

"But I can't work here if she's going to do that," she said.

"Then you tell her," I said.

"She wouldn't believe me either," she said.

She rose and ran to the women's room. When she returned she stared at me. We were two Negroes and we were silently asking ourselves if the white boss lady would believe us if we told her that her expert white cook was spitting in the food all day long as it cooked on the stove.

"I don't know," she wailed, in a whisper, and walked away.

I thought of telling the waitresses about the cook, but I could not get up enough nerve. Many of the girls were friendly with Tillie. Yet I could not let the cook spit in the food all day. That was wrong by any human standard of conduct. I washed dishes, thinking, wondering; I served breakfast, thinking, wondering; I served meals in the apartments of patrons upstairs, thinking, wondering. Each time I picked up a tray of food I felt like retching. Finally the Negro salad girl came to me and handed me her purse and hat.

"I'm going to tell her and quit, goddam," she said.

"I'll quit too, if she doesn't fire her," I said.

"Oh, she won't believe me," she wailed, in agony.

"You tell her. You're a woman. She might believe you."

Her eyes welled with tears and she sat for a long time; then she rose and went abruptly into the dining room. I went to the door and peered. Yes, she was at the desk, talking to the boss lady. She returned to the kitchen and went into the pantry; I followed her.

"Did you tell her?" I asked.

"Yes."

"What did she say?"

"She said I was crazy."

"Oh, God!" I said.

"She just looked at me with those gray eyes of hers," the girl said. "Why would Tillie do that?"

"I don't know," I said.

The boss lady came to the door and called the girl; both of them went into the dining room. Tillie came over to me; a hard cold look was in her eyes.

"What's happening here?" she asked.

"I don't know," I said, wanting to slap her across the mouth.

She muttered something and went back to the stove, coughed, and spat into a bubbling pot. I left the kitchen and went into the back areaway to breathe. The boss lady came out.

"Richard," she said.

Her face was pale. I was smoking a cigarette and I did not look at her.

"Is this true?"

"Yes, ma'am."

"It couldn't be. Do you know what you're saying?"

"Just watch her," I said.

"I don't know," she moaned.

She looked crushed. She went back into the dining room, but I saw her watching the cook through the doors. I watched both of them, the boss lady and the cook, praying that the cook would spit again. She did. The boss lady came into the kitchen and stared at Tillie, but she did not utter a word. She burst into tears and ran back into the dining room.

"What's happening here?" Tillie demanded.

No one answered. The boss lady came out and tossed Tillie her hat, coat, and money.

"Now, get out of here, you dirty dog!" she said.

Tillie stared, then slowly picked up her hat, coat, and the money; she stood a moment, wiped sweat from her forehead with her hand, then spat—this time on the floor. She left.

Nobody was ever able to fathom why Tillie liked to spit into the food.

Brooding over Tillie, I recalled the time when the boss man in Mississippi had come to me and had tossed my wages to me and said:

"Get out, nigger! I don't like your looks."

And I wondered if a Negro who did not smile and grin was morally loathsome to whites as a cook who spat into the food.

The following summer I was called for temporary duty in the post office, and the work lasted into the winter. Aunt Cleo succumbed to a severe cardiac condition and, hard on the heels of her illness, my brother developed stomach ulcers. To rush my worries to a climax, my mother also became ill. I felt that I was maintaining a private hospital. Finally, the post-office work ceased altogether and I haunted the city for jobs. But when I went into the streets in the morning I saw sights that killed my hope for the rest of the day. Unemployed men loitered in doorways with blank looks in their eyes, sat dejectedly on front steps in shabby clothing, congregated in sullen groups on street corners, and filled all the empty benches in the parks of Chicago's South Side.

Luck of a sort came when a distant cousin of mine, who was a superintendent for a Negro burial society, offered me a position on his staff as an agent. The thought of selling insurance policies to ignorant Negroes disgusted me.

"Well, if you don't sell them, somebody else will," my cousin told me. "You've got to eat, haven't you?"

During that year I worked for several burial and insurance societies that operated among Negroes, and I received a new kind of education. I found that the burial societies, with some exceptions, were mostly "rackets." Some of them conducted their business legitimately, but there were many that exploited the ignorance of their black customers.

I was paid under a system that netted me fifteen dollars for every dollar's worth of new premiums that I placed upon the company's books, and for every dollar's worth of old premiums that lapsed I was penalized fifteen dollars. In addition, I was paid a commission of ten per cent on total premiums collected, but during the Depression it was extremely difficult to persuade a black family to buy a policy carrying even a dime premium. I considered myself lucky if, after subtracting lapses from new business, there remained fifteen dollars that I could call my own.

This "gambling" method of remuneration was practiced by some of the burial companies because of the tremendous "turnover" in policyholders, and the companies had to have a constant stream of new business to keep afloat. Whenever a black family moved or suffered a slight reverse in fortune, it usually let its policy lapse and later bought another policy from some other company.

Each day now I saw how the Negro in Chicago lived, for I visited hundreds of dingy flats filled with rickety furniture and ill-clad children. Most of the policyholders were illiterate and did not know that their policies carried clauses severely restricting their benefit payments, and, as an insurance agent, it was not my duty to tell them.

After tramping the streets and pounding on doors to collect premiums, I was dry, strained, too tired to read or write. I hungered for relief and, as a salesman of insurance to many young black girls, I found it. There were many comely black housewives who, trying desperately to keep up their insurance payments, were willing to make bargains to escape paying a ten-cent premium. I had a long, tortured affair with one girl by paying her ten-cent premium each week. She was an illiterate black child with a baby whose father she did not know. During the entire period of my relationship with her, she had but one demand to make of me: she wanted me to take her to a circus. Just what significance circuses had for her, I was never able to learn.

After I had been with her one morning—in exchange for the dime premium—I sat on the sofa in the front room and began to read a book I had with me. She came over shyly.

"Lemme see that," she said.

"What?" I asked.

"That book," she said.

I gave her the book; she looked at it intently. I saw that she was holding it upside down.

"What's in here you keep reading?" she asked.

"Can't you really read?" I asked.

"Naw," she giggled. "You know I can't read."

"You can read *some*," I said.

"Naw," she said.

I stared at her and wondered just what a life like hers meant in the scheme of things, and I came to the conclusion that it meant absolutely nothing. And neither did my life mean any-thing.

"How come you looking at me that way for?"

"Nothing."

"You don't talk much."

"There isn't much to say."

"I wished Jim was here," she sighed.

"Who's Jim?" I asked, jealous. I knew that she had other men, but I resented her mentioning them in my presence.

"Just a friend," she said.

I hated her then, then hated myself for coming to her.

"Do you like Jim better than you like me?" I asked.

"Naw. Jim just likes to talk."

"Then why do you be with me, if you like Jim better?" I asked, trying to make an issue and feeling a wave of disgust be-cause I wanted to.

"You all right," she said, giggling. "I like you."

"I could kill you," I said.

"What?" she exclaimed.

"Nothing," I said, ashamed.

"Kill me, you said? You crazy, man," she said.

"Maybe I am," I muttered, angry that I was sitting beside a human being to whom I could not talk, angry with myself for coming to her, hating my wild and restless loneliness.

"You oughta go home and sleep," she said. "You tired."

"What do you ever think about?" I demanded harshly.

"Lotta things."

"What, for example?"

"You," she said, smiling.

"You know I mean just one dime to you each week," I said.

"Naw, I thinka lotta you."

"Then what do you think?"

" 'Bout how you talk when you talk. I wish I could talk like you," she said seriously.

"Why?" I taunted her.

"When you gonna take me to a circus?" she demanded sud-denly.

"You ought to be in a circus," I said.

"I'd like it," she said, her eyes shining.

I wanted to laugh, but her words sounded so sincere that I could not.

"There's no circus in town," I said.

"I bet there is and you won't tell me 'cause you don't wanna take me," she said, pouting.

"But there's no circus in town, I tell you!"

"When will one come?"

"I don't know."

"Can't you read it in the papers?" she asked.

"There's nothing in the papers about a circus."

"There is," she said. "If I could read, I'd find it."

I laughed, and she was hurt.

"There *is* a circus in town," she said stoutly.

"There's no circus in town," I said. "But if you want to learn to read, then I'll teach you."

She nestled at my side, giggling.

"See that word?" I said, pointing.

"Yeah."

"That's an 'and,' " I said.

She doubled, giggling.

"What's the matter?" I asked.

She rolled on the floor, giggling.

"What's so funny?" I demanded.

"You," she giggled. "You so funny."

I rose.

"The hell with you," I said.

"Don't you go and cuss me now," she said. "I don't cuss you."

"I'm sorry," I said.

I got my hat and went to the door.

"I'll see you next week?" she asked.

"Maybe," I said.

When I was on the sidewalk, she called to me from a window.

"You promised to take me to a circus, remember?"

"Yes." I walked close to the window. "What is it you like about a circus?"

"The animals," she said simply.

I felt that there was a hidden meaning, perhaps, in what she had said, but I could not find it. She laughed and slammed the window shut.

Each time I left her I resolved not to visit her again. I could not talk to her; I merely listened to her passionate desire to see a circus. She was not calculating; if she liked a man, she just liked him. Sex relations were the only relations she had ever had; no others were possible with her, so limited was her intelligence.

Most of the other agents also had their bought girls and they were extremely anxious to keep other agents from tampering with them. One day a new section of the South Side was given to me as a part of my collection area, and the agent from whom the territory had been taken suddenly became very friendly with me.

"Say, Wright," he asked, "did you collect from Ewing on Champlain Avenue yet?"

"Yes," I answered, after consulting my book.

"How did you like her?" he asked, staring at me.

"She's a good-looking number," I said.

"You had anything to do with her yet?" he asked.

"No, but I'd like to," I said laughing.

"Look," he said. "I'm a friend of yours."

"Since when?" I countered.

"No, I'm really a friend," he said.

"What's on your mind?"

"Listen, that gal's sick," he said seriously.

"What do you mean?"

"She's got the clap," he said. "Keep away from her. She'll lay with anybody."

"Gee, I'm glad you told me," I said.

"You had your eye on her, didn't you?" he asked.

"Yes, I did," I said.

"Leave her alone," he said. "She'll get you down."

That night I told my cousin what the agent had said about Miss Ewing. My cousin laughed.

"That gal's all right," he said. "That agent's been fooling around with her. He told you she had a disease so that you'd be scared to bother her. He was protecting her from you."

That was the way the black women were regarded by the black agents. Some of the agents were vicious; if they had claims to pay to a sick black woman and if the woman was able to have sex relations with them, they would insist upon it, using the claims money as a bribe. If the woman refused, they would report to the office that the woman was a malingerer. The average black woman would submit because she needed the money badly.

As an insurance agent, it was necessary for me to take part in one swindle. It appears that the burial society had originally issued a policy that was—from their point of view—too liberal in its provisions, and the officials decided to exchange the policies then in the hands of their clients for other policies carrying stricter clauses. Of course, this had to be done in a manner that would not allow the policyholder to know that his policy was being switched—that he was being swindled. I did not like it, but there was only one thing I could do to keep from being a party to it: I could quit and starve. But I did not feel that being honest was worth the price of starvation.

The swindle worked in this way. In my visits to the homes of the policyholders to collect premiums, I was accompanied by the superintendent who claimed to the policyholder that he was making a routine inspection. The policyholder, usually an illiterate black woman, would dig up her policy from the bottom of a trunk or chest and hand it to the superintendent. Meanwhile I would be marking the woman's premium book, an act which would distract her from what the superintendent was doing. The superintendent would exchange the old policy for a new one which was identical in color, serial number, and beneficiary, but which carried smaller payments. It was dirty work and I wondered how I could stop it. And when I could think of no safe way I would curse myself and the victims and forget about it. (The black owners of the burial societies were leaders in the Negro communities and were respected by whites.)

When I reached the relief station, I felt that I was making a public confession of my hunger. I sat waiting for hours, resentful of the mass of hungry people about me. My turn finally came and I was questioned by a middle-class Negro woman who asked me for a short history of my life. As I waited, I became aware of something happening in the room. The black men and women were mumbling quietly among themselves; they had not known one another before they had come here, but now their timidity and shame were wearing off and they were exchanging experiences. Before this they had lived as individuals, each somewhat afraid of the other, each seeking his own pleasure, each stanch in that degree of Americanism that had been allowed him. But now life had tossed them together, and they were learning to know the sentiments of their neighbors for the first time; their talking was enabling them to sense the collectivity of their lives, and some of their fear was passing.

Did the relief officials realize what was happening? No. If they had, they would have stopped it. But they saw their "clients" through the eyes of their profession, saw only what their "science" allowed them to see. As I listened to the talk, I could see black minds shedding many illusions. These people now knew that the past had betrayed them, had cast them out; but they did not know what the future would be like, did not know what they wanted. Yes, some of the things that the Communists said were true; they maintained that there came times in history when a ruling class could no longer rule. And now I sat looking at the beginnings of anarchy. To permit the birth of this new consciousness in these people was proof that those who ruled did not quite know what they were doing, assuming that they were trying to save themselves and their class. Had they understood what was happening, they would never have allowed millions of perplexed and defeated people to sit together for long hours and talk, for out of their talk was rising a new realization of life. And once this new conception of themselves had formed, no power on earth could alter it.

I left the relief station with the promise that food would be sent to me, but I also left with a knowledge that the relief officials had not wanted to give to me. I had felt the possibility of creating a new understanding of life in the minds of people rejected by the society in which they lived, people to whom the Chicago *Tribune* referred contemptuously as the "idle" ones, as though these people had deliberately sought their present state of helplessness.

Who would give these people a meaningful way of life? Communist theory defined these people as the molders of the future of mankind, but the Communist speeches I had heard in the park had mocked that definition. These people, of course, were not ready for a revolution; they had not abandoned their past lives by choice, but because they simply could not live the old way any longer. Now, what new faith would they embrace? The day I begged bread from the city officials was the day that showed me I was not alone in my loneliness; society had cast millions of others with me. But how could I be with them? How many understood what was happening? My mind swam with questions that I could not answer.

I was slowly beginning to comprehend the meaning of my environment; a sense of direction was beginning to emerge from the conditions of my life. I began to feel something more powerful than I could express. My speech and manner changed. My cynicism slid from me. I grew open and questioning. I wanted to know.

If I were a member of the class that rules, I would post men in all the neighborhoods of the nation, not to spy upon or club rebellious workers, not to break strikes or disrupt unions, but to ferret out those who no longer respond to the system under which they live. I would make it known that the real danger does not stem from those who seek to grab their share of wealth through force, or from those who try to defend their property through violence, for both of these groups, by their affirmative acts, support the values of the system under which they live. The millions that I would fear are those who do not dream of the prizes that the nation holds forth, for it is in them, though they may not know it, that a revolution has taken place and is biding its time to translate itself into a new and strange way of life.

I feel that the Negroes' relation to America is symbolically peculiar, and from the Negroes' ultimate reactions to their trapped state a lesson can be learned about America's future. Negroes are told in a language they cannot possibly misunderstand that their native land is not their own; and when, acting upon impulses which they share with whites, they try to assert a claim to their birthright, whites retaliate with terror, never pausing to consider the consequences should the Negroes give up completely. The whites never dream that they would face a situation far more terrifying if they were confronted by Negroes who made no claims at all than by those who are buoyed up by social aggressiveness. My knowledge of how Negroes react to their plight makes me declare that no man can possibly be individually guilty of treason, that an insurgent act is but a man's desperate answer to those who twist his environment so that he cannot fully share the spirit of his native land. Treason is a crime of the State.

Christmas came and I was once more called to the post office for temporary work. This time I met many young white men and we discussed world happenings, the vast armies of unemployed, the rising tide of radical action. I now detected a change in the attitudes of the whites I met; their privations were making them regard Negroes with new eyes, and, for the first time, I was invited to their homes.

When the work in the post office ended, I was assigned by the relief system as an orderly to a medical research institute in one of the largest and wealthiest hospitals in Chicago. I cleaned operating rooms, dog, rat, mice, cat, and rabbit pans, and fed guinea pigs. Four of us Negroes worked there and we occupied an underworld position, remembering that we must restrict ourselves—when not engaged upon some task—to the basement corridors, so that we would not mingle with white nurses, doctors, or visitors.

The sharp line of racial division drawn by the hospital au-
thorities came to me the first morning when I walked along an
underground corridor and saw two long lines of women coming
toward me. A line of white girls marched past, clad in starched
uniforms that gleamed white; their faces were alert, their step
quick, their bodies lean and shapely, their shoulders erect, their
faces lit with the light of purpose. And after them came a line
of black girls, old, fat, dressed in ragged gingham, walking
loosely, carrying tin cans of soap powder, rags, mops, brooms
. . . I wondered what law of the universe kept them from being
mixed? The sun would not have stopped shining had there
been a few black girls in the first line, and the earth would not
have stopped whirling on its axis had there been a few white
girls in the second line. But the two lines I saw graded social
status in purely racial terms.

Of the three Negroes who worked with me, one was a boy
about my own age, Bill, who was either sleepy or drunk most of
the time. Bill straightened his hair and I suspected that he kept
a bottle hidden somewhere in the piles of hay which we fed to
the guinea pigs. He did not like me and I did not like him,
though I tried harder than he to conceal my dislike. We had
nothing in common except that we were both black and lost.
While I contained my frustration, he drank to drown his.
Often I tried to talk to him, tried in simple words to convey to
him some of my ideas, and he would listen in sullen silence.
Then one day he came to me with an angry look on his face.

"I got it," he said.

"You've got what?" I asked.

"This old race problem you keep talking about," he said.

"What about it?"

"Well, it's this way," he explained seriously. "Let the government give every man a gun and five bullets, then let us all start
over again. Make it just like it was in the beginning. The ones
who come out on top, white or black, let them rule."

His simplicity terrified me. I had never met a Negro who was
so irredeemably brutalized. I stopped pumping my ideas into
Bill's brain for fear that the fumes of alcohol might send him
reeling toward some fantastic fate.

The two other Negroes were elderly and had been employed in the institute for fifteen years or more. One was Brand, a short, black, morose bachelor; the other was Cooke, a tall, yellow, spectacled fellow who spent his spare time keeping track of world events through the Chicago *Tribune*. Brand and Cooke hated each other for a reason that I was never able to determine, and they spent a good part of each day quarreling.

When I began working at the institute, I recalled my adolescent dream of wanting to be a medical research worker. Daily I saw young Jewish boys and girls receiving instruction in chemistry and medicine that the average black boy or girl could never receive. When I was alone, I wandered and poked my fingers into strange chemicals, watched intricate machines trace red and black lines on ruled paper. At times I paused and stared at the walls of the rooms, at the floors, at the wide desks at which the white doctors sat; and I realized—with a feeling that I could never quite get used to—that I was looking at the world of another race.

My interest in what was happening in the institute amused the three other Negroes with whom I worked. They had no curiosity about "white folks' things," while I wanted to know if the dogs being treated for diabetes were getting well; if the rats and mice in which cancer had been induced showed any signs of responding to treatment. I wanted to know the principle that lay behind the Aschheim-Zondek tests that were made with rabbits, the Wassermann tests that were made with guinea pigs. But when I asked a timid question I found that even Jewish doctors had learned to imitate the sadistic method of humbling a Negro that the others had cultivated.

"If you know too much, boy, your brains might explode," a doctor said one day.

Each Saturday morning I assisted a young Jewish doctor in slitting the vocal cords of a fresh batch of dogs from the city pound. The object was to devocalize the dogs so that their howls would not disturb the patients in the other parts of the hospital. I held each dog as the doctor injected Nembutal into its veins to make it unconscious; then I held the dog's jaws open as the doctor inserted the scalpel and severed the vocal

cords. Later, when the dogs came to, they would lift their heads
to the ceiling and gape in a soundless wail. The sight became
lodged in my imagination as a symbol of silent suffering.

To me Nembutal was a powerful and mysterious liquid, but
when I asked questions about its properties I could not obtain a
single intelligent answer. The doctor simply ignored me with:

"Come on. Bring me the next dog. I haven't got all day."

One Saturday morning, after I had held the dogs for their
vocal cords to be slit, the doctor left the Nembutal on a bench.
I picked it up, uncorked it, and smelled it. It was odorless. Suddenly Brand ran to me with a stricken face.

"What're you doing?" he asked.

"I was smelling this stuff to see if it had any odor," I said.

"Did you really smell it?" he asked me.

"Yes."

"Oh, God!" he exclaimed.

"What's the matter?" I asked.

"You shouldn't've done that!" he shouted.

"Why?"

He grabbed my arm and jerked me across the room.

"Come on!" he yelled, snatching open the door.

"What's the matter?" I asked.

"I gotta get you to a doctor 'fore it's too late," he gasped.

Had my foolish curiosity made me inhale something dangerous?

"But—is it poisonous?"

"Run, boy!" he said, pulling me. "You'll fall dead."

Filled with fear, with Brand pulling my arm, I rushed out of
the room, raced across a rear areaway, into another room, then
down a long corridor. I wanted to ask Brand what symptoms I
must expect, but we were running too fast. Brand finally
stopped, gasping for breath. My heart beat wildly and my blood
pounded in my head. Brand then dropped to the concrete floor,
stretched out on his back, and yelled with laughter, shaking all
over. He beat his fists against the concrete; he moaned, giggled,
he kicked.

I tried to master my outrage, wondering if some of the white doctors had told him to play the joke. He rose and wiped tears from his eyes, still laughing. I walked away from him. He knew that I was angry and he followed me.

"Don't get mad," he gasped through his laughter.

"Go to hell," I said.

"I couldn't help it," he giggled. "You looked at me like you'd believe anything I said. Man, you was scared."

He leaned against the wall, laughing again, stomping his feet. I was angry, for I felt that he would spread the story. I knew that Bill and Cooke never ventured beyond the safe bounds of Negro living, and they would never blunder into anything like this. And if they heard about this, they would laugh for months.

"Brand, if you mention this, I'll kill you," I swore.

"You ain't mad?" he asked, laughing, staring at me through tears.

Sniffing, Brand walked ahead of me. I followed him back into the room that housed the dogs. All day, while at some task, he would pause and giggle, then smother the giggling with his hand, looking at me out of the corner of his eyes, shaking his head. He laughed at me for a week. I kept my temper and let him amuse himself. I finally found out the properties of Nembutal by consulting medical books; but I never told Brand.

One summer morning, just as I began work, a young Jewish boy came to me with a stop watch in his hand.

"Dr.— wants me to time you when you clean a room," he said. "We're trying to make the institute more efficient."

"I'm doing my work, and getting through on time," I said.

"This is the boss's order," he said.

"Why don't you work for a change?" I blurted, angry.

"Now, look," he said. "*This* is my work. Now *you* work."

I got a mop and pail, sprayed a room with disinfectant, and scrubbed at coagulated blood and hardened dog, rat, and rabbit feces. The normal temperature of a room was ninety, but, as the sun beat down upon the skylights, the temperature rose above a hundred. Stripped to my waist, I slung the mop, moving steadily like a machine, hearing the boy press the button on the stop watch as I finished cleaning a room.

"Well, how is it?" I asked.

"It took you seventeen minutes to clean that last room," he said. "That ought to be the time for each room."

"But that room was not very dirty," I said.

"You have seventeen rooms to clean," he went on as though I had not spoken. "Seventeen times seventeen makes four hours and forty-nine minutes." He wrote upon a little pad. "After lunch, clean the five flights of stone stairs. I timed a boy who scrubbed one step and multiplied that time by the number of steps. You ought to be through by six."

"Suppose I want relief?" I asked.

"You'll manage," he said, and left.

Never had I felt so much the slave as when I scoured those stone steps each afternoon. Working against time, I would wet five steps, sprinkle soap powder, and then a white doctor or a nurse would come along and, instead of avoiding the soapy steps, would walk on them and track the dirty water onto the steps that I had already cleaned. To obviate this, I cleaned but two steps at a time, a distance over which a ten-year-old child could step. But it did no good. The white people still plopped their feet down into the dirty water and muddied the other clean steps. If I ever really hotly hated unthinking whites, it was then. Not once during my entire stay at the institute did a single white person show enough courtesy to avoid a wet step. I would be on my knees, scrubbing, sweating, pouring out what limited energy my body could wring from my meager diet, and I would hear feet approaching. I would pause and curse with tense lips:

"These sonofabitches are going to dirty these steps again, goddamn their souls to hell!"

Sometimes a sadistically observant white man would notice that he had tracked dirty water up the steps, and he would look back down at me and smile and say:

"Boy, we sure keep you busy, don't we?"

And I would not be able to answer.

The feud that went on between Brand and Cooke continued. Although they were working daily in a building where scientific history was being made, the light of curiosity was never in their eyes. They were conditioned to their racial "place," had learned to see only a part of the whites and the white world; and the whites, too, had learned to see only a part of the lives of the blacks and their world.

Perhaps Brand and Cooke, lacking interests that could absorb them, fuming like children over trifles, simply invented their hate of each other in order to have something to feel deeply about. Or perhaps there was in them a vague tension stemming from their chronically frustrating way of life, a pain whose cause they did not know; and, like those devocalized dogs, they would whirl and snap at the air when their old pain struck them. Anyway, they argued about the weather, sports, sex, war, race, politics, and religion; neither of them knew much about the subjects they debated, but it seemed that the less they knew the better they could argue.

The tug of war between the two elderly men reached a climax one winter day at noon. It was incredibly cold and an icy gale swept up and down the Chicago streets with blizzard force. The door of the animal-filled room was locked, for we always insisted that we be allowed one hour in which to eat and rest. Bill and I were sitting on wooden boxes, eating our lunches out of paper bags. Brand was washing his hands at the sink. Cooke was sitting on a rickety stool, munching an apple and reading the Chicago *Tribune.*

Now and then a devocalized dog lifted his nose to the ceiling and howled soundlessly. The room was filled with many rows of high steel tiers. Perched upon each of these tiers were layers of steel cages containing the dogs, rats, mice, rabbits, and guinea pigs. Each cage was labeled in some indecipherable scientific jargon. Along the walls of the rooms were long charts with zig-zagging red and black lines that traced the success or failure of some experiment. The lonely piping of guinea pigs floated unheeded about us. Hay rustled as a rabbit leaped restlessly about in its pen. A rat scampered around in its steel prison. Cooke tapped the newspaper for attention.

"It says here," Cooke mumbled through a mouthful of apple, "that this is the coldest day since 1888."

Bill and I sat unconcerned. Brand chuckled softly.

"What in hell you laughing about?" Cooke demanded of Brand.

"You can't believe what that damn *Tribune* says," Brand said.

"How come I can't?" Cooke demanded. "It's the world's greatest newspaper."

Brand did not reply; he shook his head pityingly and chuckled again.

"Stop that damn laughing at me!" Cooke said angrily.

"I laugh as much as I wanna," Brand said. "You don't know what you talking about. The *Herald-Examiner* says it's the coldest day since 1873."

"But the *Trib* oughta know," Cooke countered. "It's older'n that *Examiner*."

"That damn *Trib* don't know nothing!" Brand drowned out Cooke's voice.

"How in hell you know?" Cooke asked with rising anger.

The argument waxed until Cooke shouted that if Brand did not shut up he was going to "cut his black throat."

Brand whirled from the sink, his hands dripping soapy water, his eyes blazing.

"Take that back," Brand said.

"I take nothing back! What you wanna do about it?" Cooke taunted.

The two elderly Negroes glared at each other. I wondered if the quarrel was really serious, or if it would turn out harmlessly as so many others had done.

Suddenly Cooke dropped the Chicago *Tribune* and pulled a long knife from his pocket; his thumb pressed a button and a gleaming steel blade leaped out. Brand stepped back quickly and seized an ice pick that was stuck in a wooden board above the sink.

"Put that knife down," Brand said.

"Stay 'way from me, or I'll cut your throat," Cooke warned.

Brand lunged with the ice pick. Cooke dodged out of range. They circled each other like fighters in a prize ring. The cancerous and tubercular rats and mice leaped about in their cages. The guinea pigs whistled in fright. The diabetic dogs bared their teeth and barked soundlessly in our direction. The Aschheim-Zondek rabbits flopped their ears and tried to hide in the corners of their pens. Cooke now crouched and sprang forward with the knife. Bill and I jumped to our feet, speechless with surprise. Brand retreated. The eyes of both men were hard and unblinking; they were breathing deeply.

"Say, cut it out!" I called in alarm.

"Them damn fools is really fighting," Bill said in amazement.

Slashing at each other, Brand and Cooke surged up and down the aisles of steel tiers. Suddenly Brand uttered a bellow and charged into Cooke and swept him violently backward. Cooke grasped Brand's hand to keep the ice pick from sinking into his chest. Brand broke free and charged Cooke again, sweeping him into an animal-filled steel tier. The tier balanced itself on its edge for an indecisive moment, then toppled.

Like kingpins, one steel tier lammed into another, then they all crashed to the floor with a sound as of the roof falling. The whole aspect of the room altered quicker than the eye could follow. Brand and Cooke stood stock-still, their eyes fastened upon each other, their pointed weapons raised; but they were dimly aware of the havoc that churned about them.

The steel tiers lay jumbled; the doors of the cages swung open. Rats and mice and dogs and rabbits moved over the floor in wild panic. The Wassermann guinea pigs were squealing as though judgment day had come. Here and there an animal had been crushed beneath a cage.

All four of us looked at one another. We knew what this meant. We might lose our jobs. We were already regarded as black dunces; and if the doctors saw this mess they would take it as final proof. Bill rushed to the door to make sure that it was locked. I glanced at the clock and saw that it was 12:30. We had one half-hour of grace.

"Come on," Bill said uneasily. "We got to get this place cleaned."

Brand and Cooke stared at each other, both doubting.

"Give me your knife, Cooke," I said.

"Naw! Take Brand's ice pick *first*," Cooke said.

"The hell you say!" Brand said. "Take his knife *first*."

A knock sounded at the door.

"Sssssh," Bill said.

We waited. We heard footsteps going away. We'll all lose our jobs, I thought.

Persuading the fighters to surrender their weapons was a difficult task, but at last it was done and we could begin to set things right. Slowly Brand stooped and tugged at one end of a steel tier. Cooke stooped to help him. Both men seemed to be acting in a dream. Soon, however, all four of us were working frantically, watching the clock.

As we labored we conspired to keep the fight a secret; we agreed to tell the doctors—if any should ask—that we had not been in the room during our lunch hour; we felt that that lie would explain why no one had unlocked the door when the knock had come.

We righted the tiers and replaced the cages; then we were faced with the impossible task of sorting the cancerous rats and mice, the diabetic dogs, the Aschheim-Zondek rabbits, and the Wasserman guinea pigs. Whether we kept our jobs or not depended upon how shrewdly we could cover up all evidence of the fight. It was pure guesswork, but we had to try to put the animals back into the correct cages. We knew that certain rats or mice went into certain cages, but we did not know *what* rat or mouse went into *what* cage. We did not know a tubercular mouse from a cancerous mouse—the white doctors had made sure that we would not know. They had never taken time to answer a single question; though we worked in the institute, we were as remote from the meaning of the experiments as if we lived in the moon. The doctors had laughed at what they felt was our childlike interest in the fate of the animals.

First we sorted the dogs; that was fairly easy, for we could remember the size and color of most of them. But the rats and mice and guinea pigs baffled us completely.

We put our heads together and pondered, down in the underworld of the great scientific institute. It was a strange scientific conference; the fate of the entire medical research institute rested in our ignorant, black hands.

We remembered the number of rats, mice, or guinea pigs— we had to handle them several times a day—that went into a given cage, and we supplied the number helter-skelter from those animals that we could catch running loose on the floor. We discovered that many rats, mice, and guinea pigs were missing—they had been killed in the scuffle. We solved that problem by taking healthy stock from other cages and putting them into cages with sick animals. We repeated this process until we were certain that, numerically at least, all the animals with which the doctors were experimenting were accounted for.

The rabbits came last. We broke the rabbits down into two general groups; those that had fur on their bellies and those that did not. We knew that all those rabbits that had shaven bellies—our scientific knowledge adequately covered this point because it was our job to shave the rabbits—were undergoing the Aschheim-Zondek tests. But in what pen did a given rabbit belong? We did not know. I solved the problem very simply. I counted the shaven rabbits; they numbered seventeen. I counted the pens labeled "Aschheim-Zondek," then proceeded to drop a shaven rabbit into each pen at random. And again we were numerically successful. At least white America had taught us to count . . .

Lastly we carefully wrapped all the dead animals in newspapers and hid their bodies in a garbage can.

At a few minutes to one the room was in order; that is, the

kind of order that we four Negroes could figure out. I unlocked the door and we sat waiting, whispering, vowing secrecy, wondering what the reaction of the doctors would be.

Finally a doctor came, gray-haired, white-coated, spectacled, efficient, serious, taciturn, bearing a tray upon which sat a bottle of mysterious fluid and a hypodermic needle.

"My rats, please."

Cooke shuffled forward to serve him. We held our breath. Cooke got the cage which he knew the doctor always called for at that hour and brought it forward. One by one, Cooke took out the rats and held them as the doctor solemnly injected the mysterious fluid under their skins.

"Thank you, Cooke," the doctor murmured.

"Not at all, sir," Cooke mumbled with a suppressed gasp.

When the doctor had gone we looked at one another, hardly daring to believe that our secret would be kept. We were so anxious that we did not know whether to curse or laugh. Another doctor came.

"Give me A-Z rabbit number 14."

"Yes, sir," I said.

I brought him the rabbit and he took it upstairs to the operating room. We waited for repercussions. None came.

All that afternoon the doctors came and went. I would run into the room—stealing a few seconds from my step-scrubbing —and ask what progress was being made and would learn that the doctors had detected nothing. At quitting time we felt triumphant.

"They won't ever know," Cooke boasted in a whisper.

I saw Brand stiffen. I knew that he was aching to dispute Cooke's optimism, but the memory of the fight he had just had was so fresh in his mind that he could not speak.

Another day went by and nothing happened. Then another day. The doctors examined the animals and wrote in their little black books, in their big black books, and continued to trace red and black lines upon the charts.

A week passed and we felt out of danger. Not one question had been asked.

Of course, we four black men were much too modest to make our contribution known, but we often wondered what went on in the laboratories after that secret disaster. Was some scientific hypothesis, well on its way to validation and ultimate public use, discarded because of unexpected findings on that cold winter day? Was some tested principle given a new and strange refinement because of fresh, remarkable evidence? Did some brooding research worker—those who held stop watches and slopped their feet carelessly in the water of the steps I tried so hard to keep clean—get a wild, if brief, glimpse of a new scientific truth? Well, we never heard . . .

I brooded upon whether I should have gone to the director's office and told him what had happened, but each time I thought of it I remembered that the director had been the man who had ordered the boy to stand over me while I was working and time my movements with a stop watch. He did not regard me as a human being. I did not share his world. I earned thirteen dollars a week and I had to support four people with it, and should I risk that thirteen dollars by acting idealistically? Brand and Cooke would have hated me and would have eventually driven me from the job had I "told" on them. The hospital kept us four Negroes as though we were close kin to the animals we tended, huddled together down in the underworld corridors of the hospital, separated by a vast psychological distance from the significant processes of the rest of the hospital —just as America had kept us locked in the dark underworld of American life for three hundred years—and we had made our own code of ethics, values, loyalty.

Gwendolyn Brooks

The Sundays of Satin-Legs Smith

Inamorata, with an approbation,
Bestowed his title. Blessed his inclination.)

He wakes, unwinds, elaborately: a cat
Tawny, reluctant, royal. He is fat
And fine this morning. Definite. Reimbursed.

He waits a moment, he designs his reign,
That no performance may be plain or vain,
Then rises in a clear delirium.

He sheds, with his pajamas, shabby days.
And his desertedness, his intricate fear, the
Postponed resentments and the prim precautions.

Now, at his bath, would you deny him lavender
Or take away the power of his pine?
What smelly substitute, heady as wine,
Would you provide? Life must be aromatic.
There must be scent, somehow there must be some.
Would you have flowers in his life? suggest
Asters? a Really Good geranium?
A white carnation? would you prescribe a Show
With the cold lilies, formal chrysanthemum
Magnificence, poinsettias, and emphatic

Red of prize roses? might his happiest
Alternative (you muse) be, after all,
A bit of gentle garden in the best
Of taste and straight tradition? Maybe so.
But you forget, or did you ever know,
His heritage of cabbage and pigtails,
Old intimacy with alleys, garbage pails,
Down in the deep (but always beautiful) South
Where roses blush their blithest (it is said)
And sweet magnolias put Chanel to shame.

No! He has not a flower to his name.
Except a feather one, for his lapel.
Apart from that, if he should think of flowers
It is in terms of dandelions or death.
Ah, there is little hope. You might as well—
Unless you care to set the world a-boil
And do a lot of equalizing things,
Remove a little ermine, say, from kings,
Shake hands with paupers and appoint them men,
For instance—certainly you might as well
Leave him his lotion, lavender and oil.

Let us proceed. Let us inspect, together
With his meticulous and serious love,
The innards of this closet. Which is a vault
Whose glory is not diamonds, not pearls,
Not silver plate with just enough dull shine.
But wonder-suits in yellow and in wine,
Sarcastic green and zebra-striped cobalt.
All drapes. With shoulder padding that is wide
And cocky and determined as his pride;
Ballooning pants that taper off to ends
Scheduled to choke precisely.
                                        Here are hats
Like bright umbrellas; and hysterical ties
Like narrow banners for some gathering war.

People are so in need, in need of help.
People want so much that they do not know.

Below the tinkling trade of little coins
The gold impulse not possible to show
Or spend. Promise piled over and betrayed.

These kneaded limbs receive the kiss of silk.
Then they receive the brave and beautiful
Embrace of some of that equivocal wool.
He looks into his mirror, loves himself—
The neat curve here; the angularity
That is appropriate at just its place;
The technique of a variegated grace.

Here is all his sculpture and his art
And all his architectural design.
Perhaps you would prefer to this a fine
Value of marble, complicated stone.
Would have him think with horror of baroque,
Rococo. You forget and you forget.

He dances down the hotel steps that keep
Remnants of last night's high life and distress.
As spat-out purchased kisses and spilled beer,
He swallows sunshine with a secret yelp.
Passes to coffee and a roll or two.
Has breakfasted.
        Out. Sounds about him smear,
Become a unit. He hears and does not hear
The alarm clock meddling in somebody's sleep;
Children's governed Sunday happiness;
The dry tone of a plane; a woman's oath;
Consumption's spiritless expectoration;
An indignant robin's resolute donation
Pinching a track through apathy and din;
Restaurant vendors weeping; and the L
That comes on like a slightly horrible thought.

Pictures, too, as usual, are blurred.
He sees and does not see the broken windows
Hiding their shame with newsprint; little girl
With ribbons decking wornness, little boy
Wearing the trousers with the decentest patch,
To honor Sunday; women on their way
From "service," temperate holiness arranged
Ably on asking faces; men estranged
From music and from wonder and from joy
But far familiar with the guiding awe
Of foodlessness.
                    He loiters.
                              Restaurant vendors
Weep, or out of them rolls a restless glee.
The Lonesome Blues, the Long-lost Blues, I Want A
Big Fat Mama. Down these sore avenues
Comes no Saint-Saëns, no piquant elusive Grieg,
And not Tchaikovsky's wayward eloquence
And not the shapely tender drift of Brahms.
But could he love them? Since a man must bring
To music what his mother spanked him for
When he was two: bits of forgotten hate,
Devotion: whether or not his mattress hurts:
The little dream his father humored: the thing
His sister did for money: what he ate
For breakfast—and for dinner twenty years
Ago last autumn: all his skipped desserts.

The pasts of his ancestors lean against
Him. Crowd him. Fog out his identity.
Hundreds of hungers mingle with his own,
Hundreds of voices advise so dexterously
He quite considers his reactions his,
Judges he walks most powerfully alone,
That everything is—simply what it is.

But movie-time approaches, time to boo
The hero's kiss, and boo the heroine

Whose ivory and yellow it is sin
For his eye to eat of. The Mickey Mouse,
However, is for everyone in the house.

Squires his lady to dinner at Joe's Eats.
His lady alters as to leg and eye,
Thickness and height, such minor points as these,
From Sunday to Sunday. But no matter what
Her name or body positively she's
In Queen Lace stockings with ambitious heels
That strain to kiss the calves, and vivid shoes
Frontless and backless, Chinese fingernails,
Earrings, three layers of lipstick, intense hat
Dripping with the most voluble of veils.
Her affable extremes are like sweet bombs
About him, whom no middle grace or good
Could gratify. He had no education
In quiet arts of compromise. He would
Not understand your counsels on control, nor
Thank you for your late trouble.

                    At Joe's Eats
You get your fish or chicken on meat platters.
With coleslaw, macaroni, candied sweets,
Coffee and apple pie. You go out full.
("The end is—isn't it?—all that really matters.)

    And even and intrepid come
    The tender boots of night to home.

Her body is like new brown bread
Under the Woolworth mignonette.
Her body is a honey bowl
Whose waiting honey is deep and hot.
Her body is like summer earth,
Receptive, soft, and absolute . . .

Langston Hughes

Harlem

What happens to a dream deferred?

Does it dry up
like a raisin in the sun?

Or fester like a sore—
And then run?
Does it stink like rotten meat?
Or crust and sugar over—
like a syrupy sweet?

Maybe it just sags
like a heavy load.

Or does it explode?

Ralph Ellison

Riot *

When I reached Morningside the shooting sounded like a distant celebration of the Fourth of July, and I hurried forward. At St. Nicholas the street lights were out. A thunderous sound arose and I saw four men running toward me pushing something that jarred the walk. It was a safe.

"Say," I began.

"Get the hell out the way!"

I leaped aside, into the street, and there was a sudden and brilliant suspension of time, like the interval between the last ax stroke and the felling of a tall tree, in which there had been a loud noise followed by a loud silence. Then I was aware of figures crouching in doorways and along the curb; then time burst and I was down in the street, conscious but unable to rise, struggling against the street and seeing the flashes as the guns went off back at the corner of the avenue, aware to my left of the men still speeding the rumbling safe along the walk as back up the street, behind me, two policemen, almost invisible in black shirts, thrust flaming pistols before them. One of the safe rollers pitched forward, and farther away, past the corner, a bullet struck an auto tire, the released air shrieking like a huge animal in agony. I rolled, flopping around, willing myself to crawl closer to the curb but unable, feeling a sudden wet warmth upon my face and seeing the safe shooting wildly into the intersection and the men rounding the corner into the dark, pounding, gone; gone now, as the skittering safe bounded off at

* From *Invisible Man*, 1952. The title of this selection was supplied by the editor.

a tangent, shot into the intersection and lodged in the third rail and sent up a curtain of sparks that lit up the block like a blue dream; a dream I was dreaming and through which I could see the cops braced as on a target range, feet forward, free arms akimbo, firing with deliberate aim.

"Get hold of Emergency!" one of them called, and I saw them turn and disappear where the dull glint of trolley rails faded off into the dark.

Suddenly the block leaped alive. Men who seemed to rise up out of the sidewalks were rushing into the store fronts above me, their voices rising excitedly. And now the blood was in my face and I could move, getting to my knees as someone out of the crowd was helping me to stand.

"You hurt, daddy?"

"Some—I don't know—" I couldn't quite see them.

"Damn! He's got a hole in his head!" a voice said.

A light flashed in my face, came close. I felt a hard hand upon my skull and moved away.

"Hell, it's just a nick," a voice said. "One them forty-fives hit your little finger you got to go down!"

"Well, this one over here is gone down for the last time," someone called from the walk. "They got him clean."

I wiped my face, my head ringing. Something was missing.

"Here, buddy, this yours?"

It was my brief case, extended to me by its handles. I seized it with sudden panic, as though something infinitely precious had almost been lost to me.

"Thanks," I said, peering into their dim, blue-tinted features. I looked at the dead man. He lay face forward, the crowd working around him. I realized suddenly that it might have been me huddled there, feeling too that I had seen him there before, in the bright light of noon, long ago . . . how long? Knew his name, I thought, and suddenly my knees flowed forward. I sat there, my fist that gripped the brief case bruising against the street, my head slumped forward. They were going around me.

"Get off my foot, man," I heard. "Quit shoving. There's plenty for everybody."

There was something I had to do and I knew that my forget-fulness wasn't real, as one knows that the forgotten details of certain dreams are not truly forgotten but evaded. I knew, and in my mind I was trying to reach through the gray veil that now seemed to hang behind my eyes as opaquely as the blue curtain that screened the street beyond the safe. The dizziness left and I managed to stand, holding onto my brief case, press-ing a handkerchief to my head. Up the street there sounded the crashing of huge sheets of glass and through the blue mysteri-ousness of the dark the walls shimmered like shattered mir-rors. All the street's signs were dead, all the day sounds had lost their stable meaning. Somewhere a burglar alarm went off, a meaningless blangy sound, followed by the joyful shouts of looters.

"Come on," someone called nearby.

"Let's go, buddy," the man who had helped me said. He took my arm, a thin man who carried a large cloth bag slung over his shoulder.

"The shape you in wouldn't do to leave you round here," he said. "You act like you drunk."

"Go where?" I said.

"Where? Hell, man. Everywhere. We git to moving, no tell-ing where we might go—Hey, Dupre!" he called.

"Say, man—Goddam! Don't be calling my name so loud," a voice answered. "Here, I am over here, gitting me some work shirts."

"Git some for me, Du," he said.

"All right, but don't think I'm your papa," the answer came.

I looked at the thin man, feeling a surge of friendship. He didn't know me, his help was disinterested . . .

"Hey, Du," he called, "we go'n do it?"

"Hell yes, soon as I git me these shirts."

The crowd was working in and out of the stores like ants around spilled sugar. From time to time there came the crash of glass, shots; fire trucks in distant streets.

"How you feel?" the man said.

"Still fuzzy," I said, "and weak."

"Le's see if it's stopped bleeding. Yeah, you'll be all right."

I saw him vaguely though his voice came clear.

"Sure," I said.

"Man, you lucky you ain't dead. These sonsabitches is really shooting now," he said. "Over on Lenox they was aiming up in the air. If I could find me a rifle, I'd show 'em! Here, take you a drink of this good Scotch," he said, taking a quart bottle from a hip pocket. "I got me a whole case stashed what I got from a liquor store over there. Over there all you got to do is breathe, and you drunk, man. Drunk! Hundred proof bonded whiskey flowing all in the gutters."

I took a drink, shuddering as the whiskey went down but thankful for the shock it gave me. There was a bursting, tearing movement of people around me, dark figures in a blue glow.

"Look at them take it away," he said, looking into the dark action of the crowd. "Me, I'm tired. Was you over on Lenox?"

"No," I said, seeing a woman moving slowly past with a row of about a dozen dressed chickens suspended by their necks from the handle of a new straw broom . . .

"Hell, you ought to see it, man. Everything is tore up. By now the womens is picking it clean. I saw one ole woman with a whole side of a cow on her back. Man, she was 'bout bent bowlegged trying to make it home—Here come Dupre now," he said, breaking off.

I saw a little hard man come out of the crowd carrying several boxes. He wore three hats upon his head, and several pairs of suspenders flopped about his shoulders, and now as he came toward us I saw that he wore a pair of gleaming new rubber hip boots. His pockets bulged and over his shoulder he carried a cloth sack that swung heavily behind him.

"Damn, Dupre," my friend said, pointing to his head, "you got one of them for me? What kind is they?"

Dupre stopped and looked at him. "With all them hats in there and I'm going to come out with anything but a *Dobbs*? Man, are you *mad*? All them new, pretty—colored *Dobbs*? Come on, let's get going before the cops git back. Damn, look at that thing blaze!"

I looked toward the curtain of blue fire, through which vague figures toiled. Dupre called out and several men left the crowd and joined us in the street. We moved off, my friend (Scofield, the others called him) leading me along. My head throbbed, still bled.

"Looks like you got you some loot too," he said, pointing to my brief case.

"Not much," I said, thinking, loot? *Loot?* And suddenly I knew why it was heavy, remembering Mary's broken bank and the coins; and now I found myself opening the brief case and dropping all my papers—my Brotherhood identification, the anonymous letter, along with Clifton's doll—into it.

"Fill it up, man. Don't you be bashful. You wait till we tackle one of these pawnshops. That Du's got him a cotton-picking sack fulla stuff. *He* could go into business."

"Well, I'll be damn," a man on the other side of me said. "I thought that was a cotton sack. Where'd he get that thing?"

"He brought it with him when he come North," Scofield said. "Du swears that when he goes back he'll have it full of ten-dollar bills. Hell, after tonight he'll need him a warehouse for all the stuff he's got. You fill that brief case, buddy. Get yourself something!"

"No," I said, "I've enough in it already." And now I remembered very clearly where I'd started out for but could not leave them.

"Maybe you right," Scofield said. "How I know, you might have it full of diamonds or something. A man oughtn't to be greedy. Though it's time something like this happened."

We moved along. Should I leave, get on to the district? Where were they, at the birthday celebration?

"How did all this get started?" I said.

Scofield seemed surprised. "Damn if I know, man. A cop shot a woman or something."

Another man moved close to us as somewhere a piece of heavy steel rang down.

"Hell, that wasn't what started it," he said. "It was that fellow, what's his name . . . ?"

"Who?" I said. "What's his name?"

"That young guy!"

"You know, everybody's mad about it . . ."

Clifton, I thought. It's for Clifton. A night for Clifton.

"Aw man, don't tell me," Scofield said. "Didn't I see it with my own eyes? About eight o'clock down on Lenox and 123rd this paddy slapped a kid for grabbing a Baby Ruth and the kid's mama took it up and then the paddy slapped her and that's when hell broke loose."

"You were there?" I said.

"Same's I'm here. Some fellow said the kid made the paddy mad by grabbing a candy named after a white woman."

"Damn if that's the way I heard it," another man said. "When I come up they said a white woman set it off by trying to take a black gal's man."

"Damn *who* started it," Dupre said. "All I want is for it to last a while."

"It was a white gal, all right, but that wasn't the way it was. She was drunk—" another voice said.

But it couldn't have been Sybil, I thought; it had already started.

"You wahn know who started it?" a man holding a pair of binoculars called from the window of a pawnshop. "You wahn really to know?"

"Sure," I said.

"Well, you don't need to go no further. It was started by that great leader, Ras the Destroyer!"

"That monkey-chaser?" someone said.

"Listen, bahstard!"

"Don't nobody know how it started," Dupre said.

"Somebody has to know," I said.

Scofield held his whiskey toward me. I refused it.

"Hell, man, it just exploded. These is dog days," he said.

"*Dog* days?"

"Sho, this hot weather."

"I tell you they mad over what happen to that young fellow, what's-his-name . . ."

We were passing a building now and I heard a voice calling frantically, "Colored store! Colored store!"

"Then put up a sign, motherfouler," a voice said. "You probably rotten as the others."

"Listen at the bastard. For one time in his life he's glad to be colored," Scofield said.

"Colored store," the voice went on automatically.

"Hey! You sho you ain't got some white blood?"

"No, *sir!*" the voice said.

"Should I bust him, man?"

"For what? He ain't got a damn thing. Let the motherfouler alone."

A few doors away we came to a hardware store. "This is the first stop, men," Dupre said.

"What happens now?" I said.

"Who you?" he said, cocking his thrice-hatted head.

"Nobody, just one of the boys—" I began.

"You sho you ain't somebody I know?"

"I'm pretty sure," I said.

"He's all right, Du," said Scofield. "Them cops shot him."

Dupre looked at me and kicked something—a pound of butter, sending it smearing across the hot street. "We fixing to do something what needs to be done," he said. "First we gets a flashlight for everybody . . . And let's have some organization, y'all. Don't everybody be running over everybody else. Come on!"

"Come on in, buddy," Scofield said.

I felt no need to lead or leave them; was glad to follow; was gripped by a need to see where and to what they would lead. And all the time the thought that I should go to the district was with me. We went inside the store, into the dark glinting with metal. They moved carefully, and I could hear them searching, sweeping objects to the floor. The cash register rang.

"Here some flashlights over here," someone called.

"How many?" Dupre said.

"Plenty, man."

"Okay, pass out one to everybody. They got batteries?"

"Naw, but there's plenty them too, 'bout a dozen boxes."

"Okay, give me one with batteries so I can find the buckets. Then every man get him a light."

"Here some buckets over here," Scofield said.

"Then all we got to find is where he keeps the oil."

"Oil?" I said.

"Coal oil, man. And hey, y'all," he called, "don't nobody be smoking in here."

I stood beside Scofield listening to the noise as he took a stack of zinc buckets and passed them out. Now the store leaped alive with flashing lights and flickering shadows.

"Keep them lights down on the floor," Dupre called. "No use letting folks see who we are. Now when you get your buckets line up and let me fill 'em."

"Listen to ole Du lay it down—he's a bitch, ain't he, buddy? He always liked to lead things. And always leading me into trouble."

"What are we getting ready to do?" I said.

"You'll see," Dupre said. "Hey, you over there. Come on from behind that counter and take this bucket. Don't you see ain't nothing in that cash register, that if it was I'd have it myself?"

Suddenly the banging of buckets ceased. We moved into the back room. By the light of a flash I could see a row of fuel drums mounted on racks. Dupre stood before them in his new hip boots and filled each bucket with oil. We moved in slow order. Our buckets filled, we filed out into the street. I stood there in the dark feeling a rising excitement as their voices played around me. What was the meaning of it all? What should I think of it, *do* about it?

"With this stuff," Dupre said, "we better walk in the middle of the street. It's just down around the corner."

Then as we moved off a group of boys ran among us and the men started using their lights, revealing darting figures in blonde wigs, the tails of their stolen dress coats flying. Behind them in hot pursuit came a gang armed with dummy rifles taken from an Army & Navy Store. I laughed with the others, thinking: A holy holiday for Clifton.

"Put out them lights!" Dupre commanded.

Behind us came the sound of screams, laughter; ahead the footfalls of the running boys, distant fire trucks, shooting, and in the quiet intervals, the steady filtering of shattered glass. I could smell the kerosene as it sloshed from the buckets and slapped against the street.

Suddenly Scofield grabbed my arm. "Good God, look-a-yonder!"

And I saw a crowd of men running up pulling a Borden's milk wagon, on top of which, surrounded by a row of railroad flares, a huge woman in a gingham pinafore sat drinking beer from a barrel which sat before her. The men would run furiously a few paces and stop, resting between the shafts, run a few paces and rest, shouting and laughing and drinking from a jug, as she on top threw back her head and shouted passionately in a full-throated voice of blues singer's timbre:

If it hadn't been for the referee,
Joe Louis woulda killed
Jim Jefferie
Free beer!!

—sloshing the dipper of beer around.

We stepped aside, amazed, as she bowed graciously from side to side like a tipsy fat lady in a circus parade, the dipper like a gravy spoon in her enormous hand. Then she laughed and drank deeply while reaching over nonchalantly with her free hand to send quart after quart of milk crashing into the street. And all the time the men running with the wagon over the debris. Around me there were shouts of laughter and disapproval.

"Somebody better stop them fools," Scofield said in outrage. "That's what I call taking things too far. Goddam, how the hell they going to get her down from there after she gits fulla beer? Somebody answer me that. How they going to get her down? 'Round here throwing away all that good milk!"

The big woman left me unnerved. Milk and beer—I felt sad, watching the wagon careen dangerously as they went around a corner. We went on, avoiding the broken bottles as now the spilling kerosene splashed into the pale spilt milk. How much has happened? Why was I torn? We moved around a corner. My head still ached.

Scofield touched my arm. "Here we is," he said.

We had come to a huge tenement building.

"Where are we?" I said.

"This the place where most of us live," he said. "Come on."

So that was it, the meaning of the kerosene. I couldn't believe it, couldn't believe they had the nerve. All the windows seemed empty. They'd blacked it out themselves. I saw now only by flash or flame.

"Where will you live?" I said, looking up, up.

"You call *this* living?" Scofield said. "It's the only way to git rid of it, man . . ."

I looked for hesitation in their vague forms. They stood looking at the building rising above us, the liquid dark of the oil simmering dully in the stray flecks of light that struck their pails, bent forward, their shoulders bowed. None said "no," by word or stance. And in the dark windows and on the roofs above I could now discern the forms of women and children.

Dupre moved toward the building.

"Now look ahere, y'all," he said, his triple-hatted head showing grotesquely atop the stoop. "I wants all the women and chillun and the old and the sick folks brought out. And when you takes your buckets up the stairs I wants you to go clean to the top. I mean the *top!* And when you git there I want you to start using your flashlights in every room to make sure nobody gits left behind, then when you git 'em out start splashing coal oil. Then when you git it splashed I'm going to holler, and when I holler three times I want you to light them matches and git. After that it's every tub on its own black bottom!"

It didn't occur to me to interfere, or to question . . . They had a plan. Already I could see the women and children coming down the steps. A child was crying. And suddenly everyone paused, turning, looking off into the dark. Somewhere nearby an incongruous sound shook the dark, an air hammer pounding like a machine gun. They paused with the sensitivity of grazing deer, then returned to their work, the women and children once more moving.

"That's right, y'all. You ladies move on up the street to the folks you going to stay with," Dupre said. "And keep holt them kids!"

Someone pounded my back and I swung around, seeing a woman push past me and climb up to catch Dupre's arm, their two figures seeming to blend as her voice arose, thin, vibrant and desperate.

"Please, Dupre," she said, "*please*. You know my time's almost here . . . you *know* it is. If you do it now, where am I going to go?"

Dupre pulled away and rose to a higher step. He looked down at her, shaking his thrice-hatted head. "Now git on out the way, Lottie," he said patiently. "Why you have to start this now? We done been all over it and you know I ain't go'n change. And lissen here, the resta y'all," he said, reaching into the top of his hip boot and producing a nickel-plated revolver and waving it around, "don't think they's going to be any *mind*-changing either. And I don't aim for no arguments neither."

"You goddam right, Dupre. We wid you!"

"My kid died from the t-bees in that deathtrap, but I bet a man ain't no more go'n be *born* in there," he said. "So now, Lottie, you go on up the street and let us mens git going."

She stood back, crying. I looked at her, in house shoes, her breasts turgid, her belly heavy and high. In the crowd, women's hands took her away, her large liquid eyes turned for a second toward the man in the rubber boots.

What type of man is he, what would Jack say of him? Jack. *Jack!* And where was he in this?

"Let's go, buddy," Scofield said, nudging me. I followed him, filled with a sense of Jack's outrageous unreality. We went in, up the stairs, flashing our lights. Ahead I saw Dupre moving. He was a type of man nothing in my life had taught me to see, to understand, or respect, a man outside the scheme till now. We entered rooms littered with the signs of swift emptying. It was hot, close.

"This here's my own apartment," Scofield said. "And ain't the bedbugs going to get a surprise!"

We slopped the kerosene about, upon an old mattress, along the floor; then moved into the hall, using the flashlights. From all through the building came the sounds of footsteps, of splashing oil, the occasional prayerful protest of some old one being forced to leave. The men worked in silence now, like moles deep in the earth. Time seemed to hold. No one laughed. Then from below came Dupre's voice.

"Okay, mens. We got everybody out. Now starting with the top floor I want you to start striking matches. Be careful and don't set yourself on fire . . ."

There was still some kerosene left in Scofield's bucket and I saw him pick up a rag and drop it in; then came the sputtering of a match and I saw the room leap to flame. The heat flared up and I backed away. He stood there silhouetted against the red flare, looking into the flames, shouting.

"Goddam you rotten sonsabitches. You didn't think I'd do it but there it is. You wouldn't fix it up. Now see how you like it."

"Let's go," I said.

Below us, men shot downstairs five and six steps at a time, moving in the weird light of flash and flame in long, dreambounds. On each floor as I passed, smoke and flame arose. And now I was seized with a fierce sense of exaltation. They've done it, I thought. They organized it and carried it through alone; the decision their own and their own action. Capable of their own action . . .

There came a thunder of footfalls above me, someone calling, "Keep going man, it's hell upstairs. Somebody done opened the door to the roof and them flames is leaping."

"Come on," Scofield said.

I moved, feeling something slip and was halfway down the next flight before realizing that my brief case was gone. For a second I hesitated, but I'd had it too long to leave it now.

"Come on, buddy," Scofield called, "we caint be fooling around."

"In a second," I said.

Men were shooting past. I bent over, holding on to the hand-rail and shouldered my way back up the stairs, using my flash along each step, back slowly, finding it, an oily footstep embedded with crushed pieces of plaster showing upon its leather side; getting it now and turning to bound down again. The oil won't come off easily, I thought with a pang. But this was it, what I had known was coming around the dark corner of my mind, had known and tried to tell the committee and which they had ignored. I plunged down, shaking with fierce excitement.

At the landing I saw a bucket half full of kerosene and seized it, flinging it impulsively into a burning room. A huge puff of smoke-fringed flame filled the doorway, licking outward toward me. I ran, choking and coughing as I plunged. They did it themselves, I thought, holding my breath—planned it, organized it, applied the flame.

I burst into the air and the exploding sounds of the night, and I did not know if the voice was that of a man, woman or child, but for a moment I stood on the stoop with the red doorway behind me and heard the voice call me by my Brotherhood name.

It was as though I had been aroused from sleep and for an instant I stood there looking, listening to the voice almost lost in the clamour of shouts, screams, burglar alarms and sirens.

"Brother, ain't it wonderful," it called. "You said you would lead us, you really said it . . ."

I went down into the street, going slowly but filled with a feverish inner need to be away from that voice. Where had Scofield gone?

Most of their eyes, white in the flame-flushed dark, looked toward the building.

But now I heard someone say, "Woman, who you say that is?" And she proudly repeated my name.

"Where he go? Get him, mahn, Ras wahnt him!"

I went into the crowd, walking slowly, smoothly into the dark crowd, the whole surface of my skin alert, my back chilled, looking, listening to those moving with a heaving and sweating and a burr of talk around me and aware that now that I wanted to see them, needed to see them, I could not; feeling them, a dark mass in motion on a dark night, a black river ripping through a black land; and Ras or Tarp could move beside me and I wouldn't know. I was one with the mass, moving down the littered street over the puddles of oil and milk, my personality blasted. Then I was in the next block, dodging in and out, hearing them somewhere in the crowd behind me; moving on through the sound of sirens and burglar alarms to be swept into a swifter crowd and pushed along, half-running, half-walking, trying to see behind me and wondering where the others had gone. There was shooting back there now, and on either side of me they were throwing garbage cans, bricks and pieces of metal into plate glass windows. I moved, feeling as though a huge force was on the point of bursting. Shouldering my way to the side I stood in a doorway and watched them move, feeling a certain vindication as now I thought of the message that had brought me here. Who had called, one of the district members or someone from Jack's birthday celebration? Who wanted me at the district after it was too late? Very well, I'd go there now. I'd see what the master minds thought now. Where were they anyway, and what profound conclusions were they drawing? What *ex post facto* lessons of history? And that crash over the telephone, had that been the beginning, or had Jack simply dropped his eye? I laughed drunkenly, the eruption paining my head.

Suddenly the shooting ceased and in the silence there was the sound of voices, footfalls, labor.

"Hey, buddy," somebody said beside me, "where you going?" It was Scofield.

"It's either run or get knocked down," I said. "I thought you were still back there."

"I cut out, man. A building two doors away started to burn and they had to git the fire department . . . Damn! wasn't for this noise I'd swear those bullets was mosquitoes."

"Watch out!" I warned, pulling him away from where a man lay propped against a post, tightening a tourniquet around his gashed arm.

Scofield flashed his light and for a second I saw the black man, his face gray with shock, watching the jetting pulsing of his blood spurting into the street. Then, compelled, I reached down and twisted the tourniquet, feeling the blood warm upon my hand, seeing the pulsing cease.

"You done stopped it," a young man said, looking down.

"Here," I said, "you take it, hold it tight. Get him to a doctor."

"Ain't you a doctor?"

"Me?" I said. "*Me?* Are you crazy? If you want him to live, get him away from here."

"Albert done gone for one," the boy said. "But I thought you was one. You—"

"No," I said, looking at my bloody hands, "no, not me. You hold it tight until the doctor comes. I couldn't cure a headache."

I stood wiping my hands against the brief case, looking down at the big man, his back resting against the post with his eyes closed, the boy holding desperately to the tourniquet made of what had been a bright new tie.

"Come on," I said.

"Say," Scofield said when we were past, "wasn't that you that woman was calling *brother* back yonder?"

"Brother? No, it must have been some other guy."

"You know, man, I think I seen you before somewhere. You ever was in Memphis . . . ? Say, look what's coming," he said, pointing, and I looked through the dark to see a squad of white-helmeted policemen charge forward and break for shelter as a rain of bricks showered down from the building tops. Some of the white helmets, racing for the doorways, turned to fire, and I heard Scofield grunt and go down and I dropped beside him, seeing the red burst of fire and hearing the shrill scream, like an arching dive, curving from above to end in a crunching thud in the street. It was as though it landed in my stomach, sickening me, and I crouched, looking down past Scofield, who lay just ahead of me, to see the dark crushed form from the roof; and farther away, the body of a cop, his helmet making a small white luminous mound in the dark.

I moved now to see whether Scofield was hit, just as he squirmed around and cursed at the cops who were trying to rescue the one who was down, his voice furious, as he stretched full length firing away with a nickel-plated pistol like that Dupre had waved.

"Git the hell down, man," he yelled over his shoulder. "I been wanting to blast 'em a long time."

"No, not with that thing," I said. "Let's get out of here."

"Hell, man, I can *shoot* this thing," he said.

I rolled behind a pile of baskets filled with rotting chickens now, and to my left, upon the littered curb, a woman and man crouched behind an upturned delivery cart.

"Dehart," she said, "let's get up on the hill, Dehart. Up with the respectable people!"

"Hill, hell! We stay right here," the man said. "This thing's just starting. If it becomes a sho 'nough race riot I want to be here where there'll be some fighting back."

The words struck like bullets fired close range, blasting my satisfaction to earth. It was as though the uttered word had given meaning to the night, almost as though it had created it, brought it into being in the instant his breath vibrated small against the loud, riotous air. And in defining, in giving organization to the fury, it seemed to spin me around, and in my mind I was looking backward over the days since Clifton's death . . . Could this be the answer, could this be what the committee had planned, the answer to why they'd surrendered our influence to Ras? Suddenly I heard the hoarse explosion of a shotgun, and looked past Scofield's glinting pistol to the huddled form from the roof. It was suicide, without guns it was suicide, and not even the pawnshops here had guns for sale; and yet I knew with a shattering dread that the uproar which for the moment marked primarily the crash of men against things—against stores, markets—could swiftly become the crash of men against men and with most of the guns and numbers on the other side. I could see it now, see it clearly and in growing magnitude. It was not suicide, but murder. The committee had planned it. And I had helped, had been a tool. A tool just at the very moment I had thought myself free. By pretending to agree I *had* indeed agreed, had made myself responsible for that huddled form lighted by flame and gunfire in the street, and all the others whom now the night was making ripe for death.

The brief case swung heavy against my leg as I ran, going away, leaving Scofield cursing his lack of bullets behind me, running wildly and swinging the brief case hard against the head of a dog that leaped at me out of the crowd, sending him yelping away. To my right lay a quiet residential street with trees, and I entered it, going toward Seventh Avenue, toward the district, filled now with horror and hatred. They'll pay, they'll pay, I thought. They'll pay.

The street lay dead quiet in the light of the lately risen moon, the gunfire thin and for a moment, distant. The rioting seemed in another world. For a moment I paused beneath a low, thickly leaved tree, looking down the well-kept doily-shadowed walks past the silent houses. It was as though the tenants had vanished, leaving the houses silent with all windows shaded, refugees from a rising flood. Then I heard the single footfalls coming doggedly toward me in the night, an eerie slapping sound followed by a precise and hallucinated cry—

"*Time's flying
Souls dying
The coming of the Lord
Draweth niiiiigh!*"

—as though he had run for days, for years. He trotted past where I stood beneath the tree, his bare feet slapping the walk in the silence, going for a few feet and then the high, hallucinated cry beginning again.

I ran into the avenue where in the light of a flaming liquor store I saw three old women scurrying toward me with raised skirts loaded with canned goods.

"I can't stop it just yet, but have mercy, Lord," one of them said. "Do, Jesus, do sweet Jesus . . ."

I moved ahead, the fumes of alcohol and burning tar in my nostrils. Down the avenue to my left a single street lamp still glowed where the long block was intersected on my right by a street, and I could see a crowd rushing a store that faced the intersection, moving in, and a fusillade of canned goods, salami, liverwurst, hogsheads and chitterlings belching out to those outside and a bag of flour bursting white upon them; as now out of the dark of the intersecting street two mounted policemen came at a gallop, heaving huge and heavy-hooved, charging straight into the swarming mass. And I could see the great forward lunge of the horses and the crowd breaking and rolling back like a wave, back, and screaming and cursing, and some laughing—back and around and out into the avenue, stumbling and pushing, as the horses, heads high and bits froth-flecked, went over the curb to land stiff-legged and slide over the cleared walk as upon ice skates and past, carried by the force of the charge, sideways now, legs stiff, sparks flying, to where another crowd looted another store. And my heart tightened as the first crowd swung imperturbably back to their looting with derisive cries, like sandpipers swinging around to glean the shore after a furious wave's recession.

Cursing Jack and the Brotherhood I moved around a steel grill torn from the front of a pawnshop, seeing the troopers galloping back and the riders lifting the horses to charge again, grim and skillful in white steel helmets, and the charge beginning. This time a man went down and I saw a woman swinging a gleaming frying pan hard against the horse's rump and the horse neighing and beginning to plunge. They'll pay, I thought, they'll pay. They came toward me as I ran, a crowd of men and women carrying cases of beer, cheese, chains of linked sausage, watermelons, sacks of sugar, hams, cornmeal, fuel lamps. If only it could stop right here, here; here before the others came with their guns. I ran.

There was no firing. But *when*, I thought, how long before it starts?

"Git a side of bacon, Joe," a woman called. "Git a side of bacon, Joe, git Wilson's."

"Lord, Lord, Lord," a dark voice called from the dark.

I went on, plunged in a sense of painful isolation as I reached

125th Street and started east. A squad of mounted police galloped past. Men with sub-machine guns were guarding a bank and a large jewelry store. I moved out to the center of the street, running down the trolley rails.

The moon was high now and before me the shattered glass glittered in the street like the water of a flooded river upon the surface of which I ran as in a dream, avoiding by fate alone the distorted objects washed away by the flood. Then suddenly I seemed to sink, sucked under: Ahead of me the body hung, white, naked, and horribly feminine from a lamppost. I felt myself spin around with horror and it was as though I had turned some nightmarish somersault. I whirled, still moving by reflex, back-tracking and stopped and now there was another and another, seven—all hanging before a gutted storefront. I stumbled, hearing the cracking of bones underfoot and saw a physician's skeleton shattered on the street, the skull rolling away from the backbone, as I steadied long enough to notice the unnatural stiffness of those hanging above me. They were mannequins—"Dummies!" I said aloud. Hairless, bald and sterilely feminine. And I recalled the boys in the blonde wigs, expecting the relief of laughter, but suddenly was more devastated by the humor than by the horror. But are they unreal, I thought: *are* they? What if one, even *one* is real—is . . . Sybil? I hugged my brief case, backing away, and ran . . .

V Children

The impact of racism (hidden and explicit) has had its most devastating effects on the Negro family structure, the principal sufferers being children. In Junius Edwards's story it is clear that one child is regarded as less desirable because he is darker than the others. The lost, deracinated black children of the city are recorded in Gwendolyn Brooks's "We Real Cool" and William Melvin Kelley's "The Life You Save." And John A. Williams's "Son in the Afternoon" describes with chilling effect his protagonist's calculated cruelty to a white child as vengeance for his own deprived childhood.

Junius Edwards

Mother Dear and Daddy

They came in the night while we slept. We knew they were coming, but not when, and we expected to see them when they did. We never thought that they would come at night. When we got up, well, when John, my brother, got up (he was always getting up early), when he got up, he looked out of the window and ran and jumped back in bed and shook me and called my name.

"Jim, Jim, they here. They here already. Wake up, Jim. They —"

"Hey, quit shaking me. I been woke long time."

"They here," he ran to the window. "Come on look."

He didn't have to tell me "come on look" because I was at the window when he got there, almost, anyway. They had come all right; we could see the cars parked in the yard, like big cats crouching, backs hunched, ready to attack.

"I'll go tell Mary, then," John said, and bolted out of the room as fast as you could blow out a coal oil lamp.

While he was out telling our three sisters, I stood there at the window and counted the cars. There were five in all, besides our car, and they were all black and shiny as my plate whenever I got through eating red beans and rice. Our car sat over there by itself, dusty and dirty as one of those bums that come by all the time wanting a meal.

I stood there, leaning on the windowsill, with my right foot on top of my left foot, scratching my left foot with my toes, and looking at our car. I could feel my eyes burning, burning, and the tears coming and washing the burns, and me sucking

205

my tongue because of the burning and trying not to make a sound. My body went cold and inside it I could feel something surging up; not like being sick, this surging came up my whole body, my arms, too, and ended with my eyes burning. I fought to hold it back, keep it buried. Even when I was alone, I always fought it, always won and kept it down, even at times when it was sudden and fast and got to my eyes and burned like hot needles behind my eyelids, hot needles with legs running around trying to get past my eyelids and spill out on my cheeks, even then I kept it down.

I had fought it for two weeks and I was good at it and getting better. Maybe I was good at it because of that first day. I had not fought it then. I had let it come, right in front of Aunt Mabel, I let it come, not trying to stop it, control it; I let it come.

"What we going to do?" I asked Aunt Mabel, after it had come, had shaken me and left me as empty as an unfilled grave. "What we going to do, Aunt Mabel?"

"Lord knows, son. Lord knows," Aunt Mabel said, sitting in her rocker, moving, slow, back and forth, looking down at me, on my knees, my arms resting on her huge right thigh and my head turned up to her, watching that round face, her lips tight now, her head shaking side to side, and her eyes clouded, and me not understanding her answer, but thinking I should and not daring to ask again and feeling the question pounding my brain: What we going to do? What we going to do?

"The Lord giveth and the Lord taketh away."

But, what we going to do? I could not understand Aunt Mabel. I did not know what her mumbling about The Lord had to do with this. All I knew was she had just told me Mother Dear and Daddy were dead. Mother Dear and Daddy were dead. Mother Dear and Daddy would not come back. Mother Dear and Daddy wouldn't take us home again. What we going to do?

"I want to go home. I want to go home," I screamed and got to my feet and ran to the door, realizing it was Aunt Mabel calling my name. I ran out to the yard where John and our sisters played, and right past them. I did not feel my feet move; I did not feel I owned a body. I wanted to get home. And hearing Aunt Mabel call my name, seeing houses, cars, people, trees, like one big thing made of windows, walls, wheels, heads, branches, arms and legs and behind that one big thing, our house, with our car out front, and our yard and our tree, and then the big thing was gone and I was at our house, running up the steps across the porch, as fast as I could, straight to the screened door, wham! and I lay on my back on the porch looking up at the screen, at the imprints made in it by my head and hands and my right knee. I got right up and started banging on the door, trying to twist the knob.

"Mother Dear! Daddy! Mother Dear! Daddy!" I called as loud as I could and kept banging on the door. Then, I ran to the back door and called again and banged and kicked the door. They did not come.

They would not come.

"Mother Dear! Daddy! It's me. Let me in. Open the door!"

They would not come.

I ran to the front, out to the street and turned and looked up to their room and saw the shades were drawn just as they were drawn when Mother Dear and Daddy took us over to Aunt Mabel's house to stay for the weekend while they went away fishing with cousin Bob.

I cupped my hands up to my mouth.

"Mother Dear. Daddy. Mother Dear! Daddy!"

I called, and called again and all the while I kept my eyes glued on that window, waiting. Any moment now, any second now, now, *now*, waited to see that white shade zoom up and then the window, and then Mother Dear and Daddy, both together, lean out, smiling, laughing, waving, calling my name, now, now, *now*.

They did not come.

They would not come. The shade stood still, stayed still, with the sun shining on it through the window pane; stayed still, as if the sun were a huge nail shooting through the pane and holding it down. It did not go up. It would not go up.

They would not come.

I knew it. Suddenly, just like that, snap, I knew they would not come; could not come. The shades would stay still. I knew they would not come. I lowered my hands, my eyes darting from shaded window to shaded window, around the yard, under the house, searching, for what? I did not know, and then there was the car. My eyes were glued to the car, and I started over to it, slowly at first, and then I ran and I stopped short and pressed my head up against the glass in the front door beside the steering wheel. The glass was hot on my nose and lips and forehead, and burned them, but I did not care, I pressed harder, as if by doing so I could push right through the glass, not breaking it, but melting through it. Then, I felt as though I *was* inside, in my favorite spot up front with Daddy, and in back were Mother Dear and John and our sisters; Daddy whistling and the trees going by and the farms and green, green, green, and other cars and Daddy starting to sing and all of us joining him singing "Choo-choo Train to Town," even Jo Ann and Willie Mae, who had not learned the words yet, singing, singing, and ending laughing and feeling Daddy's hand on my head.

"Jim." I turned from the window, and it was Aunt Mabel's hand on my head.

"Come on, son." She took my right hand and led me up the street as if I were a baby just starting to walk.

"What we going to do, Aunt Mabel?"

"You got to be brave, Jim. You the oldest. You got to look out for your brother and sisters."

I decided then that I would not let my brother and sisters see me cry, ever. I was twelve years old and the oldest and I had to take care of them.

"When can we go back home, Aunt Mabel?"

"I guess we ought to move over to your house while we wait for the family to get here," Aunt Mabel said. "It's bigger than mine and your clothes there."

I looked up at Aunt Mabel. I had not expected her to move back with us. I wanted only we children to move back home.

When we got back to Aunt Mabel's house I told John about the automobile accident and that Mother Dear and Daddy were dead. John was only eight, but he understood and he cried and I understood just how he felt, so I left him alone.

The next day we moved back to our house. Aunt Mabel, too. Every time one of our sisters would ask for Mother Dear and Daddy we always said they were gone away. They were too young to understand about death.

Aunt Mabel told me that our Uncles and Aunts and Grandparents were coming. I didn't know any of them. I remembered Christmas presents from them and Mother Dear and Daddy talking about them, but I had never seen them.

"They're good folks," Aunt Mable said, "and it won't make no difference which one you all go to live with."

"But, Aunt Mabel. We going to stay home."

"You can't, son. You all too young to stay here by yourself and I can't take care of you."

"I can take care of us, Aunt Mabel. I'm the oldest. I can take care of us."

Aunt Mabel smiled. "Bet you could, too. But you all need somebody to be a Mama and a Papa to you. You all got to go live with one of your Aunts and Uncles."

I knew right away that Aunt Mabel was right. I told John about it and we started trying to guess where we would go. The family was scattered all over, mostly in big cities like New York, Philadelphia and Boston. Our Grandfather on Daddy's side was in Texas. John and I couldn't decide what we liked best: Texas and horses or big cities and buildings. We talked about it every day while we waited for them to come, and now they were here.

I left the window and started to get dressed. John ran back into the room.

"Them won't wake up."

"They can sleep, then," I said. "Let's go see where the cars came from."

We got dressed and ran out to the yard and looked at the license plates. There were two from New York, two from Pennsylvania and one from Massachusetts.

"None of them from Texas," I said.

"Which one you like best?" asked John.

"That one," I said, pointing to the one from Massachusetts. I liked it because it was the biggest one. The five of us could get in it without any trouble at all.

We examined each car carefully for an hour and then Aunt Mabel called us and told us to come in the house.

"They all here," she said, "all that's coming, I guess. Now, you all be good so they'll like you."

I followed Aunt Mabel into the living room. I could feel John right behind me, up close, and I could hear his breathing.

"Here the boys," Aunt Mabel announced, and walked across the room and sat down.

John and I stopped at the door. Our sisters were lined up, side by side, in the middle of the room, smiling. I had heard voices before we came into the room, but now, there was silence and all eyes were on us. They sat in a half circle in straight back chairs, near the walls around the room. I looked at them. I stared at each face. Aunt Mabel and our sisters were the only smiling faces I saw. I didn't know about John, but right at that moment, I was scared. I wanted to turn and run away as fast as I could. I felt as if I had committed the worst crime and those faces hated me for it. Besides Aunt Mabel, there were five men and five women, all dressed in black. Each man had a black line above his upper lip. The two men who were fat had thick black lines and the other three had thinner ones. I didn't like the lines. Daddy never wore one and I always thought his face was cleaner and friendlier and happier than other men I had seen who wore them.

I noticed the features of these people right away. They were all like Mother Dear, Aunt Mabel and our sisters, and they were pink rose. I knew they were Mother Dear's relatives. Daddy didn't have any brothers or sisters and he used to tell John and me whenever we got into a fight with each other that we should be kind to each other because we were brothers and it was good to have a brother and that he wished he had had brothers and sisters. Mother Dear had plenty of brothers and sisters. She had three brothers, and I knew them right away as the three who weren't fat, and three sisters, Aunt Mabel, of course, and the two women who sat beside the fat men.

I stood there looking, staring at those faces that looked as if they had just taken straight castor oil. I looked at John, now standing at my right. He stood there with his mouth hanging open and his eyes straight ahead. I could tell he was scared and as soon as I knew he was scared, I wasn't scared any more and I wanted to tell him not to be scared because I wasn't going to let anything happen to him. Just when I was about to tell him, Aunt Mabel broke the silence.

"Come on over here next to your sisters," she said.

We shuffled over to where our sisters were and stood there like slaves on auction.

"They good children," Aunt Mabel said. "No trouble at all."

The others still kept quiet, except for whispers among themselves.

"Say your names, boys," Aunt Mabel said.

"James," I said.

"John," said John.

"We call James, Jim," Aunt Mabel said, and smiled at me.

I looked at her. It was all right for her to call me Jim. Mother Dear and Daddy called me Jim. I looked back at those faces. I didn't want *them* to call me Jim.

"Well," Aunt Mabel said to them, "You all going to tell the boys your names?"

They introduced themselves to us, not smiling, not changing those castor oil expressions. Apparently they had already introduced themselves to our sisters.

"Mabel," one of the fat men said, "why don't you get these kids out of here so we can talk."

"Jim, you and the children go in the dining room," Aunt Mabel said, and when we were going, she added, "And close the door."

We went into the dining room and I closed the door. Our sisters sat down in the middle of the floor and played. John stood over them, watching, but when he saw me with my ear to the door, he came over and joined me. We faced each other with our heads pressed up against the door and we listened. The only voice I could recognize was Aunt Mabel's.

"Carol and I have thought this thing over and we can see our way clear to take the girls," one of the men said.

"Now, wait a minute, Sam," another man said. "We thought we'd take *one* of the girls, at least."

Then, for a minute it sounded as if they were all trying to get a word in. They talked all at the same time, even yelled. It sounded as if everyone wanted a girl.

"Lord have mercy. You mean you going to split them up? You mean they won't be together?"

"Five kids? Frankly, we can't afford two, but we'd be willing to take the three girls."

There was another minute of all of them trying to speak at the same time, at the top of their voices, each one wanting a girl.

"Why don't you all talk like people? I don't like to see them split up, but I guess five is too many for anybody, specially when they not your own."

"Then you understand that they'll have to be separated? There's no other way, and since we already have a son, we thought we would take one of the girls."

"Well," Aunt Mabel said, "look like to me all you all want a girl. I didn't hear nobody say nothing about the boys, yet."

There was silence. John and I pressed harder against the door. John's mouth was open, his bottom lip hanging, and he was staring at me hard. I could tell he was scared and I must have looked scared to him so I closed my own mouth and tried to swallow. There was nothing to swallow and I had to open my mouth again and take a deep breath.

"Come to think of it, you all didn't say one word to them boys," Aunt Mabel said. "Why don't you all want boys?"

"We have a boy."

"We do, too."

"Girls are easier."

"Boys are impossible."

"Lord have mercy!"

"Listen, Mabel, you don't understand the situation."

"Don't get on your high horse with me. Talk plain."

"All right, Mabel. The fact is, the boys are—well—they're too, well, too much like the father."

"What?"

"You heard me. I know that's why *we* don't want one, and it's probably why the others here don't want one and it's no use avoiding it."

"Is that right? Is that why you all don't want one, too?" Aunt Mabel asked.

There was silence.

"Lord have mercy. I never heard such a thing in all my life. Your own sister's children, too."

"You don't understand, Mabel."

"No, I don't. Lord knows I don't. What you all doing up there? Passing? Huh? That what you doing? No. No. You couldn't be doing that. Even if you wanted to, you couldn't be doing that. You not that light that you can pass, none of you all. Lord have mercy. They too black for you. Your own sister's children."

John looked down at his hands, at the back of his hands and then at me and down at our sisters and at his hands again.

"I never thought I'd live to see the day my own flesh and blood would talk like that, and all the trouble in the world. My own sisters and brothers," Aunt Mabel said.

"Mabel, you've been here in this town all your life. This town isn't the world. You don't know how it is."

John rubbed the back of his hand on his pants and looked at it again.

I kept listening.

"It's hard enough like it is without having these boys, having to always explain about them. You can see that, Mabel. Look at us, how light we are. We'd always have to explain to everyone they're our dead sister's boys and people who we don't explain to will jump to all kinds of conclusions. Socially, we'd be out, too. No, Mabel. That's just the way it is and we can't do a thing about it. I, for one, have certain standards I want to live up to and having these boys won't help."

"I never thought it. I never thought it."

"That's the way it is, Mabel. Those boys will do none of us any good."

John went over to where our sisters played and stood over them, examining them.

Aunt Mabel said: "So that's how come you didn't want her to get married. That's how come you tried to get her away from here."

John kneeled down and touched each one of our sisters. He looked at them and at his hand, at them and at his hand, and then to me. Then, his eyes became shiny and he started batting his eyes and the sides of his face grew, his cheeks puffed way out, his mouth closed tight. He fought it all he could and I knew it was useless, he would not succeed. I could feel the same thing happening to me, but I held it back and concentrated on him, watched his swelling face until it exploded and thinking he might yell out, I rushed to him and got down on my knees and held him, held him close, just as Daddy would have, with my left arm around his back and my right hand behind his head, holding his head to my chest and felt his body shaking like a balloon when you let out the air and I listened to him groan like a whipped dog. I didn't say one word to him. I couldn't. I let him cry and I held him and watched our sisters and they suddenly realized he was crying and they came to us and helped me hold him and tried to get him to tell why he cried and when he would not tell they asked me and when I would not tell they stood there holding both of us until John got control of himself. He sat back on his heels and sobbed and the girls stepped back and watched him. I stood up and watched all of them. The girls stood there and watched him and waited, their faces alert, ready to run to him and help him. It was as if they knew, now, this was not a physical wound that made him cry, not a twisted arm, a stubbed toe, or a beating, and certainly not a cry that would make them laugh and yell "cry baby" at him. It was as if they knew it was a wound they had never had and that it was deeper than skin.

I heard the voices in the living room, louder now, and wilder, so I started back to my place at the door, but before I got there, John lost control again. We got to him at the same time and tried to hold him, but this time he pushed us away, fought us off, and got to his feet and ran into the living room. I got to my feet as fast as I could and ran after him into the living room. He was screaming now and when I ran into the living room, I stopped short at what I saw. John had run in and jumped in the lap of the first man he came to and he was there on his knees in the man's lap screaming and pounding the man's chest and face. The man pushed him off and John fell to the floor on his back and got right up and jumped in the man's lap again, still screaming, and pounded the man's chest and face with both his little fists.

"John, John, John!" I yelled, and ran to him and pulled him out of the man's lap, just in time, too, because the man swung at him back handed, but I had John down and the man missed. John, still screaming, kicking, struggled with me, trying to get away from me so he could get back to the man.

"John, John!" I yelled, shaking him, trying to make him hear me. "John, John!" but I could see he wasn't listening to me even though he was looking straight at me as I stood in front of him holding both of his arms and shouting his name. He only screamed.

Suddenly, I started walking backwards from him, holding his arms still, pulling him along with me until we were in the center of the room and then I smiled at him. "Come on, John, come on, John," I said, and laughed, laughed hard, looking into his eyes, I kept it up, laughed loud and harder still and felt my body shake from it. Then I saw John's face change, first a smile, then he broke into a laugh, too. I stared into his eyes and we laughed. We laughed. We laughed. We laughed. We threw our heads back and we laughed. We held each other's hands and danced round and round and laughed. Our sisters came and joined our dance. We formed a circle, all of us laughing, laughing, and we danced round and round. We were the only people in the world. We danced round and round and laughed and laughed.

"Hey," I said, "Choo-Choo Train, Choo-Choo Train" and they joined me:

"Choo-choo train, choo-choo train
We going to take that choo-choo train
Choo-choo train to town
Choo-choo train
Choo-choo train"

Round and round, "Choo-choo train" louder and louder I sang, "CHOO-CHOO TRAIN, CHOO-CHOO TRAIN, CHOO-CHOO TRAIN TO TEXAS" round and round "CHOO-CHOO TRAIN" until I realized what I had said and I screamed happily and said it again and again until they caught on and said it, too. We went faster and faster and said it louder and louder sounding like a Choo-choo Train: TEXAS, TEXAS, TEXAS, TEXAS, TEXAS . . .

Gwendolyn Brooks

We Real Cool

The Pool Players.
Seven at the Golden Shovel.

We real cool. We
Left school. We

Lurk late. We
Strike straight. We

Sing sin. We
Thin gin. We

Jazz June. We
Die soon.

William Melvin Kelley

The Life You Save

"You mean his brother really tried to burn him alive?" Peter leaned forward onto the table, and smiled involuntarily at the horror of it.

The director nodded; he too could not help smiling. "Right. Carlyle, the older brother, told the mother he was just initiating Mance into a club. But she didn't buy it. She told the father, but he wouldn't believe it, not about his oldest boy, his name-sake. He doesn't even know what kind of place we got here. He thinks it's just a regular day camp. He'd probably pull the kid out if he found out—disgrace and all that stuff."

Peter sat back. "Wow!" He shook out a cigarette and lit it.

The director tore the cellophane from a cigar. "So anyway, that's what you got. At eleven, this Mance Bedlow's seen it all. I can only tell you one thing: don't hit him, don't even try to punish him, or any of them. They've been smacked enough to last them a lifetime. That's why they're here. If you hit them, you'll lose them, sure." He pulled himself forward, lit the cigar, and continued through dense smoke. "I'll give you all this stuff." He tapped Mance Bedlow's folder with a thick brown finger. "Okay?"

"Okay." Peter sighed, put out his cigarette and left the direc-tor's office. He went down the hall to the room, where, in an hour, he would greet his eight eleven-year-olds. They were all so-called emotionally disturbed children. Some of them had al-ready flirted with minor crime. Peter would be their counselor for the next eight weeks.

The settlement house had recently moved from a small, old

218

building to the ground floor of one of the buildings in a new low-rent housing project; the walls of the room were bleak, bare, pale-green cinder blocks. In the room, there were only two tables and ten folding chairs. Peter sat in one of the chairs, lit a cigarette, and waited for his boys to come, a bit nervous now with the thought that in a short while he would have the responsibility of helping to guide, or even the opportunity to change the lives of eight small human beings. When he realized what was running through his mind, he laughed at his earnestness. The feeling was honest, but to put it into words made it seem conceited and pompous. He would have to watch such attitudes. If his boys sensed them, they would never trust him.

The boys entered one by one, in shapeless, beltless dungarees, in torn and faded T-shirts. Each carried, in a brown paper bag, his lunch. Their mothers had pomaded and brushed their heads fervently, flattening the tiny beads of black hair. As they came in, Peter introduced himself, and each in turn, mumbled a name. Finally, eight had arrived. But there was no Mance Bedlow.

"I guess one of us isn't here." Peter, seated now at the head of one of the tables, scanned their dark faces. "Anybody here know Mance Bedlow?"

The boys glanced at one another. One of them, who had introduced himself as Randolph Wayne, said he did.

"Have you seen him, Randolph?"

"I seed him on the way over here, Mister Dunford. He say he ain't making it. He say this a wasted gig." There was an impish look on the boy's dark-brown face, as if he held the same view. His eyes were dark, and twinkled.

"Okay. You fellows wait here." Peter got up. "I'll go check on him." He left the room and headed for the director's office. Halfway down the hall he realized there was no Randolph Wayne on the list the director had given him.

"What's the problem, Peter?" The director was reading his mail.

Peter remained in the doorway. "I have the right number of kids, but no Mance Bedlow."

"Oh?" The director put down a letter he had just opened. "Who's the extra?"

"A kid named Randolph Wayne."

The director sighed. "They do that sometimes. They see their buddies on the way here and just tag along." He got up.

They walked back down the hall and stopped at the door. The director looked in at the boys. "Which is the Wayne boy?"

The boys turned to the door now, some smiling politely.

Peter indicated Randolph Wayne.

The director shook his head and chuckled. "That is Mance Bedlow."

The room filled with high squealing and cackling, the boys talking to each other: "Man, you see that cat go for that shit?"

"Yeah. Man, he dumb!"

Mance Bedlow sat at the table, basking in his triumph, staring at Peter, interested to see what he might do. Peter felt his embarrassed anger bubbling, and knowing he could not afford to let the boys see it, left the door, took two steps, and leaned against the wall, trying to control himself.

The director put a hand on Peter's shoulder. "Don't let it get you. That's the way they live."

Peter nodded.

The director went back to his office.

Peter fixed a smile on his face, and entered the room. "That's a point for you, Mance." He looked into hard brown eyes, understanding now what the director had told him before. Mance Bedlow's eyes were not at all those of an eleven-year-old. Peter realized suddenly that at eleven, he would not have survived in Mance Bedlow's world, even though he had always lived in Harlem. Peter's father was a doctor and earned a good living; Peter had been sent to private schools.

Mance returned his stare. Finally Peter looked at another boy. "Well, let's paint a little bit."

The boys were not enthusiastic. They waited quietly as Peter brought out huge sheets of paper, brushes, and jars of paint, and passed them around. Finally one of them, George, light-skinned and shaved bald, asked what Peter wanted them to paint.

"What do you guys want to paint?" Peter was sitting again, and looked around the table. The boys were surprised. The director had told Peter that most of the time boys like these were told exactly what to do. Their choice was to obey or rebel. Obedience brought little reward or admiration; rebellion brought harsh punishment. "You can paint anything you want. But if you can't think of anything, paint a picture of your family." He suggested that purposely, knowing the settlement house psychologist might learn something from the paintings.

Automatically, the boys painted their families. Peter walked around behind them. As he approached, they would usually tighten their bony shoulders. He encouraged them all and from time to time received smiles.

Mance Bedlow's picture was entirely in brown. There were three figures, the two biggest on one side of the page, the smallest on the other side. Peter asked Mance to name them. The two big ones were his father and brother. He was the small one.

"Where's your mother?"

"She's in the kitchen cooking their dinner." He looked up at Peter. "Mister Dunford, what color should I paint the sun?"

"Any color you want; it's your picture." Peter smiled and went on to George, who smiled at him timidly.

Behind him, Peter heard scuffling. "Cut that shit out, boy."

Peter turned around to find Mance glaring at the boy on the other side of him. Then he picked up his own picture and began ripping it into tiny pieces. Peter decided not to stop him.

When he was through destroying his picture, Mance turned to Peter. "This place is shit!"

Peter smiled.

"And you're a cock-sucker!"

Still Peter smiled, although now it was an effort.

"I'm going home!" Standing up, he knocked over his chair, then raced around the table away from Peter, and scrambled out the door. Peter stood his ground. The boy would come back.

Five minutes later, Mance had not re-appeared. Peter, who had started the boys painting again, told them he would return in a few moments and went down to the front door and looked out.

The settlement house was in one of twenty buildings in the red-brick project. Black asphalt paths connected the buildings, which were separated by chained-off plots of grass. Wooden benches lined the paths. Mance sat watching the door of the settlement house. When he saw Peter at the door window, he stood up.

Peter opened the door. "Why don't you come back inside?"

"I'm going home!"

Peter stepped through the door. "What do you want to do that for?"

"I'm going home!" His fists were clenched; he was yelling.

Peter came part way down the front stairs, speaking softly. "Come on, Mance, don't . . ."

He had gotten too close and the boy was running. Peter trotted after him, closing the space between them. He did not want to catch and drag him back, knowing it would be better to convince the boy to return of his own free will. They ran past a brown woman wheeling a baby carriage, shouting at a toddler clinging to her skirts, past a seated old man leaning his white-whiskered chin on his cane, past a group of young girls chanting and skipping rope. Finally, Mance neared the curb, the outer boundary of the project, and without looking, darted out into the street, avoiding cars, the drivers startled behind their windshields, stopping only when he had reached the other side.

Peter waited until the cars passed, then started across. "Why don't you tell me what's wrong?"

Mance watched Peter drawing closer to him until they were only five steps apart, then began to run again, along the sidewalks now, in front of the brownstone houses' high stairs, occupied by Negro men and women sitting in undershirts and housecoats. They ran around groups of conversing brown people, through mobs of playing children. Peter could see Mance was tiring now, his thin legs growing heavy and wobbly.

Peter slowed to a walk. Mance looked over his shoulder, and began to walk himself. "Why don't you tell me what's wrong?" Peter was shouting; several people turned around. He felt foolish.

"I don't like painting pictures!" They were still walking, a distance now of two cars between them.

"We aren't going to paint pictures all day."

Mance stopped. "What was we going to do?"

They stood shouting at each other. "I don't know—we were going to the park and play some ball."

"Who wants to do that?"

Peter wondered if Mance would sit down if he did, and moved back to some empty steps behind him. "We're taking trips downtown and on the Staten Island ferry, and to the car show." He saw Mance Bedlow's face flicker with interest, but did not know exactly what had interested him. He guessed. "You like cars?"

"When you got a car nobody can mess with you." Mance inched closer. He was standing in the gutter directly in front of Peter. "One of these days I'll hit the number and buy me a Cadillac and won't nobody mess with me." He was staring at the middle of the sidewalk.

Peter wanted to keep this conversation going and grabbed at a question. "What color car will you get?"

"I'm getting me a black one, with air conditioning and a radio." He was in the middle of the sidewalk now. "Some niggers run out and get white Cadillacs; they get dirty and look jive. But I'm getting me a black one, and even when it dirty it'll still look good." He paused for an instant. "I'll get in that car and nobody'll mess with me and I'll go away."

Peter was tempted to ask why Mance wanted to go away, but he suspected the boy would balk. "Why did you want to go home?"

"I told you—I don't want to paint no pictures."

"Well, you don't have to. You can do something else when the other guys are painting."

"What?" His chin was lifted high.

"I don't know. You decide." Peter got up, planning something new. Mance backed up. "Look, I'd like you to come back. You don't have to, of course, but I do, because I'm taking the other guys to the park." Peter descended the steps. Mance had retreated to the gutter. "Why don't you come along? We'll have a good time." Peter knew he was overacting but he did not think Mance would see it. "Well, so long. I hope you come back." He started up the street.

He walked slowly, not turning around and came to a store, the window of which was slated so he could see behind himself. At a distance of three cars, Mance was following him. Peter smiled to himself, a little proud. Perhaps, he had broken through.

Peter soon found it was not that easy. Mance ran out two times that afternoon, racing in a different direction each time. Contrary to the declaration—"I'm going home!"—he never seemed to be heading toward any particular place. He simply ran until he got tired, or until Peter could engage him in conversation. Between flights he talked to no one. He would seem as engrossed as the other boys, then suddenly, he would bolt.

At the end of the day, alone now, Peter had a chance to read Mance Bedlow's report. Two things particularly interested him. The first was that Mance had a recurring nightmare: He would be standing with his parents on a grassy mound. He would be quite happy. A wolf would appear then, and, snapping at his legs, would drive him off the mound, away from his parents. He would try to outsmart the wolf by running around to the other side of the mound to sneak to the top again. But the wolf would always get there before him and keep him away.

The second thing was that Mance lived in the Bronx. Yet, though the settlement house was in Manhattan, when he ran away, he never went anywhere near the subway.

Next day, Peter had the boys paint animals. Predictably, Mance painted a wolf standing on top of a mound of grass. Peter stood watching. "What's that?" He tried to give the question no weight.

"That's my wolf." Mance seemed indignant. "Didn't they tell you about my wolf? They all know about it—all the people here."

Peter was startled by the answer, but went on as he had planned. "They didn't tell me about him."

"Hell, they should-a. He's important. I got this wolf, see? I dream about him most every night and . . ." He stopped short. "You're jiving me. You know all about my wolf."

Peter shook his head. "No. No, I don't know a thing about it."

Mance tilted his head, studying Peter. "Then," he started slowly, "you are one stupid bastard and I ain't wasting my time telling you." He stood up, rather slowly this time. "I'm going home." He did not even bother to run; he ambled.

Peter stood fighting anger, waited until he had calmed himself before he followed, catching up to the boy in a small playground at the other end of the project. He was still a bit angry, but remembered all the director had told him, and all he had learned from the report. He told himself again that a counselor was supposed to be a good example for boys like Mance. He fixed a gentle look on his face, but before he could say anything, Mance was coming toward him. "You go to college?"

"Yes, I do." Peter sat down and was surprised when the boy sat beside him, quite close.

"What they teach you there?" The boy was genuinely interested. Peter wished he knew what turn his mind had taken.

"I guess the same things you learn, only harder." Mance Bedlow's interest in his personal affairs was a good sign.

"You ever get into any fights there?" Mance was inspecting Peter's hands.

"No, I don't." Peter had the unsettling feeling his answers were all wrong.

"What happens when somebody robs your stuff?"

"Nobody does." In front of them, two small boys were pretending to be airplanes.

Mance scowled. "Don't nobody hate you at college?"

"I hope not." Peter chuckled. "I don't think so."

"Must be a jive place." He stood up. "I guess you want me to go back, huh?"

"Yes, I do." Peter did not know what to make of all this.

"Okay. I'll save you a speech. Come on." Mance started toward the settlement house, Peter following obediently.

Mance did not run away again. But as the weeks went by, Peter realized this was not a sign of progress. Mance got along no better with the rest of the boys. He got into his share of fights. But despite these brief signs of involvement, Peter knew Mance was lonely and unhappy. It seemed that he knew he had to attend the day camp, and had decided to endure it, but no more. Even Peter's success with the other boys did not balance the disappointment of having failed with Mance Bedlow.

Peter did not know if it was this failure, or simply the demands the entire group made on him, but he began to get more tense, more tired, and more frustrated. When he arrived home at night, he would skip dinner with his parents, go to his room, and sleep. He could not rid himself of his tight feelings and could not show them to the boys, and so after six weeks of hiding them, each day was harder to get through. He was fighting anger all the time.

In the afternoons, if they had not gone on a trip, Peter would take his boys to the project's large playground, which was used not only by the settlement house, but by all of the children, boys, and young men in the neighborhood. One hot, humid day, the air conditioner had burned out and the room had steamed, forcing sweat down the dark faces of his boys, staining their shirts. Peter took them to the playground an hour early; Mance as usual tagged behind.

Peter organized seven of the boys into a game of basketball, leaving Mance to wander the playground alone. Then he sat down to watch, mopping himself with an already damp and wilted handkerchief.

The game would have been laughable if Peter had felt like laughing. The boys' shots either did not reach the backboard or went over it. Instead of dribbling, they ran, and when one had the ball, the others, no matter what team, descended on him like a mob. Even so, they seemed to be having a good time.

Peter did not see the older boys until it was too late. They were standing at the far end of the court, watching and laughing. They wore tight dark pants, button-down shirts in brown and wine-red, and thin brimmed hats.

George, his bald head glistening with sweat, threw the wild pass. It bounced down the court and was caught by one of the older boys, who began to dribble it, neatly, between his legs. George ran down the court after it, yelling: "Hey, man! Hey! Give me that ball!"

The older boy, thin and dark, ignored him, continued to bounce the ball, low and hard, behind his back.

"Hey, man, give me the ball!" George stood ten feet away, watching, and after asking for the ball once more, charged the boy, who laughing, passed the ball to one of his friends.

George did not change directions. He was swinging his fists wildly, his blows falling on the boy's thighs and stomach. Peter was up now, running down the court, telling George to stop. Just as Peter reached them, the older boy stopped laughing, stepped back, and punched George square in the face, knocking him to the ground, where he burst into fuming tears.

Peter, whose only aim until then had been to retrieve the ball and to stop George, found himself flying at the boy, a loud rushing, like heavy rain, filling his ears, his fists clenched. He caught the boy by surprise with a punch on the ear, and when the boy turned, shocked, followed through with two punches to the stomach and one to the eye. The boy stumbled, and backed up, holding his eye. "Hey, man, what you do that for?"

Peter was screaming. "What did you hit that kid for?"

"Awh, man, I was only playing." The boy was still backing up. His friends stood behind him, timidly, not looking at him.

"Well, you play some place else or I'll break your ass for you!" Peter marched forward and took the ball from the boy who was holding it. Then suddenly he realized what he had done. He spun around and found his boys in a group, staring at him, their mouths open. To one side of them, his hands in his pockets, a scowl on his face, stood Mance Bedlow.

Avoiding their gaze, Peter helped George up and hurried his boys back to the settlement house, where he let them go home immediately though it was a half hour early. He sat alone in the room, smoking, thinking how he would repair the damage he had done. All summer, he had tried to build an image they could see and perhaps copy; he had tried to show them there were people in the world who were completely different from their aggressive, brutal fathers and brothers. In ten seconds, he had destroyed six weeks' work, and now he could not discover a way to salvage himself in their eyes.

As he was just about to push open the front door, he saw Mance sitting on one of the benches in front of the settlement house. He was still scowling.

Peter did not want to speak to him; he pushed open the door quickly and waved: "Good night, Mance." He walked as fast as he could.

Behind him, he heard running footsteps. "You learn to fight like that in college?"

"No!" He stopped now, and spun on his heels, expecting to find the boy taunting him. The boy's face was blank. Peter changed his tone. "No, I didn't. Look, Mance, it's not good to settle things by—"

Mance cut him off. "Where'd you learn to fight?"

Peter sighed. "I don't know—I guess my father taught me." He started to walk again.

Mance tagged along at his elbow. "What do he do?"

"My father? He's a doctor."

"And he really taught you how to fight?" Mance did not seem to believe him.

"That's right." They were out of the project now, almost to the corner where Peter waited for his bus. He hoped one would come soon.

"You mean, doctors really get in fights?"

He looked up the block for the bus. "Sometimes. I guess sometimes everybody gets into a fight."

"Just like me."

Something in the boy's tone forced Peter to look at him. Mance was staring at him. "When I was a kid I wanted to be a doctor."

Peter was about to speak, when behind him, he heard the gasping of a bus door. He turned around uncertain whether to get on. This was too good to let slip.

"He leaving without you. You better get on."

Peter did as the boy directed. After he had paid his fare and found a seat, and the bus had begun to move, he looked out of the window, back to the bus stop and saw Mance Bedlow, standing on tiptoes, his hand just at ear level, waving him a timid, tentative good-by.

John A. Williams

Son in the Afternoon

It was hot. I tend to be a bitch when it's hot. I goosed the little Ford over Sepulveda Boulevard toward Santa Monica until I got stuck in the traffic that pours from L.A. into the surrounding towns. I'd had a very lousy day at the studio.

I was—still am—a writer and this studio had hired me to check scripts and films with Negroes in them to make sure the Negro moviegoer wouldn't be offended. The signs were already clear one day the whole of American industry would be racing pell-mell to get a Negro, showcase a spade. I was kind of a pioneer. I'm a *Negro* writer, you see. The day had been tough because of a couple of verbs—slink and walk. One of those Hollywood hippies had done a script calling for a Negro waiter to slink away from the table where a dinner party was glaring at him. I said the waiter should walk, not slink, because later on he becomes a hero. The Hollywood hippie, who understood it all because he had some colored friends, said that it was essential to the plot that the waiter slink. I said you don't slink one minute and become a hero the next; there has to be some consistency. The Negro actor I was standing up for said nothing either way. He had played Uncle Tom roles so long that he had become Uncle Tom. But the director agreed with me.

Anyway . . . hear me out now. I was on my way to Santa Monica to pick up my mother, Nora. It was a long haul for such a hot day. I had planned a quiet evening: a nice shower, fresh clothes, and then I would have dinner at the Watkins and talk with some of the musicians on the scene for a quick taste before they cut to their gigs. After, I was going to the Pigalle down on Figueroa and catch Earl Grant at the organ, and still later, if nothing exciting happened, I'd pick up Scottie and make it to the Lighthouse on the Beach or to the Strollers and listen to some of the white boys play. I liked the long drive, especially while listening to Sleepy Stein's show on the radio. Later, much later of course, it would be home, back to Watts.

So you see, this picking up Nora was a little inconvenient. My mother was a maid for the Couchmans. Ronald Couchman was an architect, a good one I understood from Nora who has a fine sense for this sort of thing; you don't work in some hundred-odd houses during your life without getting some idea of the way a house should be laid out. Couchman's wife, Kay, was a playgirl who drove a white Jaguar from one party to another. My mother didn't like her too much; she didn't seem to care much for her son, Ronald, junior. There's something wrong with a parent who can't really love her own child, Nora thought. The Couchmans lived in a real fine residential section, of course. A number of actors lived nearby, character actors, not really big stars.

Somehow it is very funny. I mean that the maids and butlers knew everything about these people, and these people knew nothing at all about the help. Through Nora and her friends I knew who was laying whose wife; who had money and who *really* had money; I knew about the wild parties hours before the police, and who smoked marijuana, when, and where they got it.

To get to Couchman's driveway I had to go three blocks up one side of a palm-planted center strip and back down the other. The driveway bent gently, then swept back out of sight of the main road. The house, sheltered by slim palms, looked like a transplanted New England Colonial. I parked and walked to the kitchen door, skirting the growling Great Dane who was tied to a tree. That was the route to the kitchen door.

I don't like kitchen doors. Entering people's houses by them, I mean. I'd done this thing most of my life when I called at places where Nora worked to pick up the patched or worn sheets or the half-eaten roasts, the battered, tarnished silver—

the fringe benefits of a housemaid. As a teen-ager I'd told Nora I was through with that crap; I was not going through anyone's kitchen door. She only laughed and said I'd learn. One day soon after, I called for her and without knocking walked right through the front door of this house and right on through the living room. I was almost out of the room when I saw feet behind the couch. I leaned over and there was Mr. Jorgensen and his wife making out like crazy. I guess they thought Nora had gone and it must have hit them sort of suddenly and they went at it like the hell-bomb was due to drop any minute. I've been that way too, mostly in the spring. Of course, when Mr. Jorgensen looked over his shoulder and saw me, you know what happened. I was thrown out and Nora right behind me. It was the middle of winter, the old man was sick and the coal bill three months overdue. Nora was right about those kitchen doors: I learned.

My mother saw me before I could ring the bell. She opened the door. "Hello," she said. She was breathing hard, like she'd been running or something. "Come in and sit down. I don't know *where* that Kay is. Little Ronald is sick and she's probably out gettin' drunk again." She left me then and trotted back through the house, I guess to be with Ronnie. I hated the combination of her white nylon uniform, her dark brown face and the wide streaks of gray in her hair. Nora had married this guy from Texas a few years after the old man had died. He was all right. He made out okay. Nora didn't have to work, but she just couldn't be still; she always had to be doing something. I suggested she quit work, but I had as much luck as her husband. I used to tease her about liking to be around those white folks. It would have been good for her to take an extended trip around the country visiting my brothers and sisters. Once she got to Philadelphia, she could go right out to the cemetery and sit awhile with the old man.

I walked through the Couchman home. I liked the library. I thought if I knew Couchman I'd like him. The room made me feel like that. I left it and went into the big living room. You could tell that Couchman had let his wife do that. Everything in it was fast, dart-like, with no sense of ease. But on the walls were several of Couchman's conceptions of buildings and homes. I guess he was a disciple of Wright. My mother walked rapidly through the room without looking at me and said, "Just be patient, Wendell. She should be here real soon."

"Yeah," I said, "with a snootful." I had turned back to the drawings when Ronnie scampered into the room, his face twisted with rage.

"Nora!" he tried to roar, perhaps the way he'd seen the parents of some of his friends roar at their maids. I'm quite sure Kay didn't shout at Nora, and I don't think Couchman would. But then no one shouts at Nora. "Nora, you come right back here this minute!" the little bastard shouted and stamped and pointed to a spot on the floor where Nora was supposed to come to roost. I have a nasty temper. Sometimes it lies dormant for ages and at other times, like when the weather is hot and nothing seems to be going right, it's bubbling and ready to explode. "Don't talk to *my* mother like that, you little—!" I said sharply, breaking off just before I cursed. I wanted him to be large enough for me to strike. "How'd you like for me to talk to *your* mother like that?"

The nine-year-old looked up at me in surprise and confusion. He hadn't expected me to say anything. I was just another piece of furniture. Tears rose in his eyes and spilled out onto his pale cheeks. He put his hands behind him, twisted them. He moved backwards, away from me. He looked at my mother with a "Nora, come help me" look. And sure enough, there was Nora, speeding back across the room, gathering the kid in her arms, tucking his robe together. I was too angry to feel hatred for myself.

Ronnie was the Couchmans' only kid. Nora loved him. I suppose that was the trouble. Couchman was gone ten, twelve hours a day. Kay didn't stay around the house any longer than she had to. So Ronnie had only my mother. I think kids should have someone to love, and Nora wasn't a bad sort. But somehow when the six of us, her own children, were growing up we never had her. She was gone, out scuffling to get those crumbs

to put into our mouths and shoes for our feet and praying for
something to happen so that all the space in between would be
taken care of. Nora's affection for us took the form of rushing
out into the morning's five o'clock blackness to wake some silly
bitch and get her coffee; took form in her trudging five miles
home every night instead of taking the streetcar to save money
to buy tablets for us, to use at school, we said. But the truth
was that all of us liked to draw and we went through a writing
tablet in a couple of hours every day. Can you imagine? There's
not a goddamn artist among us. We never had the physical
affection, the pat on the head, the quick, smiling kiss, the
"gimme a hug" routine. All of this Ronnie was getting.

Now he buried his little blond head in Nora's breast and
sobbed. "There, there now," Nora said. "Don't you cry, Ronnie. Ol' Wendell is just jealous, and he hasn't much sense either. He didn't mean nuthin'."

I left the room. Nora had hit it of course, hit it and passed
on. I looked back. It didn't look so incongruous, the white and
black together, I mean. Ronnie was still sobbing. His head
bobbed gently on Nora's shoulder. The only time I ever got
that close to her was when she trapped me with a bearhug so
she could whale the daylights out of me after I put a snowball
through Mrs. Grant's window. I walked outside and lit a cigarette. When Ronnie was in the hospital the month before,
Nora got me to run her way over to Hollywood every night to
see him. I didn't like that worth a damn. All right, I'll admit it:
it did upset me. All that affection I didn't get nor my brothers
and sisters going to that little white boy who, without a doubt,
when away from her called her the names he'd learned from
adults. Can you imagine a nine-year-old kid calling Nora a
"girl," "our girl"? I spat at the Great Dane. He snarled and
then I bounced a rock off his fanny. "Lay down, you bastard," I
muttered. It was a good thing he was tied up.

I heard the low cough of the Jaguar slapping against the road.
The car was throttled down, and with a muted roar it swung
into the driveway. The woman aimed it for me. I was evil
enough not to move. I was tired of playing with these people.

At the last moment, grinning, she swung the wheel over and braked. She bounded out of the car like a tennis player vaulting over a net.

"Hi," she said, tugging at her shorts.

"Hello."

"You're Nora's boy?"

"I'm Nora's son." Hell, I was as old as she was; besides, I can't stand "boy."

"Nora tells us you're working in Hollywood. Like it?"

"It's all right."

"You must be pretty talented."

We stood looking at each other while the dog whined for her attention. Kay had a nice body and it was well tanned. She was high, boy, was she high. Looking at her, I could feel myself going into my sexy bastard routine; sometimes I can swing it great. Maybe it all had to do with the business inside. Kay took off her sunglasses and took a good look at me. "Do you have a cigarette?"

I gave her one and lit it. "Nice tan," I said. Most white people I know think it's a great big deal if a Negro compliments them on their tans. It's a large laugh. You have all this volleyball about color and come summer you can't hold the white folks back from the beaches, anyplace where they can get some sun. And of course the blacker they get, the more pleased they are. Crazy. If there is ever a Negro revolt, it will come during the summer and Negroes will descend upon the beaches around the nation and paralyze the country. You can't conceal cattle prods and bombs and pistols and police dogs when you're showing your birthday suit to the sun.

"You like it?" she asked. She was pleased. She placed her arm next to mine. "Almost the same color," she said.

"Ronnie isn't feeling well," I said.

"Oh, the poor kid. I'm so glad we have Nora. She's such a charm. I'll run right in and look at him. Do have a drink in the bar. Fix me one too, will you?" Kay skipped inside and I went to the bar and poured out two strong drinks. I made hers stronger than mine. She was back soon. "Nora was trying to put him to sleep and she made me stay out." She giggled. She quickly tossed off her drink. "Another, please?" While I was fixing her drink she was saying how amazing it was for Nora to have such a talented son. What she was really saying was that it was amazing for a servant to have a son who was not also a servant. "Anything can happen in a democracy," I said. "Servants' sons drink with madames and so on."

"Oh, Nora isn't a servant," Kay said. "She's part of the family."

Yeah, I thought. Where and how many times had I heard *that* before?

In the ensuing silence, she started to admire her tan again. "You think it's pretty good, do you? You don't know how hard I worked to get it." I moved close to her and held her arm. I placed my other arm around her. She pretended not to see or feel it, but she wasn't trying to get away either. In fact she was pressing closer and the register in my brain that tells me at the precise moment when I'm in, went off. Kay was very high. I put both arms around her and she put both hers around me. When I kissed her, she responded completely.

"Mom!"

"Ronnie, come back to bed," I heard Nora shout from the other room. We could hear Ronnie running over the rug in the outer room. Kay tried to get away from me, push me to one side, because we could tell that Ronnie knew where to look for his Mom: he was running right for the bar, where we were. "Oh, please," she said, "don't let him see us." I wouldn't let her push me away. "Stop!" she hissed. "He'll *see* us!" We stopped struggling just for an instant, and we listened to the echoes of the word *see*. She gritted her teeth and renewed her efforts to get away.

Me? I had the scene laid right out. The kid breaks into the room, see, and sees his mother in this real wriggly clinch with this colored guy who's just shouted at him, see, and no matter how his mother explains it away, the kid has the image—the colored guy and his mother—for the rest of his life, see?

That's the way it happened. The kid's mother hissed under

her breath, *"You're crazy!"* and she looked at me as though she were seeing me or something about me for the very first time. I'd released her as soon as Ronnie, romping into the bar, saw us and came to a full, open-mouthed halt. Kay went to him. He looked first at me, then at his mother. Kay turned to me, but she couldn't speak.

Outside in the living room my mother called, "Wendell, where are you? We can go now."

I started to move past Kay and Ronnie. I felt many things, but I made myself think mostly, *There, you little bastard, there.*

My mother thrust her face inside the door and said, "Good-bye, Mrs. Couchman. See you tomorrow. 'Bye, Ronnie."

"Yes," Kay said, sort of stunned. "Tomorrow." She was reaching for Ronnie's hand as we left, but the kid was slapping her hand away. I hurried quickly after Nora, hating the long drive back to Watts.

VI Church

Since the Civil War the institution that has best managed to survive the upheavals of Negro history has been the Negro church. One reason, undoubtedly, has been the ability of black ministers to convey to their congregations a sense of community among themselves and commonality with persons and events in the Bible. James Weldon Johnson's "The Creation" captures something of the black preacher's rhythms, rhetoric and metaphor. When the church followed Negroes to the cities, it often performed even more vital services in bolstering the sagging spirits of migrants in a strange and bewildering environment. But of course the cities offered greater opportunity for fraud and charlatanism as well among unscrupulous churchmen. Langston Hughes's "Rock, Church" is a lively account of one such charlatan and his comeuppance. James Baldwin's "The Outing" is a rich story in several ways, among them the manner in which the church service acts as a psychological buffer to the humiliated, the angered, the frustrated and the lost.

James Weldon Johnson

The Creation

A Negro Sermon

And God stepped out on space,
And He looked around and said,
"I'm lonely—
I'll make me a world."

And far as the eye of God could see
Darkness covered everything,
Blacker than a hundred midnights
Down in a cypress swamp.

Then God smiled,
And the light broke,
And the darkness rolled up on one side,
And the light stood shining on the other,
And God said, *"That's good!"*

Then God reached out and took the light in His hands,
And God rolled the light around in His hands,
Until He made the sun;
And He set that sun a-blazing in the heavens.
And the light that was left from making the sun
God gathered up in a shining ball
And flung against the darkness,
Spangling the night with the moon and stars.
Then down between

The darkness and the light
He hurled the world:
And God said, *"That's good!"*

Then God himself stepped down—
And the sun was on His right hand,
And the moon was on His left;
The stars were clustered about His head,
And the earth was under His feet.
And God walked, and where He trod
His footsteps hollowed the valleys out
And bulged the mountains up.

Then He stopped and looked and saw
That the earth was hot and barren.
So God stepped over to the edge of the world
And He spat out the seven seas;
He batted His eyes, and the lightnings flashed;
He clapped His hands, and the thunders rolled;
And the waters above the earth came down,
The cooling waters came down.

Then the green grass sprouted,
And the little red flowers blossomed,
The pine-tree pointed his finger to the sky,
And the oak spread out his arms;
The lakes cuddled down in the hollows of the ground,
And the rivers ran down to the sea;
And God smiled again,
And the rainbow appeared,
And curled itself around His shoulder.

Then God raised His arm and He waved His hand
Over the sea and over the land,
And He said, *"Bring forth! Bring forth!"*
And quicker than God could drop His hand,
Fishes and fowls
And beast and birds
Swam the rivers and the seas,

Roamed the forests and the woods,
And split the air with their wings,
And God said, *"That's good!"*

Then God walked around
And God looked around
On all that He had made.
He looked at His sun,
And He looked at His moon,
And He looked at His little stars;
He looked on His world
With all its living things,
And God said, *"I'm lonely still."*

Then God sat down
On the side of a hill where He could think;
By a deep, wide river He sat down;
With His head in His hands,
God thought and thought,
Till He thought, *"I'll make me a man!"*

Up from the bed of the river
God scooped the clay;
And by the bank of the river
He kneeled Him down;
And there the great God Almighty,
Who lit the sun and fixed it in the sky,
Who flung the stars to the most far corner of the night,
Who rounded the earth in the middle of His hand—
This Great God,
Like a mammy bending over her baby,
Kneeled down in the dust
Toiling over a lump of clay
Till He shaped it in His own image;

Then into it He blew the breath of life,
And man became a living soul.
Amen. Amen.

Rock, Church

Elder William Jones was one of them rock-church preachers who know how to make the spirit rise and the soul get right. Sometimes in the pulpit he used to start talking real slow, and you'd think his sermon warn't gonna be nothing, but by the time he got through, the walls of the building would be almost rent, the doors busted open, and the benches turned over from pure shouting on the part of the brothers and sisters.

He were a great preacher, was Reverend William Jones. But he warn't satisfied—he wanted to be greater than he was. He wanted to be another Billy Graham or a Aimee McPherson or a resurrected Reverend Becton. And that's what brought about his downfall—ambition!

Now, Reverend Jones had been for nearly a year the pastor of one of them little colored churches in the back alleys of St. Louis that are open every night in the week for preaching, singing, and praying, where sisters come to shake tambourines, shout, sing gospel songs, and get happy while the Reverend presents the Word.

Elder Jones always opened his part of the services with "In His Hand," his theme song, and he always closed his services with the same. Now, the rhythm of "In His Hand" was such that once it got to swinging, you couldn't help but move your arms or feet or both, and since the Reverend always took up collection at the beginning and ending of his sermons, the dancing movement of the crowd at such times was always toward the collection table—which was exactly where the Elder wanted it to be.

In His hand!
In His hand!
I'm safe and sound
I'll be bound—
Settin' in Jesus' hand!

"Come one! Come all! Come, my Lambs," Elder Jones would shout, "and put it down for Jesus!"

Poor old washerladies, big fat cooks, long lean truck drivers, and heavy-set roustabouts would come up and lay their money down, two times every evening for Elder Jones.

That minister was getting rich right there in that St. Louis alley.

In His hand!
In His hand!
I'll have you know
I'm white as snow—
Settin' in Jesus' hand!

With the piano just a-going, tambourines a-flying, and people shouting right on up to the altar.

"Rock, church, rock!" Elder Jones would cry at such intensely lucrative moments.

But he were too ambitious. He wouldn't let well enough alone. He wanted to be a big shot and panic Harlem, gas Detroit, sew up Chicago, then move on to Hollywood. He warn't satisfied with just St. Louis.

So he got to thinking now what can I do to get everybody excited, to get everybody talking about my church, to get the streets outside crowded and my name known all over, even unto the far reaches of the nation? Now, what can I do?

Billy Sunday had a sawdust trail, so he had heard. Reverend Becton had two valets in the pulpit with him as he cast off garment after garment in the heat of preaching, and used up dozens of white handkerchiefs every evening wiping his brow while calling on the Lord to come. Meanwhile, the Angel of Angelus

Temple had just kept on getting married and divorced and making the front pages of everybody's newspapers.

"I got to be news, too, in my day and time," mused Elder Jones. "This town's too small for me! I want the world to hear my name!"

Now, as I've said before, Elder Jones was a good preacher— and a good-looking preacher, too. He could cry real loud and moan real deep, and he could move the sisters as no other black preacher on this side of town had ever moved them before. Besides, in his youth, as a sinner, he had done a little light hustling around Memphis and Vicksburg—so he knew just how to appeal to the feminine nature.

Since his recent sojourn in St. Louis, Elder Jones had been looking for a special female Lamb to shelter in his private fold. Out of all the sisters in his church, he had finally chosen Sister Maggie Bradford. Not that Sister Maggie was pretty. No, far from it. But Sister Maggie was well fed, brownskin, good-natured, fat, and *prosperous*. She owned four two-family houses that she rented out, upstairs and down, so she made a good living. Besides, she had sweet and loving ways as well as the interest of her pastor at heart.

Elder Jones confided his personal ambitions to said Sister Bradford one morning when he woke up to find her by his side.

"I want to branch out, Maggie," he said. "I want to be a really big man! Now, what can I do to get the 'tention of the world on me? I mean in a religious way?"

They thought and they thought. Since it was a Fourth of July morning, and Sister Maggie didn't have to go collect rents, they just lay there and thought.

Finally, Sister Maggie said, "Bill Jones, you know something I ain't never forgot that I seed as a child? There was a preacher down in Mississippi named old man Eubanks who one time got himself dead and buried and then rose from the dead. Now, I ain't never forgot that. Neither has nobody else in that part of the Delta. That's something mem'rable. Why don't you do something like that?"

"How did he do it, Sister Maggie?"

"He ain't never told nobody how he do it, Brother Bill. He say it were the Grace of God, that's all."

"It might a-been," said Elder Jones. "It might-a-been."

He lay there and thought awhile longer. By and by, he said, "But, honey, I'm gonna do something better'n that. I'm gonna be nailed on a cross."

"Do, Jesus!" said Sister Maggie Bradford. "Jones, you's a mess!"

Now, the Elder, in order to pull off his intended miracle, had, of necessity, to take somebody else into his confidence, so he picked out Brother Hicks, his chief deacon, one of the main pillars of the church long before Jones came as pastor.

It was too bad, though, that Jones never knew that Brother Hicks (more familiarly known as Bulldog) used to be in love with Sister Bradford. Sister Bradford neglected to tell the new Reverend about any of her former sweethearts. So how was Elder Jones to know that some of them still coveted her, and were envious of him in their hearts?

"Hicks," whispered Elder Jones in telling his chief deacon of his plan to die on the cross and then come back to life, "that miracle will make me the greatest minister in the world. No doubt about it! When I get to be world-renowned, Bulldog, and go traveling about the firmament, I'll take you with me as my chief deacon. You shall be my right hand, and Sister Maggie Bradford shall be my left. Amen!"

"I hear you," said Brother Hicks. "I hope it comes true."

But if Elder Jones had looked closely, he would have seen an evil light in his deacon's eyes.

"It will come true," said Elder Jones, "if you keep your mouth shut and follow out my instructions—exactly as I lay 'em down to you. I trust you, so listen! You know and I know that I ain't gonna *really* die. Neither is I *really* gonna be nailed. That's why I wants you to help me. I wants you to have me a great big cross made, higher than the altar—so high I has to have a step-ladder to get up to it to be nailed thereon, and you to nail me. The higher the better, so's they won't see the straps—'cause I'm gonna be tied on by straps, you hear. The light'll be rose-colored so they can't see the straps. Now, here you come and do the nailin'—nobody else but you. Put them nails *between* my fingers and toes, not through 'em—*between*—and don't nail too deep. Leave the heads kinder stickin' out. You get the jibe?"

"I get the jibe," said Brother Bulldog Hicks.

"Then you and me'll stay right on there in the church all night and all day till the next night when the people come back to see me rise. Ever so often, you can let me down to rest a little bit. But as long as I'm on the cross, I play off like I'm dead, particularly when reporters come around. On Monday night— Hallelujah! I will rise, and take up collection!"

"Amen!" said Brother Hicks.

Well, you couldn't get a-near the church on the night that Reverend Jones had had it announced by press, by radio, and by word of mouth that he would be crucified *dead*, stay dead, and rise. Negroes came from all over St. Louis, East St. Louis, and mighty nigh everywhere else to be present at the witnessing of the miracle. Lots of 'em didn't believe in Reverend Jones, but lots of 'em *did*. Sometimes false prophets can bamboozle you so you can't tell yonder from whither—and that's the way Jones had the crowd.

The church was packed and jammed. Not a seat to be found and tears were flowing (from sorrowing sisters' eyes) long before the Elder even approached the cross which, made out of new lumber right straight from the sawmill, loomed up behind the pulpit. In the rose-colored lights, with big paper lilies that Sister Bradford had made decorating its head and foot, the cross looked mighty pretty.

Elder Jones preached a mighty sermon that night and, hot as it was, there was plenty of leaping and jumping and shouting in that crowded church. It looked like the walls would fall. Then when he got through preaching, Elder Jones made a solemn announcement. As he termed it, for a night and a day, his last pronouncement.

"Church! Tonight, as I have told the world, I'm gonna die. I'm gonna be nailed to this cross and let the breath pass from me. But tomorrow, Monday night, August the twenty-first, at twelve p.m., I am coming back to life. Amen! After twenty-four hours on the cross, Hallelujah! And all the city of St. Louis can be saved—if they will just come out to see me. Now, before I mounts the steps to the cross, let us sing for the last time 'In His Hand'—'cause I tell you, that's where I am! As we sing, let everybody come forward to the collection table and help this church before I go. Give largely!"

The piano tinkled, the tambourines rang, hands clapped. Elder Jones and his children sang:

In His hand!
In His hand!
You'll never stray
Down the Devil's way—
Settin' in Jesus' hand!

Oh, in His hand!
In His hand!
Though I may die
I'll mount on high—
Settin' in Jesus' hand!

"Let us pray." And while every back was bowed in prayer, the Elder went up the stepladder to the cross. Brother Hicks followed with the hammer and nails. Sister Bradford wailed at the top of her voice. Woe filled the Amen Corner. Emotion rocked the church.

Folks outside was saying all up and down the streets, "Lawd, I wish we could have got in. Listen yonder at that noise! I wonder what *is* going on!"

Elder Jones was about to make himself famous—that's what was going on. And all would have went well had it not been for Brother Hicks—a two-faced rascal. Somehow that night the devil got into Bulldog Hicks and took full possession.

The truth of the matter is that Hicks got to thinking about Sister Maggie Bradford, and how Reverend Jones had worked up to be her No. 1 man. That made him mad. The old green snake of jealousy began to coil around his heart, right there in the meeting, right there on the steps of the cross, at the very high point of the ceremonies. Lord, have Mercy!

Hicks had the hammer in one hand and his other hand was full of nails as he mounted the ladder behind his pastor. He was going up to nail Elder Jones on that sawmill cross.

"While I'm nailin', I might as well nail him right," Hicks thought. "A low-down klinker—comin' here out of Mississippi to take my woman away from me! He'll never know the pleasure of my help in none o' his schemes to out-Divine Father! No, sir!"

Elder Jones had himself all fixed up with a system of straps round his waist, round his shoulder blades, and round his wrists and ankles, hidden under his long black coat. These straps fastened in hooks on the back of the cross, out of sight of the audience, so he could just hang up there all sad and sorrowful-looking, and make out like he was being nailed. Brother Bulldog Hicks was to plant the nails *between* his fingers and toes. Hallelujah! Rock, church, rock!

Excitement was intense.

All went well, until the nailing began. Elder Jones removed his shoes and socks, in his bare black feet, bade farewell to his weeping congregation. As he leaned back against the cross and allowed Brother Hicks to compose him there, the crowd began to moan. But it was when Hicks placed the first nail between Elder Jones's toes that they became hysterical. Sister Bradford outyelled them all.

Hicks placed that first nail between the big toe and the next toe of the left foot and began to hammer. The foot was well strapped down, so the Elder couldn't move it. The closer the head of the nail got to his toes, the harder Hicks struck it. Finally the hammer collided with Elder Jones's foot, *bam* against his big toe.

"Aw-oh!" he moaned under his breath. "Go easy, man!"

"Have mercy," shouted the brothers and sisters of the church. "Have mercy on our Elder!"

Once more the hammer struck his toe. But the all too human

sound of his surprised and agonized "Ouch!" was lost in the tumult of the shouting church.

"Bulldog, I say, go easy," hissed the Elder. "This *ain't* real."

Brother Hicks desisted, a grim smile on his face. Then he turned his attention to the right foot. There he placed another nail between the toes, and began to hammer. Again, as the nail went into the wood, he showed no signs of stopping when the hammer reached the foot. He just kept on landing cruel, metallic blows on the Elder's bare toenails until the preacher howled with pain, no longer able to keep back a sudden hair-raising cry. The sweat popped out on his forehead and dripped down on his shirt.

At first the Elder thought, naturally, that it was just a slip of the hammer on the deacon's part. Then he thought the man must have gone crazy—like the rest of the audience. Then it hurt him so bad he didn't know what he thought—so he just hollered, "Aw-ooo-oo-o!"

It was a good thing the church was full of noise, or they would have heard a strange dialogue.

"My God, Hicks, what are you doing?" the Elder cried, staring wildly at his deacon on the ladder.

"I'm nailin' you to the cross, Jones! And, man, I'm *really* nailin'."

"Aw-oow-ow! Don't you know you're hurting me? I told you *not* to nail so hard!"

But the deacon was unruffled.

"Who'd you say's gonna be your right hand, when you get down from here and start your travelings?" Hicks asked.

"You, brother," the sweating Elder cried.

"And who'd you say was gonna be your left hand?"

"Sister Maggie Bradford," moaned Elder Jones from the cross.

"Naw, she ain't," said Brother Hicks, whereupon he struck the Reverend's toe a really righteous blow.

"Lord, help me!" cried the tortured minister. The weeping congregation echoed his cry. It was certainly real. The Elder *was* being crucified!

Brother Bulldog Hicks took two more steps up the ladder,

preparing to nail the hands. With his evil face right in front of Elder Jones, he hissed: "I'll teach you nappy-headed jack-leg ministers to come to St. Louis and think you all can walk away with any woman you's a mind to. I'm gonna teach you to leave my woman alone. Here—here's a nail!"

Brother Hicks placed a great big spike right in the palm of Elder Jones's left hand. He was just about to drive it in when the frightened Reverend let out a scream that could be heard two blocks away. At the same time, he began to struggle to get down. Jones tried to bust the straps, but they was too strong for him.

If he could just get one foot loose to kick Brother Bulldog Hicks!

Hicks lifted the hammer to let go when the Reverend's second yell, this time, was loud enough to be heard in East St. Louis. It burst like a bomb above the shouts of the crowd—and it had its effect. Suddenly the congregation was quiet. Everybody knew that was no way for a dying man to yell.

Sister Bradford realized that something had gone wrong, so she began to chant the song her beloved pastor had told her to chant at the propitious moment after the nailing was done. Now, even though the nailing was not done, Sister Bradford thought she had better sing:

Elder Jones will rise again,
Elder Jones will rise again,
Rise again, rise again!
Elder Jones will rise again,
Yes, my Lawd!

But nobody took up the refrain to help her carry it on. Everybody was too interested in what was happening in front of them, so Sister Bradford's voice just died out.

Meanwhile, Brother Hicks lifted the hammer again, but Elder Jones spat right in his face. He not only spat, but suddenly called his deacon a name unworthy of man or beast. Then he let out another frightful yell and, in mortal anguish, called, "Sister Maggie Bradford, lemme down from here! I say, come and get . . . me . . . down . . . *from here!*"

Those in the church that had not already stopped moaning and shouting, did so at once. You could have heard a pin drop. Folks were petrified.

Brother Hicks stood on the ladder glaring with satisfaction at Reverend Jones, his hammer still raised. Under his breath, the panting Elder dared him to nail another nail, and threatened to kill him stone-dead with a forty-four if he did.

"Just lemme get loose from here, and I'll fight you like a natural man," he gasped, twisting and turning like a tree in a storm.

"Come down, then," yelled Hicks, right out loud from the ladder. "Come on down! As sure as water runs, Jones, I'll show you up for what you is—a woman-chasing, no-good, low-down faker! I'll beat you to a batter with my bare hands!"

"Lawd, have mercy!" cried the church.

Jones almost broke a blood vessel trying to get loose from his cross.

"Sister Maggie, come and lemme down," he pleaded, sweat streaming from his face.

But Sister Bradford was covered with confusion. In fact, she was petrified. What could have gone wrong for the Elder to call on her like this in public in the very midst of the thing that was to bring him famous-glory and make them all rich preaching throughout the land with her at his side? Sister Bradford's head was in a whirl, her heart was in her mouth.

"Elder Jones, you means you really wants to get down?" she asked weakly from her seat in the Amen Corner.

"Yes," said the Elder, "can't you hear? I done called on you twenty times to let me down!"

At this point, Brother Hicks gave the foot nails one more good hammering. The words that came from the cross were nobody's business.

In a twinkling, Sister Bradford was at Jones's side. Realizing at last that the devil must've done got into Hicks (like it used to sometimes in the days when she knowed him), she went to the aid of her battered Elder, grabbed the foot of the ladder, and sent Hicks sprawling across the pulpit.

"You'll never crucify my Elder," she cried, "not for real." Energetically, she began to cut the straps away that bound the Reverend. Soon poor Jones slid to the floor, his feet too sore from the hammer's blows to even stand on them without help.

"Just lemme get at Hicks," was all Reverend Jones could gasp. "He knowed I didn't want them nails that close." In the dead silence that took possession of the church, everybody heard him moan, "Lawd, lemme get at Hicks," as he hobbled away on the protecting arm of Sister Maggie.

"Stand back, Bulldog," Sister Maggie said to the deacon, "and let your pastor pass. Soon as he's able, he'll flatten you out like a shadder—but now, I'm in charge. Stand back, I say, and let him pass!"

Hicks stood back. The crowd murmured. The minister made his exit.

Thus ended the ambitious career of Elder William Jones. He never did pastor in St. Louis any more. Neither did he fight Hicks. He just snuck away.

James Baldwin

The Outing

Each summer the church gave an outing. It usually took place on the Fourth of July, that being the day when most of the church-members were free from work; it began quite early in the morning and lasted all day. The saints referred to it as the 'whosoever will' outing, by which they meant that, though it was given by the Mount of Olives Pentecostal Assembly for the benefit of its members, all men were free to join them, Gentile, Jew or Greek or sinner. The Jews and the Greeks, to say nothing of the Gentiles—on whom, for their livelihood, most of the saints depended—showed themselves, year after year, indifferent to the invitation; but sinners of the more expected hue were seldom lacking. This year they were to take a boat trip up the Hudson as far as Bear Mountain where they would spend the day and return as the moon rose over the wide river. Since on other outings they had merely taken a subway ride as far as Pelham Bay or Van Cortlandt Park, this year's outing was more than ever a special occasion and even the deacon's two oldest boys, Johnnie and Roy, and their friend, David Jackson, were reluctantly thrilled. These three tended to consider themselves sophisticates, no longer, like the old folks, at the mercy of the love or the wrath of God.

The entire church was going and for weeks in advance talked of nothing else. And for weeks in the future the outing would provide interesting conversation. They did not consider this frivolous. The outing, Father James declared from his pulpit a week before the event, was for the purpose of giving the children of God a day of relaxation; to breathe a purer air and to

255

worship God joyfully beneath the roof of heaven; and there was nothing frivolous about *that*. And, rather to the alarm of the captain, they planned to hold church services aboard the ship. Last year Sister McCandless had held an impromptu service in the unbelieving subway car; she played the tambourine and sang and exhorted sinners and passed through the train distributing tracts. Not everyone had found this admirable, to some it seemed that Sister McCandless was being a little ostentatious. "I praise my Redeemer wherever I go," she retorted defiantly. "Holy Ghost don't leave *me* when I leave the church. I got a every day religion."

Sylvia's birthday was on the third, and David and Johnnie and Roy had been saving money for her birthday present. Between them they had five dollars but they could not decide what to give her. Roy's suggestion that they give her underthings was rudely shouted down: did he want Sylvia's mother to kill the girl? They were all frightened of the great, rawboned, outspoken Sister Daniels and for Sylvia's sake went to great pains to preserve what remained of her good humor. Finally, and at the suggestion of David's older sister, Lorraine, they bought a small, gold-plated pin cut in the shape of a butterfly. Roy thought that it was cheap and grumbled angrily at their combined bad taste ("Wait till it starts turning her clothes green!" he cried) but David did not think it was so bad; Johnnie thought it pretty enough and he was sure that Sylvia would like it anyway; "When's *your* birthday?" he asked David). It was agreed that David should present it to her on the day of the outing in the presence of them all. ("Man, I'm the oldest cat here," David said, "you know that girl's crazy about me"). This was the summer in which they all abruptly began to grow older, their bodies becoming troublesome and awkward and even dangerous and their voices not to be trusted. David perpetually boasted of the increase of down on his chin and professed to have hair on his chest—"and somewhere else, too," he added slyly, whereat they all laughed. "You ain't the only one," Roy said. "No," Johnnie said, "I'm almost as old as you are." "Almost ain't got it," David said. "Now ain't this a hell of a conversation for church boys?" Roy wanted to know.

The morning of the outing they were all up early; their father sang in the kitchen and their mother, herself betraying an excitement nearly youthful, scrubbed and dressed the younger children and laid the plates for breakfast. In the bedroom which they shared Roy looked wistfully out of the window and turned to Johnnie.

"Got a good mind to stay home," he said. "Probably have more fun." He made a furious gesture toward the kitchen. "Why doesn't *he* stay home?"

Johnnie, who was looking forward to the day with David and who had not the remotest desire to stay home for any reason and who knew, moreover, that Gabriel was not going to leave Roy alone in the city, not even if the heavens fell, said lightly, squirming into clean underwear: "Oh, he'll probably be busy with the old folks. We can stay out of his way."

Roy sighed and began to dress. "Be glad when I'm a man," he said.

Lorraine and David and Mrs. Jackson were already on the boat when they arrived. They were among the last; most of the church, Father James, Brother Elisha, Sister McCandless, Sister Daniels and Sylvia were seated near the rail of the boat in a little semi-circle, conversing in strident tones. Father James and Sister McCandless were remarking the increase of laxity among God's people and debating whether or not the church should run a series of revival meetings. Sylvia sat there, saying nothing, smiling painfully now and then at young Brother Elisha, who spoke loudly of the need for a revival and who continually attempted to include Sylvia in the conversation. Elsewhere on the boat similar conversations were going on. The saints of God were together and very conscious this morning of their being together and of their sainthood; and were determined that the less enlightened world should know who they were and remark upon it. To this end there were a great many cries of "Praise the Lord!" in greeting and the formal holy kiss. The children, bored with the familiar spectacle, had already drawn apart and amused themselves by loud cries and games that were no less exhibitionistic than that being played by their parents. Johnnie's nine year old sister, Lois, since she professed salvation, could not very well behave as the other children did; yet no degree of salvation could have equipped her to enter into the conversation of the grown-ups; and she was very violently disliked among the adolescents and could not join them either. She wandered about, therefore, unwillingly forlorn, contenting herself to some extent by a great display of virtue in her encounters with the unsaved children and smiling brightly at the grown-ups. She came to Brother Elisha's side. "Praise the Lord," he cried, stroking her head and continuing his conversation.

Lorraine and Mrs. Jackson met Johnnie's mother for the first time as she breathlessly came on board, dressed in the airy and unreal blue which Johnnie would forever associate with his furthest memories of her. Johnnie's baby brother, her youngest, happiest child, clung round her neck; she made him stand, staring in wonder at the strange, endless deck, while she was introduced. His mother, on all social occasions, seemed fearfully distracted, as though she awaited, at any moment, some crushing and irrevocable disaster. This disaster might be the sudden awareness of a run in her stocking or private knowledge that the trump of judgment was due, within five minutes, to sound; but, whatever it was, it lent her a certain agitated charm and people, struggling to guess what it might be that so claimed her inward attention, never failed, in the process, to be won over. She talked with Lorraine and Mrs. Jackson for a few moments, the child tugging at her skirts, Johnnie watching her with a smile; and at last, the child becoming always more restive, said that she must go—into what merciless arena one dared not imagine —but hoped, with a despairing smile which clearly indicated the improbability of such happiness, that she would be able to see them later. They watched her as she walked slowly to the other end of the boat, sometimes pausing in conversation, always (as though it were a duty) smiling a little and now and then considering Lois where she stood at Brother Elisha's knee.

"She's very friendly," Mrs. Jackson said. "She looks like you, Johnnie."

David laughed. "Now why you want to say a thing like that, Ma? That woman ain't never done nothing to you."

Johnnie grinned, embarrassed, and pretended to menace David with his fists.

"Don't you listen to that old, ugly boy," Lorraine said. "He just trying to make you feel bad. Your mother's real good-looking. Tell her I said so."

This embarrassed him even more, but he made a mock bow and said, "Thank you, Sister." And to David: "Maybe now you'll learn to keep your mouth shut."

"Who'll learn to keep whose mouth shut? What kind of talk is that?"

He turned and faced his father, who stood smiling on them as from a height.

"Mrs. Jackson, this is my father," said Roy quickly. "And this is Miss Jackson. You know David."

Lorraine and Mrs. Jackson looked up at the deacon with polite and identical smiles.

"How do you do?" Lorraine said. And from Mrs. Jackson: "I'm very pleased to meet you."

"Praise the Lord," their father said. He smiled. "Don't you let Johnnie talk fresh to you."

"Oh, no, we were just kidding around," David said. There was a short, ugly silence. The deacon said: "It looks like a good day for the outing, praise the Lord. You kids have a good time. Is this your first time with us, Mrs. Jackson?"

"Yes," said Mrs. Jackson. "David came home and told me about it and it's been so long since I've been in the country I just decided I'd take me a day off. And Lorraine's not been feeling too strong. I thought the fresh air would do her some good." She smiled a little painfully as she spoke. Lorraine looked amused.

"Yes, it will, nothing like God's fresh air to help the feeble." At this description of herself as feeble Lorraine looked ready to fall into the Hudson and coughed nastily into her handkerchief. David, impelled by his own perverse demon, looked at Johnnie quickly and murmured, "That's the truth, deacon." The deacon looked at him and smiled and turned to Mrs. Jackson. "We been hoping that your son might join our church someday. Roy brings him out to service every Sunday. Do you like the serv-

ices, son?" This last was addressed in a hearty voice to David;
who, recovering from his amazement at hearing Roy mentioned
as his especial pal (for he was Johnnie's friend, it was to be
with Johnnie that he came to church!), smiled and said, "Yes
sir, I like them alright," and looked at Roy, who considered his
father with an expression at once contemptuous, ironic and re-
signed and at Johnnie, whose face was a mask of rage. He
looked sharply at the deacon again; but he, with his arm around
Roy, was still talking.

"This boy came to the Lord just about a month ago," he said
proudly. "The Lord saved him just like that. Believe me, Sister
Jackson, ain't no better fortress for nobody, young or old, than
the arms of Jesus. My son'll tell you so, ain't it, Roy?"

They considered Roy with a stiff, cordial curiosity. He muttered murderously, "Yes sir."

"Johnnie tells me you're a preacher," Mrs. Jackson said at
last. "I'll come out and hear you sometime with David."

"Don't come out to hear me," he said. "You come out and
listen to the Word of God. We're all just vessels in His hand.
Do you know the Lord, sister?"

"I try to do His will," Mrs. Jackson said.

He smiled kindly. "We must all grow in grace." He looked at
Lorraine. "I'll be expecting to see you too, young lady."

"Yes, we'll be out," Lorraine said. They shook hands. "It's
very nice to have met you," she said.

"Goodbye." He looked at David. "Now you be good. I want
to see you saved soon." He released Roy and started to walk
away. "You kids enjoy yourselves. Johnnie, don't you get into
no mischief, you hear me?"

He affected not to have heard; he put his hands in his pants'
pockets and pulled out some change and pretended to count it.
His hand was clammy and it shook. When his father repeated
his admonition, part of the change spilled to the deck and he
bent to pick it up. He wanted at once to shout to his father the
most dreadful curses that he knew and he wanted to weep. He
was aware that they were all intrigued by the tableau presented
by his father and himself, that they were all vaguely cognizant

of an unnamed and deadly tension. From his knees on the deck he called back (putting into his voice as much asperity, as much fury and hatred as he dared):

"Don't worry about me, Daddy. Roy'll see to it that I behave."

There was a silence after he said this; and he rose to his feet and saw that they were all watching him. David looked pitying and shocked, Roy's head was bowed and he looked apologetic. His father called:

"Excuse yourself, Johnnie, and come here."

"Excuse me," he said, and walked over to his father. He looked up into his father's face with an anger which surprised and even frightened him. But he did not drop his eyes, knowing that his father saw there (and he wanted him to see it) how much he hated him.

"What did you say?" his father asked.

"I said you don't have to worry about me. I don't think I'll get into any mischief." And his voice surprised him, it was more deliberately cold and angry than he had intended and there was a sardonic stress on the word 'mischief.' He knew that his father would then and there have knocked him down if they had not been in the presence of saints and strangers.

"You be careful how you speak to me. Don't you get grown too fast. We get home, I'll pull down those long pants and we'll see who's the man, you hear me?"

Yes we will, he thought and said nothing. He looked with a deliberate casualness about the deck. Then they felt the lurch of the boat as it began to move from the pier. There was an excited raising of voices and "I'll see you later," his father said and turned away.

He stood still, trying to compose himself to return to Mrs. Jackson and Lorraine. But as he turned with his hands in his pants' pockets he saw that David and Roy were coming toward him and he stopped and waited for them.

"It's a bitch," Roy said.

David looked at him, shocked. "That's no language for a saved boy." He put his arm around Johnnie's shoulder. "We're

off to Bear Mountain," he cried, "*up* the glorious Hudson"—
and he made a brutal gesture with his thumb.

"Now suppose Sylvia saw you do that," said Roy, "what
would you say, huh?"

"We needn't worry about her," Johnnie said. "She'll be sitting with the old folks all day long."

"Oh, we'll figure out a way to take care of *them*," said David.
He turned to Roy. "Now you the saved one, why don't you talk
to Sister Daniels and distract her attention while we talk to the
girl? You the baby, anyhow, girl don't want to talk to you."

"I ain't got enough salvation to talk to that hag," Roy said.
"I got a Daddy-made salvation. I'm saved when I'm with
Daddy." They laughed and Roy added, "And I ain't no baby,
either, I got everything my Daddy got."

"And a lot your Daddy don't dream of," David said.

Oh, thought Johnnie, with a sudden, vicious, chilling anger,
he doesn't have to dream about it!

"Now let's act like we Christians," David said. "If we was
real smart now, we'd go over to where she's sitting with all
those people and act like we wanted to hear about God. Get on
the good side of her mother."

"And suppose *he* comes back?" asked Johnnie.

Gabriel was sitting at the other end of the boat, talking with
his wife. "Maybe he'll stay there," David said; there was a note
of apology in his voice.

They approached the saints.

"Praise the Lord," they said sedately.

"Well, praise Him," Father James said. "How are you young
men today?" He grabbed Roy by the shoulder. "Are you coming along in the Lord?"

"Yes, sir," Roy muttered, "I'm trying." He smiled into Father James's face.

"It's a wonderful thing," Brother Elisha said, "to give up to
the Lord in your youth." He looked up at Johnnie and David.
"Why don't you boys surrender? Ain't nothing in the world for
you, I'll tell you that. He says, 'Remember thy Creator in the
days of thy youth when the evil days come not.'"

"Amen," said Sister Daniels. "We're living in the last days,

children. Don't think because you're young you got plenty of
time. God takes the young as well as the old. You got to hold
yourself in readiness all the time lest when He comes He catch
you unprepared. Yes sir. Now's the time."

"You boys going to come to service today, ain't you?" asked
Sister McCandless. "We're going to have service on the ship,
you know." She looked at Father James. "Reckon we'll start
as soon as we get a little further up the river, won't we,
Father?"

"Yes," Father James said, "we're going to praise God right in
the middle of the majestic Hudson." He leaned back and released Roy as he spoke. "Want to see you children there. I
want to hear you make a *noise* for the Lord."

"I ain't never seen none of these young men Shout," said Sister Daniels, regarding them with distrust. She looked at David
and Johnnie. "Don't believe I've ever even heard you testify."

"We're not saved yet, sister," David told her gently.

"That's alright," Sister Daniels said. "You *could* get up and
praise the Lord for your life, health and strength. Praise Him
for what you got, He'll give you something more."

"That's the truth," said Brother Elisha. He smiled at Sylvia.
"I'm a witness, bless the Lord."

"They going to make a noise yet," said Sister McCandless.
"Lord's going to touch everyone of these young men one day
and bring them on their knees to the altar. You mark my
words, you'll see." And she smiled at them.

"You just stay around the house of God long enough,"
Father James said. "One of these days the Spirit'll jump on
you. I won't never forget the day It jumped on me."

"That *is* the truth," Sister McCandless cried, "so glad It
jumped on me one day, hallelujah!"

"Amen," Sister Daniels cried, "amen."

"Looks like we're having a little service right now," Brother
Elisha said smiling. Father James laughed heartily and cried,
"Well, praise Him anyhow."

"I believe next week the church is going to start a series of revival meetings," Brother Elisha said. "I want to see you boys at
every one of them, you hear?" He laughed as he spoke and

added as David seemed about to protest, "No, no, brother, don't want no excuses. You *be* there. Get you boys to the altar, then maybe you'll pay more attention in Sunday School."

At this they all laughed and Sylvia said in her mild voice, looking mockingly at Roy, "Maybe we'll even see Brother Roy Shout." Roy grinned.

"Like to see you do some Shouting too," her mother grumbled. "You got to get closer to the Lord." Sylvia smiled and bit her lip; she cast a glance at David.

"Now everybody ain't got the same kind of spirit," Brother Elisha said, coming to Sylvia's aid. "Can't *all* make as much noise as you make," he said, laughing gently, "we all ain't got your energy."

Sister Daniels smiled and frowned at this reference to her size and passion and said, "Don't care, brother, when the Lord moves inside you, you bound to do something. I've seen that girl Shout all night and come back the next night and Shout some more. I don't believe in no dead religion, no sir. The saints of God need a revival."

"Well, we'll work on Sister Sylvia," said Brother Elisha.

Directly before and behind them stretched nothing but the river; they had long ago lost sight of the point of their departure. They steamed beside the Palisades, which rose rough and gigantic from the dirty, broad and blue-green Hudson. Johnnie and David and Roy wandered downstairs to the bottom deck, standing by the rail and leaning over to watch the white, writhing spray which followed the boat. From the river there floated up to their faces a soft, cool breeze. They were quiet for a long time, standing together, watching the river and the mountains and hearing vaguely the hum of activity behind them on the boat. The sky was high and blue, with here and there a spittle-like, changing cloud; the sun was orange and beat with anger on their uncovered heads.

And David muttered finally, "Be funny if they were right."

"If who was right?" asked Roy.

"Elisha and them—"

"There's only one way to find out," said Johnnie.

"Yes," said Roy, "and I ain't homesick for heaven yet."

"You always got to be so smart," David said.

"Oh," said Roy, "you just sore because Sylvia's still up there with Brother Elisha."

"You think they going to be married?" Johnnie asked.

"Don't talk like a fool," David said.

"Well it's a cinch you ain't never going to get to talk to her till you get saved," Johnnie said. He had meant to say 'we.' He looked at David and smiled.

"Might be worth it," David said.

"*What* might be worth it?" Roy asked, grinning.

"Now be nice," David said. He flushed, the dark blood rising beneath the dark skin. "How you expect me to get saved if you going to talk that way? You supposed to be an example."

"Don't look at me, boy," Roy said.

"I want you to talk to Johnnie," Gabriel said to his wife.

"What about?"

"That boy's pride is running away with him. Ask him to tell you what he said to me this morning soon as he got in front of his friends. He's your son, alright."

"What did he say?"

He looked darkly across the river. "You ask him to tell you about it tonight. I wanted to knock him down."

She had watched the scene and knew this. She looked at her husband briefly, feeling a sudden, outraged anger, barely conscious; sighed and turned to look at her youngest child where he sat involved in a complicated and strenuous and apparently joyless game which utilized a red ball, jacks, blocks and a broken shovel.

"I'll talk to him," she said at last. "He'll be alright." She wondered what on earth she would say to him; and what he would say to her. She looked covertly about the boat, but he was nowhere to be seen.

"That proud demon's just eating him up," he said bitterly. He watched the river hurtle past. "Be the best thing in the world if the Lord would take his soul." He had meant to say 'save' his soul.

Now it was noon and all over the boat there was the activity of lunch. Paper bags and huge baskets were opened. There was then revealed splendor: cold pork chops, cold chicken, bananas, apples, oranges, pears, and soda-pop, candy and cold lemonade. All over the boat the chosen of God relaxed; they sat in groups and talked and laughed; some of the more worldly gossiped and some of the more courageous young people dared to walk off together. Beneath them the strong, indifferent river raged within the channel and the screaming spray pursued them. In the engine room children watched the motion of the ship's gears as they rose and fell and chanted. The tremendous bolts of steel seemed almost human, imbued with a relentless force that was not human. There was something monstrous about this machine which bore such enormous weight and cargo.

Sister Daniels threw a paper bag over the side and wiped her mouth with her large handkerchief. "Sylvia, you be careful how you speak to these unsaved boys," she said.

"Yes, I am, Mama."

"Don't like the way that little Jackson boy looks at you. That child's got a demon. You be careful."

"Yes, Mama."

"You got plenty of time to be thinking about boys. Now's the time for you to be thinking about the Lord."

"Yes'm."

"You *mind* now," her mother said.

"Mama, I want to go home!" Lois cried. She crawled into her mother's arms, weeping.

"Why, what's the matter, honey?" She rocked her daughter gently. "Tell Mama what's the matter? Have you got a pain?"

"I want to go home, I want to go home." Lois sobbed.

"A very fine preacher, a man of God and a friend of mine will run the service for us," said Father James.

"Maybe you've heard about him—a Reverend Peters? A real man of God, amen."

"I thought," Gabriel said, smiling, "that perhaps I could

bring the message some Sunday night. The Lord called me a long time ago. I used to have my own church down home."

"You don't want to run too fast, Deacon Grimes," Father James said. "You just take your time. You been coming along right well on Young Ministers' Nights." He paused and looked at Gabriel. "Yes, indeed."

"I just thought," Gabriel said humbly, "that I could be used to more advantage in the house of God."

Father James quoted the text which tells us how preferable it is to be a gate-keeper in the house of God than to dwell in the tent of the wicked; and started to add the dictum from Saint Paul about obedience to those above one in the Lord but decided (watching Gabriel's face) that it was not necessary yet.

"You just keep praying," he said kindly. "You get a little closer to God. He'll work wonders. You'll see." He bent closer to his deacon. "And try to get just a little closer to the *people*."

Roy wandered off with a gawky and dazzled girl named Elizabeth. Johnnie and David wandered restlessly up and down the boat alone. They mounted to the topmost deck and leaned over the railing in the deserted stern. Up here the air was sharp and clean. They faced the water, their arms around each other.

"Your old man was kind of rough this morning," David said carefully, watching the mountains pass.

"Yes," Johnnie said. He looked at David's face against the sky. He shivered suddenly in the sharp, cold air and buried his face in David's shoulder. David looked down at him and tightened his hold.

"Who do you love?" he whispered. "Who's your boy?"

"You," he muttered fiercely, "I love you."

"Roy!" Elizabeth giggled. "*Roy Grimes*. If you *ever* say a thing like that *again*."

Now the service was beginning. From all corners of the boat there was the movement of the saints of God. They gathered together their various possessions and moved their chairs from

top and bottom decks to the large main hall. It was early afternoon, not quite two o'clock. The sun was high and fell everywhere with a copper light. In the city the heat would have been
insupportable; and here, as the saints filed into the huge, high
room, once used as a ballroom, to judge from the faded and an-
tique appointments, the air slowly began to be oppressive. The
room was the color of black mahogany and coming in from the
bright deck, one groped suddenly in darkness; and took one's
sense of direction from the elegant grand piano which stood in
the front of the room on a little platform.

They sat in small rows with one wide aisle between them,
forming, almost unconsciously, a hierarchy. Father James sat in
the front next to Sister McCandless. Opposite them sat Gabriel
and Deacon Jones and, immediately behind them, Sister Daniels and her daughter. Brother Elisha walked in swiftly, just as
they were beginning to be settled. He strode to the piano and
knelt down for a second before rising to take his place. There
was a quiet stir, the saints adjusted themselves, waiting while
Brother Elisha tentatively ran his fingers over the keys. Gabriel
looked about impatiently for Roy and Johnnie, who, engaged no
doubt in sinful conversation with David, were not yet in service.
He looked back to where Mrs. Jackson sat with Lorraine, uncomfortable smiles on their faces, and glanced at his wife, who
met his questioning regard quietly, the expression on her face
not changing.

Brother Elisha struck the keys and the congregation joined in
the song, *Nothing Shall Move Me from the Love of God,* with
tambourine and heavy hands and stomping feet. The walls and
the floor of the ancient hall trembled and the candelabra wav-
ered in the high ceiling. Outside the river rushed past under the
heavy shadow of the Palisades and the copper sun beat down. A
few of the strangers who had come along on the outing appeared
at the doors and stood watching with an uneasy amusement.
The saints sang on, raising their strong voices in praises to Jehovah and seemed unaware of those unsaved who watched and
who, some day, the power of the Lord might cause to tremble.

The song ended as Father James rose and faced the congregation, a broad smile on his face. They watched him expectantly,

with love. He stood silent for a moment, smiling down upon
them. Then he said, and his voice was loud and filled with
triumph:

"Well, let us all say, Amen!"

And they cried out obediently, "Well, Amen!"

"Let us all say, praise Him!"

"Praise Him!"

"Let us all say, hallelujah!"

"Hallelujah!"

"Well, glory!" cried Father James. The Holy Ghost touched
him and he cried again, "Well, bless Him! Bless His holy name!"

They laughed and shouted after him, their joy so great that
they laughed as children and some of them cried as children do;
in the fullness and assurance of salvation, in the knowledge that
the Lord was in their midst and that each heart, swollen to anguish, yearned only to be filled with His glory. Then, in that
moment, each of them might have mounted with wings like ea-
gles far past the sordid persistence of the flesh, the depthless iniquity of the heart, the doom of hours and days and weeks; to
be received by the Bridegroom where He waited on high in
glory; where all tears were wiped away and death had no power;
where the wicked ceased from troubling and the weary soul
found rest.

"Saints, let's praise Him," Father James said. "Today, right in
the middle of God's great river, under God's great roof, beloved, let us raise our voices in thanksgiving that God has seen
fit to save us, amen!"

"Amen! Hallelujah!"

"—and to keep us saved, amen, to keep us, oh glory to God,
from the snares of Satan, from the temptation and the lust and
the evil of this world!"

"Talk about it!"

"*Preach!*"

"Ain't nothing strange, amen, about worshiping God *wherever*
you might be, ain't that right? Church, when you get this
mighty salvation you just can't keep it in, hallelujah! you got to
talk about it—"

"Amen!"

"You got to live it, amen. When the Holy Ghost touches you, you *move*, bless God!"

"Well, it's so!"

"Want to hear some testimonies today, amen! I want to hear some *singing* today, bless God! Want to see some *Shouting*, bless God, hallelujah!"

"Talk about it!"

"And I don't want to see none of the saints hold back. If the Lord saved you, amen, He give you a witness *every*where you go. Yes! My soul is a witness, bless our God!"

"Glory!"

"If you ain't saved, amen, get up and praise Him anyhow. Give God the glory for sparing your sinful life, *praise* Him for the sunshine and the rain, praise Him for all the works of His hands. Saints, I want to hear some praises today, you hear me? I want you to make this old boat *rock*, hallelujah! I want to *feel* your salvation. Are you saved?"

"Amen!"

"Are you sanctified?"

"Glory?"

"Baptized in fire?"

"Yes! So glad!"

"*Testify!*"

Now the hall was filled with a rushing wind on which forever rides the Lord, death or healing indifferently in His hands. Under this fury the saints bowed low, crying out "holy!" and tears fell. On the open deck sinners stood and watched, beyond them the fiery sun and the deep river, the black-brown-green, unchanging cliffs. That sun, which covered earth and water now, would one day refuse to shine, the river would cease its rushing and its numberless dead would rise; the cliffs would shiver, crack, fall and where they had been would then be nothing but the unleashed wrath of God.

"Who'll be the first to tell it?" Father James cried. "Stand up and talk about it!"

Brother Elisha screamed, "Have mercy, Jesus!" and rose from the piano stool, his powerful frame possessed. And the Holy Ghost touched him and he cried again, bending nearly double, while his feet beat ageless, dreadful signals on the floor, while his arms moved in the air like wings and his face, distorted, no longer his own face nor the face of a young man, but timeless, anguished, grim with ecstasy, turned blindly toward heaven. *Yes, Lord,* they cried, *yes!*

"Dearly beloved . . ."

"Talk about it!"

"Tell it!"

"I want to thank and praise the Lord, amen . . ."

"Amen!"

". . . for being here, I want to thank Him for my life, health, and strength . . ."

"Amen!"

"Well, glory!"

". . . I want to thank Him, hallelujah, for saving my soul one day . . . !"

"Oh!"

"Glory!"

". . . for causing the light, bless God, to shine in *my* heart one day when I was still a child, amen, I want to thank Him for bringing me to salvation in the days of my *youth,* hallelujah, when I have all my faculties, amen, before Satan had a chance to destroy my body in the world!"

"Talk about it!"

"He saved me, dear ones, from the world and the things of the world. Saved me, amen, from cardplaying . . ."

"Glory!"

". . . saved me from drinking, bless God, saved me from the streets, from the movies and all the filth that is in the world!"

"I *know* it's so!"

"He saved me, beloved, and sanctified me and filled me with the blessed Holy Ghost, *hallelujah!* Give me a new song, amen, which I didn't know before and set my feet on the King's highway. Pray for me beloved, that I will stand in these last and evil days."

"Bless your name, Jesus!"

During his testimony, Johnnie and Roy and David had stood quietly beside the door, not daring to enter while he spoke. The moment he sat down they moved quickly, together, to the front of the high hall and knelt down beside their seats to pray. The aspect of each of them underwent always, in this company, a striking, even an exciting change; as though their youth, barely begun, were already put away; and the animal, so vividly restless and undiscovered, so tense with power, ready to spring had been already stalked and trapped and offered, a perpetual blood-sacrifice, on the altar of the Lord. Yet their bodies continued to change and grow, preparing them, mysteriously and with ferocious speed, for manhood. No matter how careful their movements, these movements suggested, with a distinctness dreadful for the redeemed to see, the pagan lusting beneath the blood-washed robes. In them was perpetually and perfectly poised the power of revelation against the power of nature; and the saints, considering them with a baleful kind of love, struggled to bring their souls to safety in order, as it were, to steal a march on the flesh while the flesh still slept. A kind of storm, infernal, blew over the congregation as they passed; someone cried, "Bless them, Lord!" and immediately, honey-colored Sister Russell, while they knelt in prayer, rose to her feet to testify.

From the moment that they closed their eyes and covered their faces they were isolated from the joy that moved everything beside them. Yet this same isolation served only to make the glory of the saints more real; the pulse of conviction, however faint, beat in the glory of God then held an undertone of abject terror. Roy was the first to rise, sitting very straight in his seat and allowing his face to reveal nothing; just as Sister Russell ended her testimony and sat down, sobbing, her head thrown back and both hands raised to heaven. Immediately Sister Daniels raised her strong, harsh voice and hit her tambourine, singing. Brother Elisha turned on the piano stool and hit the keys. Johnnie and David rose from their knees and as they rose the congregation rose, clapping their hands, singing. The three boys did not sing; they stood together, carefully ignoring one another, their feet steady on the slightly tilting floor but their bodies moving back and forth as the music grew more savage. And someone cried aloud, a timeless sound of wailing; fire splashed the open deck and filled the doors and bathed the sinners standing there; fire filled the great hall and splashed the faces of the saints and a wind, unearthly, moved above their heads. Their hands were arched before them, moving, and their eyes were raised to heaven. Sweat stained the deacon's collar and soaked the tight headbands of the woman. Was it true then? and had there indeed been born one day in Bethlehem a Saviour who was Christ the Lord? who had died for them—for *them!*—the spat-upon and beaten with rods, who had worn a crown of thorns and seen His blood run down like rain; and who had lain in the grave three days and vanquished death and hell and risen again in glory—*was it for them?*

Lord, I want to go, show me the way!

For unto us a child is born, unto us a son is given—and His name shall be called Wonderful, the mighty God, the everlasting Father, the Prince of Peace. Yes, and He was coming back one day, the King of glory; He would crack the face of heaven and descend to judge the nations and gather up His people and take them to their rest.

Take me by my hand and lead me on!

Somewhere in the back a woman cried out and began the Shout. They looked carefully about, still not looking at one another, and saw, as from a great distance and through intolerable heat, such heat as might have been faced by the Hebrew children when cast bound into the fiery furnace, that one of the saints was dancing under the arm of the Lord. She danced out into the aisle, beautiful with a beauty unbearable, graceful with grace that poured from heaven. Her face was lifted up, her eyes were closed and the feet which moved so surely now were not her own. One by one the power of God moved others and—as it had been written—the Holy Ghost descended from heaven with a Shout. Sylvia raised her hands, the tears poured down her face, and in a moment, she too moved out into the aisle, Shouting. Is is true then? the saints rejoiced, Roy beat his tambourine. David, grave and shaken, clapped his hands and his body moved insistently in the rhythm of the dancers. Johnnie stood beside him, hot and faint and repeating yet again his struggle, summoning in panic all his forces, to save him from this frenzy. And yet daily he recognized that he was black with sin, that the secrets of his heart were a stench in God's nostrils. *Though your sins be as scarlet they shall be white as snow. Come, let us reason together, saith the Lord.*

Now there was a violent discord on the piano and Brother Elisha leapt to his feet, dancing. Johnnie watched the spinning body and listened, in terror and anguish, to the bestial sobs. Of the men it was only Elisha who danced and the women moved toward him and he moved toward the women. Johnnie felt blow over him an icy wind, all his muscles tightened, as though they furiously resisted some imminent bloody act, as the body of Isaac must have revolted when he saw his father's knife, and, sick and nearly sobbing, he closed his eyes. It was Satan, surely, who stood so foully at his shoulder; and what, but the blood of Jesus, should ever set him free? He thought of the many times he had stood in the congregation of the righteous—and yet he was not saved. He remained among the vast army of the doomed, whose lives—as he had been told, as he now, with such heart-sickness, began to discover for himself—were swamped with wretchedness and whose end was wrath and weeping. Then, for he felt himself falling, he opened his eyes and watched the rejoicing of the saints. His eyes found his father where he stood clapping his hands, glittering with sweat and overwhelming. Then Lois began to shout. For the first time he looked at Roy; their eyes met in brief, wry wonder and Roy imperceptibly shrugged. He watched his mother standing over Lois, her own face obscurely troubled. The light from the door was on her face, the entire room was filled with this strange light. There was no sound now except the sound of Roy's tambourine and the heavy rhythm of the saints; the sound of heavy feet and hands and the sound of weeping. Perhaps centuries past the children of Israel led by Miriam had made just such a noise as they came out of the wilderness. *For unto us is born this day a Saviour who is Christ the Lord.*

Yet, in the copper sunlight Johnnie felt suddenly, not the presence of the Lord, but the presence of David; which seemed to reach out to him, hand reaching out to hand in the fury of flood-time, to drag him to the bottom of the water or to carry him safe to shore. From the corner of his eye he watched his friend, who held him with such power; and felt, for that moment, such a depth of love, such nameless and terrible joy and pain, that he might have fallen, in the face of that company, weeping at David's feet.

Once at Bear Mountain they faced the very great problem of carrying Sylvia sufficiently far from her mother's sight to present her with her birthday present. This problem, difficult enough, was made even more difficult by the continual presence of Brother Elisha; who, inspired by the afternoon's service and by Sylvia's renewal of her faith, remained by her side to bear witness to the goodness and power of the Lord. Sylvia listened with her habitual rapt and painful smile. Her mother on the one side and Brother Elisha on the other seemed almost to be taking turns in advising her on her conduct as a saint of God. They began to despair, as the sun moved visibly westward, of ever giving her the gold-plated butterfly which rested uncomfortably in David's waistcoat pocket.

Of course, as Johnnie once suggested, there was really no reason they could not go up to her, surrounded as she was, and give her the jewel and get it over with—the more particularly as David evinced no desire to explore the wonders of Bear Mountain until this mission should have been fulfilled. Sister Daniels could scarcely object to an innocuous memento from three young men, all of whom attended church devoutly and one of whom professed salvation. But this was far from satisfactory for David, who did not wish to hear Sylvia's "thank-you's" in the constricting presence of the saints. Therefore they waited, wandering about the sloping park, lingering near the lake and the skating rink and watching Sylvia.

"God, why don't they go off somewhere and sleep? or pray?" cried David finally. He glared at the nearby rise where Sylvia and her mother sat talking with Brother Elisha. The sun was in their faces and struck from Sylvia's hair as she restlessly moved her head, small blue-black sparks.

Johnnie swallowed his jealousy at seeing how Sylvia filled his comrade's mind; he said, half-angrily, "I still don't see why we don't just go over and give it to her."

Roy looked at him. "Boy, you sound like you ain't got good sense," he said.

Johnnie, frowning, fell into silence. He glanced sidewise at David's puckered face (his eyes were still on Sylvia) and abruptly turned and started walking off.

"Where you going, boy?" David called.

"I'll be back," he said. And he prayed that David would follow him.

But David was determined to catch Sylvia alone and remained where he was with Roy. "Well, make it snappy," he said; and sprawled, full length, on the grass.

As soon as he was alone his pace slackened; he leaned his forehead against the bark of a tree, shaking and burning as in the teeth of a fever. The bark of the tree was rough and cold and though it offered no other comfort he stood there quietly for a long time, seeing beyond him—but it brought no peace— the high clear sky where the sun in fading glory traveled; and the deep earth covered with vivid banners, grass, flower, thorn and vine, thrusting upward forever the brutal trees. At his back he heard the voices of the children and the saints. He knew that he must return, that he must be on hand should David at last outwit Sister Daniels and present her daughter with the golden butterfly. But he did not want to go back, now he realized that he had no interest in the birthday present, no interest whatever in Sylvia—that he had had no interest all along. He shifted his stance, he turned from the tree as he turned his mind from the abyss which suddenly yawned, the abyss, depthless and terrifying, which he had encountered already in dreams. And he slowly began to walk, away from the saints and the voices of the children, his hands in his pockets, struggling to ignore the question which now screamed and screamed in his mind's bright haunted house.

It happened quite simply. Eventually Sister Daniels felt the need to visit the ladies' room, which was a long ways off. Brother Elisha remained where he was while Roy and David, like two beasts crouching in the underbrush, watched him and waited their opportunity. Then he also rose and wandered off to get cold lemonade for Sylvia. She sat quietly alone on the green rise, her hands clasped around her knees, dreaming.

They walked over to her, in terror that Sister Daniels would suddenly reappear. Sylvia smiled as she saw them coming and waved to them merrily. Roy grinned and threw himself on his belly on the ground beside her. David remained standing, fumbling in his waistcoat pocket.

"We got something for you," Roy said.

David produced the butterfly. "Happy birthday, Sylvia," he said. He stretched out his hand, the butterfly glinted oddly in the sun, and he realized with surprise that his hand was shaking. She grinned widely, in amazement and delight, and took the pin from him.

"It's from Johnnie too," he said. "I—we—hope you like it—"

She held the small gold pin in her palm and stared down at it; her face was hidden. After a moment she murmured, "I'm so surprised." She looked up, her eyes shining, almost wet. "Oh, it's wonderful," she said. "I never expected anything. I don't know what to say. It's marvelous, it's wonderful." She pinned the butterfly carefully to her light blue dress. She coughed slightly. "Thank you," she said.

"Your mother won't mind, will she?" Roy asked. "I mean—" he stammered awkwardly under Sylvia's sudden gaze—"we didn't know, we didn't want to get you in any trouble—"

"No," David said. He had not moved; he stood watching Sylvia. Sylvia looked away from Roy and up at David; his eyes met hers and she smiled. He smiled back, suddenly robbed of speech. She looked away again over the path her mother had taken and frowned slightly. "No," she said, "no, she won't mind."

Then there was silence. David shifted uncomfortably from one foot to the other. Roy lay contentedly face down on the grass. The breeze from the river, which lay below them and out of sight, grew subtly more insistent for they had passed the heat of the day; and the sun, moving always westward, fired and polished the tips of trees. Sylvia sighed and shifted on the ground.

"Why isn't Johnnie here?" she suddenly asked.

"He went off somewhere," Roy said. "He said he'd be right back." He looked at Sylvia and smiled. She was looking at David.

"You must want to grow real tall," she said mockingly. "Why don't you sit down?"

David grinned and sat down cross-legged next to Sylvia. "Well, the ladies like 'em tall." He lay on his back and stared up at the sky. "It's a fine day," he said.

She said, "Yes," and looked down at him; he had closed his eyes and was bathing his face in the slowly waning sun. Abruptly, she asked him:

"Why don't you get saved? You around the church all the time and you not saved yet? Why don't you?"

He opened his eyes in amazement. Never before had Sylvia mentioned salvation to him, except as a kind of joke. One of the things he most liked about her was the fact that she never preached to him. Now he smiled uncertainly and stared at her.

"I'm not joking," she said sharply. "I'm perfectly serious. Roy's saved—at least he *says* so—" and she smiled darkly, in the fashion of the old folks, at Roy—"and anyway, you ought to be thinking about your soul."

"Well, I don't know," David said. "I *think* about it. It's—well, I don't know if I can—well, live it—"

"All you got to do is make up your mind. If you really want to be saved, He'll save you. Yes, and He'll keep you too." She did not sound at all hysterical or transfigured. She spoke very quietly and with great earnestness and frowned as she spoke. David, taken off guard, said nothing. He looked embarrassed and pained and surprised. "Well, I don't know," he finally repeated.

"Do you ever pray?" she asked. "I mean, *really* pray?"

David laughed, beginning to recover himself. "It's not fair," he said, "you oughtn't to catch me all unprepared like that. Now I don't know what to say." But as he looked at her earnest face he sobered. "Well, I try to be decent. I don't bother nobody." He picked up a grass blade and stared at it. "I don't know," he said at last. "I do my best."

"*Do* you?" she asked.

He laughed again, defeated. "Girl," he said, "you *are* a killer."

She laughed too. "You black-eyed demon," she said, "if I don't see you at revival services I'll never speak to you again." He looked up quickly, in some surprise, and she said, still smiling, "Don't look at me like that. I mean it."

"All right, sister," he said. Then: "If I come out can I walk you home?"

"I got my mother to walk me home—"

"Well, let your mother walk home with Brother Elisha," he said, grinning. "Let the old folks stay together."

"Loose him, Satan!" she cried, laughing, "loose the boy!"

"The brother needs prayer," Roy said.

"Amen," said Sylvia. She looked down again at David. "I want to see you at church. Don't you forget it."

"All right," he said. "I'll be there."

The boat whistles blew at six o'clock, punctuating their holiday; blew, fretful and insistent, through the abruptly dispirited park and skaters left the skating rink; boats were rowed in furiously from the lake. Children were called from the swings and the seesaw and the merry-go-round and forced to leave behind the ball which had been lost in the forest and the torn kite which dangled from the top of a tree. ("Hush now," said their parents, "we'll get you another one—come along." "*Tomorrow?*"—"Come along, honey, it's time to go!") The old folks rose from the benches, from the grass, gathered together the empty lunch-basket, the half-read newspaper, the Bible which was carried everywhere; and they started down the hillside, an army in disorder. David walked with Sylvia and Sister Daniels and Brother Elisha, listening to their conversation (good Lord, thought Johnnie, don't they ever mention anything but sin?) and carrying Sylvia's lunch-basket. He seemed interested in what they were saying; every now and then he looked at Sylvia and grinned and she grinned back. Once, as Sylvia stumbled, he put his hand on her elbow to steady her and held her arm perhaps a moment too long. Brother Elisha, on the far side of Sister Daniels, noticed this and a frown passed over his face. He kept talking, staring now and then hard at Sylvia and trying, with a certain almost humorous helplessness, to discover what was in her mind. Sister Daniels talked of nothing but the service on the boat and of the forthcoming revival. She scarcely seemed to notice David's presence, though once she spoke to him, making some remark about the need, on his part, of much prayer. Gabriel carried the sleeping baby in his arms, striding beside his wife and Lois—who stumbled perpetually and held tightly to her mother's hand. Roy was somewhere in the back, joking with Elizabeth. At a turn in the road the boat and the dock appeared below them, a dead gray-white in the sun.

Johnnie walked down the slope alone, watching David and Sylvia ahead of him. When he had come back, both Roy and David had disappeared and Sylvia sat again in the company of her mother and Brother Elisha; and if he had not seen the gold butterfly on her dress he would have been aware of no change. She thanked him for his share in it and told him that Roy and David were at the skating rink.

But when at last he found them they were far in the middle of the lake in a rowboat. He was afraid of water, he could not row. He stood on the bank and watched them. After a long while they saw him and waved and started to bring the boat in so that he could join them. But the day was ruined for him; by the time they brought the boat in, the hour, for which they had hired it, was over; David went in search of his mother for more money but when he came back it was time to leave. Then he walked with Sylvia.

All during the trip home David seemed preoccupied. When he finally sought out Johnnie he found him sitting by himself on the top deck, shivering a little in the night air. He sat down beside him. After a moment Johnnie moved and put his head on David's shoulder. David put his arms around him. But now where there had been peace there was only panic and where there had been safety, danger, like a flower, opened.

VII Music

Without a doubt black music is the principal cultural achievement of Negro Americans. Indeed, it may well be the principal cultural achievement of America. How much of black music owes its origins to Africa and how much is native American are questions musicologists and critics seldom agree upon. Yet there can be little question that beginning with nineteenth-century work songs and spirituals and extending to present-day developments in jazz and "soul," black music has retained its tremendous vitality. The reason may well lie in the fact that music, the most abstract of arts, does not lend itself to the kind of curbs and repressions Negroes have been subject to in other spheres of American life. Hence, although music may be in the profoundest sense "subversive," it has paradoxically been the one means of expression blacks have felt most free to focus their creative energies on. Two of the following selections—Dunbar's "When Malindy Sings" and Robert Hayden's "Homage to the Empress of the Blues," one written early in the century and the other produced roughly fifty years later—celebrate the immense humanity of their subjects through their music. Frank London Brown's "McDougal" suggests that the truth of black jazz transcends race, while Ralph Ellison's essay "The Golden Age, Time Past" vividly evokes a period at Minton's in Harlem when a new style of music was being developed.

Paul Laurence Dunbar

When Malindy Sings

G'way an' quit dat noise, Miss Lucy—
  Put dat music book away;
What's de use to keep on tryin'?
  Ef you practice twell you're gray,
You cain't sta't no notes a-flyin'
  Lak de ones dat rants and rings
F'om the kitchen to de big woods
  When Malindy sings.

You ain't got de nachel o'gans
  Fu' to make de soun' come right,
You ain't got de tu'ns an' twistin's
  Fu' to make it sweet an' light.
Tell you one thing now, Miss Lucy,
  An' I'm tellin' you fu' true,
When hit comes to raal right singin',
  Tain't no easy thing to do.

Easy 'nough fu' folks to hollah,
  Lookin' at de lines an' dots,
When dey ain't no one kin sense it,
  An' de chune comes in, in spots;
But fu' real melojous music,
  Dat jes' strikes yo' hea't and clings,
Jes' you stan' an' listen wif me
  When Malindy sings.

Ain't you nevah hyeahd Malindy?
    Blessed soul, tek up de cross!
Look hyeah, ain't you jokin', honey?
    Well, you don't know whut you los'.
Y' ought to hyeah dat gal a-wa'blin',
    Robins, la'ks, an' all dem things,
Heish dey moufs an' hides dey faces
    When Malindy sings.

Fiddlin' man jes' stop his fiddlin',
    Lay his fiddle on de she'f;
Mockin'-bird quit try'n' to whistle,
    'Cause he jes' so shamed hisse'f.
Folks a-playin' on de banjo
    Draps dey fingahs on de strings—
Bless yo' soul—fu'gits to move 'em,
    When Malindy sings.

She jes' spreads huh mouf and hollahs,
    "Come to Jesus," twell you hyeah
Sinnahs' tremblin' steps and voices,
    Timid-lak a-drawin' neah:
Den she tu'ns to "Rock of Ages,"
    Simply to de cross she clings,
An' you fin' yo' teahs a-drappin'
    When Malindy sings.

Who dat says dat humble praises
    Wif de Master nevah counts?
Heish yo' mouf, I hyeah dat music,
    Ez hit rises up an' mounts—
Floatin' by de hills an' valleys,
    Way above dis buryin' sod,
Ez hit makes its way in glory
    To de very gates of God!

Oh, hit's sweetah dan de music
   Of an edicated band;
An' hit's dearah dan de battle's
   Song o' triumph in de lan'.
It seems holier dan evenin'
   When de solemn chu'ch bell rings,
Ez I sit an' ca'mly listen
   While Malindy sings.

Towsah, stop dat ba'kin', hyeah me!
   Mandy, mek dat chile keep still;
Don't you hyeah de echoes callin'
   F'om de valley to de hill?
Let me listen, I can hyeah it,
   Th'oo de bresh of angels' wings,
Sof' an' sweet, "Swing low, Sweet Chariot,"
   Ez Malindy sings.

Robert Hayden

Homage to the Empress of the Blues

Because there was a man somewhere in a candystripe silk shirt,
gracile and dangerous as a jaguar and because a woman moaned
for him in sixty-watt gloom and mourned him Faithless Love
Twotiming Love Oh Love Oh Careless Aggravating Love,

> She came out on the stage in yards of pearls, emerging like
> a favorite scenic view, flashed her golden smile and sang.

Because grey laths began somewhere to show from underneath
torn hurdygurdy lithographs of dollfaced heaven;
and because there were those who feared alarming fists of snow
on the door and those who feared the riot-squad of statistics,

> She came out on the stage in ostrich feathers, beaded satin,
> and shone that smile on us and sang.

286

Frank London Brown

McDougal

The bass was walking. Nothing but the bass. And the rhythm section waited, counting time with the tap of a foot or the tip of a finger against the piano top. Pro had just finished his solo and the blood in his neck was pumping so hard it made his head hurt. Sweat shone upon the brown backs of his fingers and the moisture stained the bright brass of his tenor where he held it. Jake, young eyeglass-wearing boy from Dallas, had stopped playing the drums, and he too was sweating, and slight stains were beginning to appear upon his thin cotton coat, and his dark skin caught the purple haze from the overhead spotlight and the sweat that gathered on his flat cheekbones seemed purple. Percy R. Brookins bent over the piano tapping the black keys but not hard enough to make a sound.

Everybody seemed to be waiting.

And the bass was walking. Doom-de-doom-doom-doom-doom-doom!

A tall thin white man whose black hair shone with sweat stood beside the tenorman, lanky, ginger-brown Pro.

Pro had wailed—had blown choruses that dripped with the smell of cornbread and cabbage and had roared like a late "L" and had cried like a blues singer on the last night of a good gig.

Now it was the white man's turn, right after the bass solo was over . . . and he waited and Pro waited and so did Jake the drummer, and Percy R. Brookins. Little Jug was going into his eighth chorus and showed no sign of letting up.

DOOM-DE-DOOM-DOOM-DOOM-DOOM-DOOM!

Jake looked out into the audience. And the shadowy faces were hard to see behind the bright colored lights that ringed the bandstand. Yet he felt that they too waited . . . Pro had laid down some righteous sound—he had told so much truth—told it so plainly, so passionately that it had scared everybody in the place, even Pro, and now he waited for the affirming bass to finish so that he could hear what the white man had to say.

McDougal was his name. And his young face had many wrinkles and his young body slouched and his shoulders hung round and loose. He was listening to Little Jug's bass yet he also seemed to be listening to something else, almost as if he were still listening to the truth Pro had told.

And the bass walked.

Jake leaned over his drums and whispered to Percy R. Brookins.

"That cat sure looks beat don't he?"

Percy R. Brookins nodded, and then put his hand to the side of his mouth, and whispered back.

"His old lady's pregnant again."

"Again?! What's that? Number three?"

"Number four," Percy R. Brookins answered.

"Hell I'd look sad too . . . Is he still living on Forty Seventh Street?"

The drums slid in underneath the bass and the bass dropped out amid strong applause and a few "Yeahs!" And Jake, not having realized it, cut in where McDougal was to begin his solo. He smiled sheepishly at Percy R. Brookins and the piano player hunched his shoulders and smiled.

McDougal didn't look around, he didn't move from his slouched one-sided stance, he didn't stop staring beyond the audience and beyond the room itself. Yet his left foot kept time with the light bombs the drummer dropped and the husky soft scrape of the brushes.

Little Jug pulled a handkerchief from his back pocket and wiped his cheeks and around the back of his neck, then he stared at the black, glistening back of McDougal's head and then leaned down and whispered to Percy R. Brookins.

"Your boy sure could stand a haircut. He looks as bad as Ol' Theo." And they both knew how bad Ol' Theo looked and they both frowned and laughed.

Percy R. Brookins touched a chord lightly to give some color to Jake's solo and then he said,

"Man, that cat has suffered for that brownskin woman."

Little Jug added,

"And those . . . three little brownskin crumb-crushers."

Percy R. Brookins hit another chord and then

"Do you know none of the white folks'll rent to him now?"

Little Jug laughed.

"Why hell yes . . . will they rent to me?"

"Sure they will, down on Forty Seventh Street."

Little Jug nodded at Jake and Jake made a couple of breaks that meant that he was about to give in to McDougal.

Percy R. Brookins turned to face his piano and then he got an idea and he turned to Little Jug and spoke with a serious look behind the curious smile on his face.

"You know that cat's after us? I mean he's out to blow the real thing. You know what I mean? Like he's no Harry James? Do you know that?"

Little Jug ran into some triplets and skipped a couple of beats and brought McDougal in right on time.

At the same time McDougal rode in on a long, hollow, gut bucket note that made Percy R. Brookins laugh, and caused Pro to cock his head and rub his cheek. The tall worried looking white man bent his trumpet to the floor and hunched his shoulders and closed his eyes and blew.

Little Jug answered Percy R. Brookins' question about McDougal.

"I been knowing that . . . he knows the happenings . . . I mean about where we get it, you dig? I mean like with Leola and those kids and Forty Seventh Street and those jive land-lords, you dig? The man's been burnt, Percy. Listen to that somitch—listen to him!"

McDougal's eyes were closed and he did not see the dark woman with the dark cotton suit that ballooned away from the great bulge of her stomach. He didn't see her ease into a chair at the back of the dark smoky room. He didn't see the smile on her face or the sweat upon her flat nose.

Ralph Ellison

The Golden Age, Time Past

That which we do is what we are. That which we remember is, more often than not, that which we hope to be. Thus our memory and our identity are ever at odds; our history ever a tall tale told by inattentive idealists.

It has been a long time now, and not many remember how it was in the old days; not really. Not even those who were there to see and hear as it happened, who were pressed in the crowds beneath the dim rosy lights of the bar in the smoke-veiled room, and who shared, night after night, the mysterious spell created by the talk, the laughter, grease paint, powder, perfume, sweat, alcohol and food—all blended and simmering, like a stew on the restaurant range, and brought to a sustained moment of elusive meaning by the timbres and accents of musical instruments locked in passionate recitative. It has been too long now, some seventeen years.

Above the bandstand there later appeared a mural depicting a group of jazzmen holding a jam session in a narrow Harlem bedroom. While an exhausted girl with shapely legs sleeps on her stomach in a big brass bed, they bend to their music in a quiet concatenation of unheard sound: a trumpeter, a guitarist, a clarinetist, a drummer; their only audience a small, cock-eared dog. The clarinetist is white. The guitarist strums with an enigmatic smile. The trumpet is muted. The barefooted drummer, beating a folded newspaper with whisk-brooms in lieu of a drum, stirs the eye's ear like a blast of brasses in a midnight street. A bottle of port rests on a dresser, but it, like the girl, is ignored. The artist, Charles Graham, adds mystery to, as well as illumination within, the scene by having them play by the light of a kerosene lamp. The painting, executed in a harsh documentary style reminiscent of W.P.A. art, conveys a feeling of musical effort caught in timeless and unrhetorical suspension, the sad remoteness of a scene observed through a wall of crystal.

Except for the lamp, the room might well have been one in the Hotel Cecil, the building on 118th Street in which Minton's Playhouse is located, and although painted in 1946, some time after the revolutionary doings there had begun, the mural should help recall the old days vividly. But the décor of the place has been changed and now it is covered, most of the time, by draperies. These require a tricky skill of those who would draw them aside. And even then there will still only be the girl who must sleep forever unhearing, and the men who must forever gesture the same soundless tune. Besides, the time it celebrates is dead and gone and perhaps not even those who came when it was still fresh and new remember those days as they were.

Neither do those remember who knew Henry Minton, who gave the place his name. Nor those who shared in the noisy lostness of New York the rediscovered community of the feasts, evocative of home, of South, of good times, the best and most unself-conscious of times, created by the generous portions of Negro American cuisine—the hash, grits, fried chicken, the ham-seasoned vegetables, the hot biscuits and rolls and the free whiskey—with which, each Monday night, Teddy Hill honored the entire cast of current Apollo Theatre shows. They were gathered here from all parts of America and they broke bread together and there was a sense of good feeling and promise, but what shape the fulfilled promise would take they did not know, and few except the more restless of the younger musicians even questioned. Yet it was an exceptional moment and the world was swinging with change.

Most of them, black and white alike, were hardly aware of where they were or what time it was; nor did they wish to be. They thought of Minton's as a sanctuary, where in an atmosphere blended of nostalgia and a music-and-drink-lulled suspension of time they could retreat from the wartime tensions of the town. The meaning of time-present was not their concern; thus when they try to tell it now the meaning escapes them.

For they were caught up in events which made that time exceptionally and uniquely *then*, and which brought, among the other changes which have reshaped the world, a momentous modulation into a new key of musical sensibility; in brief, a revolution in culture.

So how *can* they remember? Even in swiftly changing America there are few such moments, and at best Americans give but a limited attention to history. Too much happens too rapidly, and before we can evaluate it, or exhaust its meaning or pleasure, there is something new to concern us. Ours is the tempo of the motion picture, not that of the still camera, and we waste experience as we wasted the forest. During the time it was happening the sociologists were concerned with the riots, unemployment and industrial tensions of the time, the historians with the onsweep of the war; and the critics and most serious students of culture found this area of our national life of little interest. So it was left to those who came to Minton's out of the needs of feeling, and when the moment was past no one retained more than a fragment of its happening. Afterward the very effort to put the fragments together transformed them—so that in place of true memory they now summon to mind pieces of legend. They retell the stories as they have been told and written, glamorized, inflated, made neat and smooth, with all incomprehensible details vanished along with most of the wonder—not how it was as they themselves knew it.

When asked how it was back then, back in the forties, they will smile, then, frowning with the puzzlement of one attempting to recall the details of a pleasant but elusive dream, they'll say: "Oh, man, it was a hell of a time! A wailing time! Things were jumping, you couldn't get in here for the people. The place was packed with celebrities. Park Avenue, man! Big people in show business, college professors along with the pimps and their women. And college boys and girls. Everybody came. You know how the old words to the 'Basin Street Blues' used to go before Sinatra got hold of it? *Basin Street is the street where the dark and the light folks meet*—that's what I'm talking about. That was Minton's, man. It was a place where everybody could come to be entertained because it was a place that was jumping with good times."

Or some will tell you that it was here that Dizzy Gillespie found his own trumpet voice; that here Kenny Clarke worked out the patterns of his drumming style; where Charlie Christian played out the last creative and truly satisfying moments of his brief life, his New York home; where Charlie Parker built the monument of his art; where Thelonius Monk formulated his contribution to the chordal progressions and the hide-and-seek melodic methods of modern jazz. And they'll call such famous names as Lester Young and Ben Webster, Coleman Hawkins; or Fats Waller, who came here in the after-hour stillness of the early morning to compose. They'll tell you that Benny Goodman, Art Tatum, Count Basie and Lena Horne would drop in to join in the fun; that it was here that George Shearing played on his first night in the United States; or of Tony Scott's great love of the place; and they'll repeat all the stories of how, when and by whom the word "bebop" was coined here—but, withal, few actually remember, and these leave much unresolved.

Usually music gives resonance to memory (and Minton's was a hotbed of jazz), but not the music then in the making here. It was itself a texture of fragments, repetitive, nervous, not fully formed; its melodic lines underground, secret and taunting; its riffs jeering—"Salt peanuts! Salt peanuts!" Its timbres flat or shrill, with a minimum of thrilling vibrato. Its rhythms were out of stride and seemingly arbitrary, its drummers frozen-faced introverts dedicated to chaos. And in it the steady flow of memory, desire and defined experience summed up by the traditional jazz beat and blues mood seemed swept like a great river from its old, deep bed. We know better now, and recognize the old moods in the new sounds, but what we know is that which was then becoming. For most of those who gathered here, the enduring meaning of the great moment at Minton's took place off to the side, beyond the range of attention, like a death blow glimpsed from the corner of the eye, the revolutionary rumpus sounding like a series of flubbed notes blasting the talk with discord. So that the events which made Minton's *Minton's* arrived in conflict and ran their course—then the heat was gone and all that is left to mark its passage is the controlled fury of the music itself, sealed pure and irrevocable, banalities and excellencies alike, in the early recordings; or swept along by our restless quest for the new, to be diluted in more recent styles, the best of it absorbed like drops of fully distilled technique, mood and emotions into the great stream of jazz.

Left also to confuse our sense of what happened is the word "bop," hardly more than a nonsense syllable, by which the music synthesized at Minton's came to be known. A most inadequate word which does little, really, to help us remember. A word which throws up its hands in clownish self-deprecation before all the complexity of sound and rhythm and self-assertive passion which it pretends to name; a mask-word for the charged ambiguities of the new sound, hiding the serious face of art.

Nor does it help that so much has come to pass in the meantime. There have been two hot wars and that which continues, called "cold." And the unknown young men who brought a new edge to the sound of jazz and who scrambled the rhythms of those who used the small clear space at Minton's for dancing are no longer so young or unknown; indeed, they are referred to now by nickname in even the remotest of places. And in Paris and Munich and Tokyo they'll tell you the details of how, after years of trying, "Dizzy" (meaning John Birks Gillespie) vanquished "Roy" (meaning Roy Eldridge) during a jam session at Minton's, to become thereby the new king of trumpeters. Or how, later, while jetting over the world on the blasts of his special tilt-belled horn, he jammed with a snake charmer in Pakistan. "Sent the bloody cobra, man," they'll tell you in London's Soho. So their subsequent fame has blurred the sharp, ugly lines of their rebellion even in the memories of those who found them most strange and distasteful.

What's more, our memory of some of the more brilliant young men has been touched by the aura of death, and we feel guilt that the fury of their passing was the price paid for the art they left us to enjoy unscathed: Charlie Christian, burned out by tuberculosis like a guitar consumed in the tenement fire; Fats Navarro, wrecked by the tensions and needling temptations of his orgiastic trade, a big man physically as well as musically, shrunken to nothingness; and most notably of all, Charlie Parker, called "Bird," now deified, worshiped and studied and, like any fertility god, mangled by his admirers and imitators, who coughed up his life and died—as incredibly as the leopard which Hemingway tells us was found "dried and frozen" near the summit of Mount Kilimanjaro—in the hotel suite of a Baroness. (Nor has anyone explained what a "yardbird" was seeking at that social altitude, though we know that ideally anything is possible within a democracy, and we know quite well that upper-class Europeans were seriously interested in jazz long before Newport became hospitable.) All this is too much for memory; the dry facts are too easily lost in legend and glamour. (With jazz we are yet not in the age of history, but linger in that of folklore.) We know for certain only that the strange sounds which they and their fellows threw against the hum and buzz of vague signification that seethed in the drinking crowd at Minton's and which, like disgruntled conspirators meeting fatefully to assemble the random parts of a bomb, they joined here and beat and blew into a new jazz style—these sounds we know now to have become the clichés, the technical exercises and the standard of achievement not only for fledgling musicians all over the United States, but for Dutchmen and Swedes, Italians and Frenchmen, Germans and Belgians, and even Japanese. All these, in places which came to mind during the Minton days only as points where the war was in progress and where one might soon be sent to fight and die, are now spotted with young men who study the discs on which the revolution hatched in Minton's is preserved with all the intensity that young American painters bring to the works, say, of Kandinsky, Picasso and Klee. Surely this is an odd swing of the cultural tide. Yet Stravinsky, Webern and Berg notwithstanding, or, more recently, Boulez or Stockhausen—such young men (many of them excellent musicians in the highest European tradition) find in the music made articulate at Minton's some key to a fuller freedom of self-realization. Indeed for many young Europeans the developments which took place here and the careers of those who brought it about have become the latest episodes in the great American epic. They collect the recordings and thrive on the legends as eagerly, perhaps, as young Americans.

Today the bartenders at Minton's will tell you how they come fresh off the ships or planes, bringing their brightly expectant and—in this Harlem atmosphere—startlingly innocent European faces, to buy drinks and stand looking about for the source of the mystery. They try to reconcile the quiet reality of the place with the events which fired, at such long range, their imaginations. They come as to a shrine; as we to the Louvre, Notre Dame or St. Peter's; as young Americans hurry to the Café Flore, the Deux Magots, the Rotonde or the Café du Dôme in Paris. For some years now they have been coming to ask, with all the solemnity of pilgrims inquiring of a sacred relic, to see the nicotine-stained amplifier which Teddy Hill provided for Charlie Christian's guitar. And this is quite proper, for every shrine should have its relic.

Perhaps Minton's has more meaning for European jazz fans than for Americans, even for those who regularly went there. Certainly it has a *different* meaning. For them it is associated with those continental cafés in which great changes, political and artistic, have been plotted; it is to modern jazz what the Café Voltaire in Zurich is to the Dadaist phase of modern literature and painting. Few of those who visited Harlem during the forties would associate it so, but there is a context of meaning in which Minton's and the musical activities which took place there can be meaningfully placed.

Jazz, for all the insistence of the legends, has been far more closely associated with cabarets and dance halls than with brothels, and it was these which provided both the employment for the musicians and an audience initiated and aware of the overtones of the music; which knew the language of riffs, the unstated meanings of the blues idiom, and the dance steps developed from, and complementary to, its rhythms. And in the beginning it was in the Negro dance hall and night club that jazz was most completely a part of a total cultural expression; and in which it was freest and most satisfying, both for the musicians and for those in whose lives it played a major role. As a night club in a Negro community then, Minton's was part of a national pattern.

But in the old days Minton's was far more than this; it was also a rendezvous for musicians. As such, and although it was not formally organized, it goes back historically to the first New York center of Negro musicians, the Clef Club. Organized in 1910, during the start of the great migration of Negroes northward, by James Reese Europe, the director whom Irene Castle credits with having invented the fox trot, the Clef Club was set up on West 53rd Street to serve as a meeting place and booking office for Negro musicians and entertainers. Here wage scales were regulated, musical styles and techniques worked out, and entertainment was supplied for such establishments as Rector's and Delmonico's, and for such producers as Florenz Ziegfeld and Oscar Hammerstein. Later, when Harlem evolved into a Negro section, a similar function was served by the Rhythm Club, located then in the old Lafayette Theatre building on 132nd Street and Seventh Avenue. Henry Minton, a former saxophonist and officer of the Rhythm Club, became the first Negro delegate to Local 802 of the American Federation of Musicians and was thus doubly aware of the needs, artistic as well as economic, of jazzmen. He was generous with loans, was fond of food himself and, as an old acquaintance recalled, "loved to put a pot on the range" to share with unemployed friends. Naturally when he opened Minton's Playhouse many musicians made it their own.

Henry Minton also provided, as did the Clef and Rhythm clubs, a necessity more important to jazz musicians than food: a place in which to hold their interminable jam sessions. And it is here that Minton's becomes most important to the development of modern jazz. It is here, too, that it joins up with all the countless rooms, private and public, in which jazzmen have

worked out the secrets of their craft. Today jam sessions are offered as entertainment by night clubs and on radio and television, and some are quite exciting; but what is seen and heard is
only one aspect of the true jam session: the "cutting session,"
or contest of improvisational skill and physicial endurance between two or more musicians. But the jam session is far more
than this, and when carried out by musicians, in the privacy of
small rooms (as in the mural at Minton's) or in such places as
Halley Richardson's shoeshine parlor in Oklahoma City—where
I first heard Lester Young jamming in a shine chair, his head
thrown back, his horn even then outthrust, his feet working on
the footrests, as he played with and against Lem Johnson, Ben
Webster (this was 1929) and other members of the old Blue
Devils Orchestra—or during the after hours in Piney Brown's
old Sunset Club in Kansas City; in such places as these with
only musicians and jazzmen present, then the jam session is revealed as the jazzman's true academy.

It is here that he learns tradition, group techniques and style.
For although since the twenties many jazzmen have had conser-
vatory training and were well grounded in formal theory and in-
strumental technique, when we approach jazz we are entering
quite a different sphere of training. Here it is more meaningful
to speak, not of courses of study, of grades and degrees, but of
apprenticeship, ordeals, initiation ceremonies, of rebirth. For
after the jazzman has learned the fundamentals of his instrument and the traditional techniques of jazz—the intonations,
the mute work. manipulation of timbre, the body of traditional
styles—he must then "find himself," must be reborn, must find,
as it were, his soul. All this through achieving that subtle identification between his instrument and his deepest drives which
will allow him to express his own unique ideas and his own
unique voice. He must achieve, in short, his self-determined
identity.

In this his instructors are his fellow musicians, especially the
acknowledged masters, and his recognition of manhood depends
upon their acceptance of his ability as having reached a standard which is all the more difficult for not having been rigidly
codified. This does not depend upon his ability to simply hold a

job but upon his power to express an individuality in tone. Nor is his status ever unquestioned, for the health of jazz and the unceasing attraction which it holds for the musicians themselves lies in the ceaseless warfare for mastery and recognition —not among the general public, though commercial success is not spurned, but among their artistic peers. And even the greatest can never rest on past accomplishments, for, as with the fast guns of the old West, there is always someone waiting in a jam session to blow him literally, not only down, but into shame and discouragement.

By making his club hospitable to jam sessions even to the point that customers who were not musicians were crowded out, Henry Minton provided a retreat, a homogeneous community where a collectivity of common experience could find continuity and meaningful expression. Thus the stage was set for the birth of bop.

In 1941 Mr. Minton handed over his management to Teddy Hill, the saxophonist and former band leader, and Hill turned the Playhouse into a musical dueling ground. Not only did he continue Minton's policies, he expanded them. It was Hill who established the Monday Celebrity Nights, the house band which included such members from his own disbanded orchestra as Kenny Clarke, Dizzy Gillespie, along with Thelonius Monk, sometimes with Joe Guy, and, later, Charlie Christian and Charlie Parker; and it was Hill who allowed the musicians free rein to play whatever they liked. Perhaps no other club except Clarke Monroe's Uptown House was so permissive, and with the hospitality extended to musicians of all schools the news spread swiftly. Minton's became the focal point for musicians all over the country.

Herman Pritchard, who presided over the bar in the old days, tells us that every time they came, "Lester Young and Ben Webster used to tie up in battle like dogs in the road. They'd fight on those saxophones until they were tired out, then they'd put in long-distance calls to their mothers, both of whom lived in Kansas City, and tell them about it."

And most of the masters of jazz came either to observe or to participate and be influenced and listen to their own discoveries transformed; and the aspiring stars sought to win their approval, as the younger tenor men tried to win the esteem of Coleman Hawkins. Or they tried to vanquish them in jamming contests as Gillespie is said to have outblown his idol, Roy Eldridge. It was during this period that Eddie "Lockjaw" Davis underwent an ordeal of jeering rejection until finally he came through as an admired tenor man.

In the perspective of time we now see that what was happening at Minton's was a continuing symposium of jazz, a summation of all the styles, personal and traditional, of jazz. Here it was possible to hear its resources of technique, ideas, harmonic structure, melodic phrasing and rhythmical possibilities explored more thoroughly than was ever possible before. It was also possible to hear the first attempts toward a conscious statement of the sensibility of the younger generation of musicians as they worked out the techniques, structures and rhythmical patterns with which to express themselves. Part of this was arbitrary, a revolt of the younger against the established stylists; part of it was inevitable. For jazz had reached a crisis and new paths were certain to be searched for and found. An increasing number of the younger men were formally trained and the post-Depression developments in the country had made for quite a break between their experience and that of the older men. Many were even of a different physical build. Often they were quiet and of a reserve which contrasted sharply with the exuberant and outgoing lyricism of the older men, and they were intensely concerned that their identity as Negroes placed no restriction upon the music they played or the manner in which they used their talent. They were concerned, they said, with art, not entertainment. Especially were they resentful of Louis Armstrong, whom (confusing the spirit of his music with his clowning) they considered an Uncle Tom.

But they too, some of them, had their own myths and misconceptions: That theirs was the only generation of Negro musicians who listened to or enjoyed the classics; that to be truly free they must act exactly the opposite of what white people

might believe, rightly or wrongly, a Negro to be; that the performing artist can be completely and absolutely free of the obli-
gations of the entertainer, and that they could play jazz with
dignity only by frowning and treating the audience with aggressive contempt; and that to be in control, artistically and personally, one must be so cool as to quench one's own human fire.

Nor should we overlook the despair which must have swept
Minton's before the technical mastery, the tonal authenticity,
the authority and the fecundity of imagination of such men as
Hawkins, Young, Goodman, Tatum, Teagarden, Ellington and
Waller. Despair, after all, is ever an important force in revolu-
tions.

They were also responding to the non-musical pressures af-
fecting jazz. It was a time of big bands, and the greatest pres-
tige and economic returns were falling outside the Negro
community—often to leaders whose popularity grew from the
compositions and arrangements of Negroes—to white instru-
mentalists whose only originality lay in the enterprise with
which they rushed to market with some Negro musician's hard-
won style. Still there was no policy of racial discrimination at
Minton's. Indeed, it was very much like those Negro cabarets of
the twenties and thirties in which a megaphone was placed on
the piano so that anyone with the urge could sing a blues. Nevertheless, the inside-dopesters will tell you that the "changes" or
chord progressions and the melodic inversions worked out by
the creators of bop sprang partially from their desire to create a
jazz which could not be so easily imitated and exploited by
white musicians to whom the market was more open simply *because* of their whiteness. They wished to receive credit for what
they created, and besides, it was easier to "get rid of the trash"
who crowded the bandstand with inept playing and thus make
room for the real musicians, whether white or black. Nevertheless, white musicians like Tony Scott, Remo Palmieri and Al
Haig who were part of the development at Minton's became so
by passing a test of musicianship, sincerity and temperament.
Later, it is said, the boppers became engrossed in solving the
musical problems which they set themselves. Except for a few

sympathetic older musicians it was they who best knew the promise of the Minton moment, and it was they, caught like the rest in all the complex forces of American life which comes to focus in jazz, who made the most of it. Now the tall tales told as history must feed on the results of their efforts.

VIII Anger

The "angry black" is not so recent a phenomenon as the popular press makes out. Like all Americans, blacks have dreamed the American dream of freedom, equality and opportunity, but more often than not have discovered themselves humiliated, frustrated or threatened as a result of peculiar American notions about color. Bigger Thomas, the slum adolescent protagonist of Richard Wright's 1940 novel, Native Son, walked about with murder in his heart long before he thought of committing violence. But Wright's justly famous novel was not the first to express black rage. Perhaps its earliest literary expression may be found in William E. B. DuBois's "A Litany in Atlanta," written after the Atlanta race riot of 1906. In the 1920's, a subsequent period of heightened racial tensions and black nationalism, Claude McKay's sonnet, "America," described similar feelings. The late Malcolm X, whose address to Mississippi youth is reprinted here, has become the patron saint of a number of militant movements that have spawned since his assassination in 1965. As can be seen, Malcolm's effectiveness with the young and dispossessed resulted from a lucidity of language, an ability to underline his points with illustrative material from the black experience, and a seemingly driving, relentless logic. Mari Evans's "Black jam for dr. negro" portrays perhaps the spiritual offspring of Malcolm—young, impatient and angry.

William E. B. Du Bois

A Litany at Atlanta

O Silent God, Thou whose voice afar in mist and mystery hath
left our ears an-hungered in these fearful days—
Hear us, good Lord!

Listen to us, Thy children: our faces dark with doubt are
made a mockery in Thy sanctuary. With uplifted hands we
front Thy heaven, O God, crying:
We beseech Thee to hear us, good Lord!

We are not better than our fellows, Lord, we are but weak
and human men. When our devils do deviltry, curse Thou the
doer and the deed: curse them as we curse them, do to them all
and more than ever they have done to innocence and weakness,
to womanhood and home.
Have mercy upon us, miserable sinners!

And yet whose is the deeper guilt? Who made these devils?
Who nursed them in crime and fed them on injustice? Who
ravished and debauched their mothers and their grandmothers?
Who bought and sold their crime, and waxed fat and rich on
public iniquity?
Thou knowest, good God!

Is this Thy justice, O Father, that guile be easier than innocence, and the innocent crucified for the guilt of the untouched
guilty?
Justice, O judge of men!

Wherefore do we pray? Is not the God of the fathers dead? Have not seers seen in Heaven's halls Thine hearsed and lifeless forms stark amidst the black and rolling smoke of sin, where all along bow bitter forms of endless dead?
Awake, Thou that sleepest!

Thou art not dead, but flown afar, up hills of endless light through blazing corridors of suns, where worlds do swing of good and gentle men, of women strong and free—far from the cozenage, black hypocrisy, and chaste prostitution of this shameful speck of dust?
Turn again, O Lord, leave us not to perish in our sin!

From lust of body and lust of blood,
Great God, deliver us!

From lust of power and lust of gold,
Great God, deliver us!

From the leagued lying of despot and of brute,
Great God, deliver us!

A city lay in travail, God our Lord, and from her loins sprang twin Murder and Black Hate. Red was the midnight; clang, crack and cry of death and fury filled the air and trembled underneath the stars when church spires pointed silently to Thee. And all this was to sate the greed of greedy men who hide behind the veil of vengeance!
Bend us Thine ear, O Lord!

In the pale, still morning we looked upon the deed. We stopped our ears and held our leaping hands, but they—did they not wag their heads and leer and cry with bloody jaws: *Cease from Crime!* The word was mockery, for thus they train a hundred crimes while we do cure one.
Turn again our captivity, O Lord!

Behold this maimed and broken thing; dear God, it was an humble black man who toiled and sweat to save a bit from the pittance paid him. They told him: *Work and Rise*. He worked. Did this man sin? Nay, but some one told how some one said another did—one whom he had never seen nor known. Yet for that man's crime this man lieth maimed and murdered, his wife naked to shame, his children, to poverty and evil.

Hear us, O heavenly Father!

Doth not this justice of hell stink in Thy nostrils, O God? How long shall the mounting flood of innocent blood roar in Thine ears and pound in our hearts for vengeance? Pile the pale frenzy of blood-crazed brutes who do such deeds high on Thine altar, Jehovah Jireh, and burn it in hell forever and forever.

Forgive us, good Lord; we know not what we say!

Bewildered we are, and passion-tost, mad with the madness of a mobbed and mocked and murdered people; straining at the armposts of Thy Throne, we raise our shackled hands and charge Thee, God, by the bones of our stolen fathers, by the tears of our dead mothers, by the very blood of Thy crucified Christ: *What meaneth this?* Tell us the Plan; give us the Sign!

Keep not Thou silence, O God!

Sit no longer blind, Lord God, deaf to our prayer and dumb to our dumb suffering. Surely Thou too art not white, O Lord, a pale, bloodless, heartless thing?

Ah! Christ of all the Pities!

Forgive the thought! Forgive these wild, blasphemous words. Thou art still the God of our black fathers, and in Thy soul's soul sit some soft darkenings of the evening, some shadowings of the velvet night.

But whisper—speak—call, great God, for Thy silence is white terror to our hearts! The way, O God, show us the way and point us the path.

Whither? North is greed and South is blood; within, the coward, and without, the liar. Whither? To Death?
Amen! Welcome dark sleep!

Whither? To life? But not this life, dear God, not this. Let the cup pass from us, tempt us not beyond our strength, for there is that clamoring and clawing within, to whose voice we would not listen, yet shudder lest we must,—and it is red, Ah! God! It is a red and awful shape.
Selah!

In yonder East trembles a star.
Vengeance is mine: I will repay, saith the Lord!

Thy will, O Lord, be done!
Kyrie Eleison!

Lord, we have done these pleading, wavering words.
We beseech Thee to hear us, good Lord!

We bow our heads and hearken soft to the sobbing of women and little children.
We beseech Thee to hear us, good Lord!

Our voices sink in silence and in night.
Hear us, good Lord!

In night, O God of a godless land!
Amen!

In silence, O silent God.
Selah!

Claude McKay

America

Although she feeds me bread of bitterness,
And sinks into my throat her tiger's tooth,
Stealing my breath of life, I will confess
I love this cultured hell that tests my youth!
Her vigor flows like tides into my blood,
Giving me strength erect against her hate.
Her bigness sweeps my being like a flood.
Yet as a rebel fronts a king in state,
I stand within her walls with not a shred
Of terror, malice, not a word of jeer.
Darkly I gaze into the days ahead,
And see her might and granite wonders there,
Beneath the touch of Time's unerring hand,
Like priceless treasures sinking in the sand.

To Mississippi Youth

One of the first things I think young people, especially nowadays, should learn is how to see for yourself and listen for yourself and think for yourself. Then you can come to an intelligent decision for yourself. If you form the habit of going by what you hear others say about someone, or going by what others think about someone, instead of searching that thing out for yourself and seeing for yourself, you will be walking west when you think you're going east, and you will be walking east when you think you're going west. This generation, especially of our people, has a burden, more so than any other time in history. The most important thing that we can learn to do today is think for ourselves.

It's good to keep wide-open ears and listen to what everybody else has to say, but when you come to make a decision, you have to weigh all of what you've heard on its own, and place it where it belongs, and come to a decision for yourself; you'll never regret it. But if you form the habit of taking what someone else says about a thing without checking it out for yourself, you'll find that other people will have you hating your friends and loving your enemies. This is one of the things that our people are beginning to learn today—that it is very important to think out a situation for yourself. If you don't do it, you'll always be maneuvered into a situation where you are never fighting your actual enemies, where you will find yourself fighting your own self.

I think our people in this country are the best examples of that. Many of us want to be nonviolent and we talk very loudly, you know, about being nonviolent. Here in Harlem, where there are probably more black people concentrated than any place in the world, some talk that nonviolent talk too. But we find that they aren't nonviolent with each other. You can go out to Harlem Hospital, where there are more black patients than any hospital in the world, and see them going in there all cut up and shot up and busted up where they got violent with each other.

My experience has been that in many instances where you find Negroes talking about nonviolence, they are not nonviolent with each other, and they're not loving with each other, or forgiving with each other. Usually when they say they're nonviolent, they mean they're nonviolent with somebody else. I think you understand what I mean. They are nonviolent with the enemy. A person can come to your home, and if he's white and wants to heap some kind of brutality on you, you're nonviolent; or he can come to take your father and put a rope around his neck, and you're nonviolent. But if another Negro just stomps his foot, you'll rumble with him in a minute. Which shows you that there's an inconsistency there.

I myself would go for nonviolence if it was consistent, if everybody was going to be nonviolent all the time. I'd say, okay, let's get with it, we'll all be nonviolent. But I don't go along with any kind of nonviolence unless everybody's going to be nonviolent. If they make the Ku Klux Klan nonviolent, I'll be nonviolent. If they make the White Citizens Council nonviolent, I'll be nonviolent. But as long as you've got somebody else not being nonviolent, I don't want anybody coming to me talking any nonviolent talk. I don't think it is fair to tell our people to be nonviolent unless someone is out there making the Klan and the Citizens Council and these other groups also be nonviolent.

Now, I'm not criticizing those here who are nonviolent. I think everybody should do it the way they feel is best, and I congratulate anybody who can be nonviolent in the face of all that kind of action in that part of the world. I don't think that in 1965 you will find the upcoming generation of our people, especially those who have been doing some thinking, who will go along with any form of nonviolence unless nonviolence is going to be practiced all the way around.

If the leaders of the nonviolent movement can go into the white community and teach nonviolence, good. I'd go along with that. But as long as I see them teaching nonviolence only in the black community, we can't go along with that. We believe in equality, and equality means that you have to put the same thing over here that you put over there. And if black people alone are going to be the ones who are nonviolent, then it's not fair. We throw ourselves off guard. In fact, we disarm ourselves and make ourselves defenseless.

The Organization of Afro-American Unity is a nonreligious group of black people who believe that the problems confronting our people in this country need to be re-analyzed and a new approach devised toward trying to get a solution. Studying the problem, we recall that prior to 1939 all of our people, in the North, South, East and West, no matter how much education we had, were segregated. We were segregated in the North just as much as we were segregated in the South. Even now there's as much segregation in the North as there is in the South. There's some worse segregation right here in New York City than there is in McComb, Mississippi; but up here they're subtle and tricky and deceitful, and they make you think you've got it made when you haven't even begun to make it yet.

Prior to 1939, our people were in a very menial position or condition. Most of us were waiters and porters and bellhops and janitors and waitresses and things of that sort. It was not until war was declared with Germany, and America became involved in a manpower shortage in regards to her factories plus her army, that the black man in this country was permitted to make a few strides forward. It was never out of some kind of moral enlightenment or moral awareness on the part of Uncle Sam. Uncle Sam only let the black man take a step forward when he himself had his back to the wall.

In Michigan, where I was brought up at that time, I recall that the best jobs in the city for blacks were waiters out at the country club. In those days if you had a job waiting table in the country club, you had it made. Or if you had a job at the State House. Having a job at the State House didn't mean that you were a clerk or something of that sort; you had a shoeshine stand at the State House. Just by being there you could be around all those big-shot politicians—that made you a big-shot Negro. You were shining shoes, but you were a big-shot Negro because you were around big-shot white people and you could bend their ear and get up next to them. And ofttimes you were chosen by them to be the voice of the Negro community.

Around that time, 1939 or '40 or '41, they weren't drafting Negroes in the army or the navy. A Negro couldn't join the navy in 1940 or '41. They wouldn't take a black man in the navy except to make him a cook. He couldn't just go and join the navy, and I don't think he could just go and join the army. They weren't drafting him when the war first started. This is what they thought of you and me in those days. For one thing, they didn't trust us; they feared that if they put us in the army and trained us in how to use rifles and other things, we might shoot at some targets that they hadn't picked out. And we would have. Any thinking man knows what target to shoot at. If a man has to have someone else to choose his target, then he isn't thinking for himself—they're doing the thinking for him.

The Negro leaders in those days were the same type we have today. When the Negro leaders saw all the white fellows being drafted and taken into the army and dying on the battlefield, and no Negroes were dying because they weren't being drafted, the Negro leaders came up and said, "We've got to die too. We want to be drafted too, and we demand that you take us in there and let us die for our country too." That was what the Negro leaders did back in 1940, I remember. A. Philip Randolph was one of the leading Negroes in those days who said it, and he's one of the Big Six right now; and this is why he's one of the Big Six.

So they started drafting Negro soldiers then, and started letting Negroes get into the navy. But not until Hitler and Tojo and the foreign powers were strong enough to put pressure on this country, so that it had its back to the wall and needed us, [did] they let us work in factories. Up until that time we couldn't work in the factories; I'm talking about the North as well as the South. And when they let us work in the factories, at first they let us in only as janitors. After a year or so passed by, they let us work on machines. We became machinists, got a little more skill. If we got a little more skill, we made a little more money, which enabled us to live in a little better neighborhood. When we lived in a little better neighborhood, we went to a little better school, got a little better education and could come out and get a little better job. So the cycle was broken somewhat.

But the cycle was not broken out of some kind of sense of moral responsibility on the part of the government. No, the only time that cycle was broken even to a degree was when world pressure was brought to bear on the United States government. They didn't look at us as human beings—they just put us into their system and let us advance a little bit farther because it served their interests. They never let us advance a little bit farther because they were interested in us as human beings. Any of you who have a knowledge of history, sociology, or political science, or the economic development of this country and its race relations—go back and do some research on it and you'll have to admit that this is true.

It was during the time that Hitler and Tojo made war with this country and put pressure on it [that] Negroes in this country advanced a little bit. At the end of the war with Germany and Japan, then Joe Stalin and Communist Russia were a threat. During that period we made a little more headway. Now the point that I'm making is this: Never at any time in the history of our people in this country have we made advances or progress in any way based upon the internal good will of this country. We have made advancement in this country only when this country was under pressure from forces above and beyond its control. The internal moral consciousness of this country is bankrupt. It hasn't existed since they first brought us over here and made slaves out of us. They make it appear they have our good interests at heart, but when you study it, every time, no matter how many steps they take us forward, it's like we're standing on a—what do you call that thing?—a treadmill. The treadmill is moving backwards faster than we're able to go forward in this direction. We're not even standing still—we're going backwards.

In studying the process of this so-called progress during the past twenty years, we of the Organization of Afro-American Unity realized that the only time the black man in this country is given any kind of recognition, or even listened to, is when America is afraid of outside pressure, or when she's afraid of her image abroad. So we saw that it was necessary to expand the problem and the struggle of the black man in this country until it went above and beyond the jurisdiction of the United States.
. . .

I was fortunate enough to be able to take a tour of the African continent during the summer. I went to Egypt, then to Arabia, Kuwait, Lebanon, Sudan, Ethiopia, Kenya, Tanganyika, Zanzibar, Nigeria, Ghana, Guinea, Liberia and Algeria. I found, while I was traveling on the African continent, I had already detected it in May, that someone had very shrewdly planted the seed of division on this continent to make the Africans not show genuine concern with our problem, just as they plant seeds in your and my minds so that we won't show concern with the African problem. . . .

I also found that in many of these African countries the head of state is genuinely concerned with the problem of the black man in this country; but many of them thought if they opened their mouths and voiced their concern that they would be insulted by the American Negro leaders. Because one head of state in Asia voiced his support of the civil-rights struggle [in 1963] and a couple of the Big Six had the audacity to slap his face and say they weren't interested in that kind of help—which in my opinion is asinine. So the African leaders only had to be convinced that if they took an open stand at the governmental level and showed interest in the problem of black people in this country, they wouldn't be rebuffed.

And today you'll find in the United Nations, and it's not an accident, that every time the Congo question or anything on the African continent is being debated, they couple it with what is going on, or what is happening to you and me, in Mississippi and Alabama and these other places. In my opinion, the greatest accomplishment that was made in the struggle of the black man in America in 1964 toward some kind of real progress was the successful linking together of our problem with the African problem, or making our problem a world problem. Because now, whenever anything happens to you in Mississippi, it's not just a case of somebody in Alabama getting indignant, or somebody in New York getting indignant. The same repercussions that you see all over the world when an imperialist or foreign power interferes in some section of Africa—you see repercussions, you see the embassies being bombed and burned and overturned—nowadays, when something happens to black people in Mississippi, you'll see the same repercussions all over the world.

I wanted to point this out to you because it is important for you to know that when you're in Mississippi, you're not alone. As long as you think you're alone, then you take a stand as if you're a minority or as if you're outnumbered, and that kind of stand will never enable you to win a battle. You've got to know that you've got as much power on your side as that Ku Klux Klan has on its side. And when you know that you've got as much power on your side as the Klan has on its side, you'll talk the same kind of language with that Klan as the Klan is talking with you. . . .

I think in 1965, whether you like it, or I like it, or they like it, or not, you will see that there is a generation of black people becoming mature to the point where they feel that they have no more business being asked to take a peaceful approach than anybody else takes, unless everybody's going to take a peaceful approach.

So we here in the Organization of Afro-American Unity are with the struggle in Mississippi one thousand per cent. We're with the efforts to register our people in Mississippi to vote one thousand per cent. But we do not go along with anybody telling us to help nonviolently. We think that if the government says that Negroes have a right to vote, and then some Negroes come out to vote, and some kind of Ku Klux Klan is going to put them in the river, and the government doesn't do anything about it, it's time for us to organize and band together and equip ourselves and qualify ourselves to protect ourselves. And once you can protect yourself, you don't have to worry about being hurt. . . .

If you don't have enough people down there to do it, we'll come down there and help you do it. Because we're tired of this old runaround that our people have been given in this country. For a long time they accused me of not getting involved in politics. They should've been glad I didn't get involved in politics, because anything I get in, I'm in it all the way. If they say we don't take part in the Mississippi struggle, we will organize brothers here in New York who know how to handle these kind of affairs, and they'll slip into Mississippi like Jesus slipped into Jerusalem.

That doesn't mean we're against white people, but we sure are against the Ku Klux Klan and the White Citizens Councils; and anything that looks like it's against us, we're against it. Excuse me for raising my voice, but this thing, you know, gets me upset. Imagine that—a country that's supposed to be a democracy, supposed to be for freedom and all of that kind of stuff when they want to draft you and put you in the army and send you to Saigon to fight for them—and then you've got to turn around and all night long discuss how you're going to just get a right to register and vote without being murdered. Why, that's the most hypocritical government since the world began! . . .

I hope you don't think I'm trying to incite you. Just look here: Look at yourselves. Some of you are teen-agers, students. How do you think I feel—and I belong to a generation ahead of you—how do you think I feel to have to tell you, "We, my generation, sat around like a knot on a wall while the whole world was fighting for its human rights—and you've got to be born into a society where you still have that same fight." What did we do, who preceded you? I'll tell you what we did: Nothing. And don't you make the same mistake we made. . . .

You get freedom by letting your enemy know that you'll do anything to get your freedom; then you'll get it. It's the only way you'll get it. When you get that kind of attitude, they'll label you as a "crazy Negro," or they'll call you a "crazy nigger" —they don't say Negro. Or they'll call you an extremist or a subversive, or seditious, or a red or a radical. But when you stay radical long enough, and get enough people to be like you, you'll get your freedom. . . .

So don't you run around here trying to make friends with somebody who's depriving you of your rights. They're not your friends, no, they're your enemies. Treat them like that and fight them, and you'll get your freedom; and after you get your freedom, your enemy will respect you. And we'll respect you. And I say that with no hate. I don't have hate in me. I have no hate at all. I don't have any hate. I've got some sense. I'm not going to let somebody who hates me tell me to love him. I'm not that way-out. And you, young as you are, and because you start thinking, you're not going to do it either. The only time you're going to get in that bag is if somebody puts you there. Somebody else, who doesn't have your welfare at heart. . . .

I want to thank all of you for taking the time to come to Harlem and especially here. I hope that you've gotten a better understanding about me. I put it to you just as plain as I know how to put it; there's no interpretation necessary. And I want you to know that we're not in any way trying to advocate any kind of indiscriminate, unintelligent action. Any kind of action that you are ever involved in that's designed to protect the lives and property of our mistreated people in this country, we're with you one thousand per cent. And if you don't feel you're qualified to do it, we have some brothers who will slip in, as I said earlier, and help train you and show you how to equip yourself and let you know how to deal with the man who deals with you. . . .

Mari Evans

Black jam for dr. negro

Pullin me in off the corner to wash my face an
cut my afro turn
my collar
down
when that aint my
thang I
walk heels first
nose round an tilted
up
my ancient
eyes
see your thang
baby
an it aint
shit
your thang
puts my eyes out baby
turns my seeking fingers
   into splintering fists
messes up my head
an I scream you out
your thang
is whats wrong
   an you keep
   pilin it on rubbin it
   in
   smoothly

doin it
    to death

what you sweatin
baby your
            guts
puked an rotten
waitin
to be defended

IX Men and Women

For many black writers, American racism is rooted in sexual guilt and sexual fantasy. In part, they say, the guilt stems from the white man's desires for black women and also from his failure to protect or acknowledge the children he has sired of black women. (It is estimated that fewer than 5 per cent of American Negroes are of unadulterated African blood.) Further, they assert, whites have projected their own asocial libidinal impulses onto blacks and have justified repression of blacks on the ground that such unrestrained savage primitives would otherwise ravage and destroy the white race. Thus, in the fantasies of whites blacks are sexual champions, but black males who are forbidden from partaking of activities reserved for whites sometimes feel themselves psychologically emasculated. Their women, consequently, especially among the lower economic strata, often become the mainstays of black families and occasionally their sole financial support. Meanwhile, the white woman is sometimes regarded by black males with both hostility and desire: hostility because they see her as the source of their caste deprivation, desire because she is presumably taboo. With the exception of Audre Lorde's sensuous love poem "Pirouette," the following pieces explore the relationship of the sexes in a racist world. Sadly, neither whites nor blacks fully confront their sexuality or their emotions.

Chester Himes

*Morning After**

The gold-plated Swiss clock on the nightstand whirred softly, curdling the silence of the small dark room. A woman stirred tentatively on the three-quarter-size bed, flung a heavy bare arm searchingly across the faded blue sheet. It encountered a human body, and the panic that had begun to well up inside of her abruptly subsided. Dave? she wondered, and cracked a bleary eye. On the adjacent pillow a fuzzy round object, like a frizzled coconut, black in the dim light, showed faintly in her thin scope of vision. Jesse! she remembered. She closed her eyes and, recalling his abject acceptance of her atrocious behavior, felt pleased. "I'll make him eat roots," she resolved and silently kneed him in the back.

"Uh!" he grunted, coming awake as furiously as he'd gone to sleep. His startled gaze searched the dim cell-like room and, finding everything strange, he felt a shattering of emotion. He was on the verge of leaping up and searching for the light of reason when his hand encountered a body beside him in the bed. Peering from bloodshot eyes, he recognized the matted head of Kriss. "Ready to light out and run, eh, son?" he thought, laughing at himself with self-disparagement.

She appeared to be asleep. He moved towards her. "Maybe she won't awaken," he thought hopefully. Half-laughing, he recalled a burlesque skit of a guy in a hotel room eavesdropping on a honeymoon couple in the next room who were trying to close an over-stuffed suitcase.

* From *The Primitive*, 1955. The title of this selection was supplied by the editor.

"No, not that way," he said as she tried to close it with her hands. "I'll put it on the floor and you get on top."

The eavesdropper's ears perked up.

But it still wouldn't close, so she said, "Oh shucks, it won't fit—you get on top."

The eavesdropper's ears wagged in a frenzy.

But it still wouldn't close, so he said, "Let's both get on top."

That's where the eavesdropper broke down the adjoining door. *"This I gotta see!"* he cried.

But Kriss pushed him viciously and said in a cold, dictatorial voice, "Jesse, I've got to go to work. You don't have anything to do but hang around some Harlem bar and you can sleep all day."

"Fine," he said, and turned over as if to go back to sleep.

"You can't sleep here!" she said, trying to push him from the bed. "My maid's coming this morning to clean up," she lied, then, to infuriate him, she added, "Go back to your wife then, she'll let you sleep all day. She always has." And when getting to his feet, he said, "Go to hell!" she giggled maliciously.

He found the switch for the hall light and went into the bathroom without replying. She had a glimpse of his body before he closed the door, smooth sepia skin, strong back and broad shoulders, his well-formed legs and smooth calves, almost hairless, that could have been a woman's; she thought of other women who'd seen him in the morning and she resented his body bitterly. "He's five years older than I am," she thought, indulging in the complicated reasoning of attributing his youthful appearance to the fact that white people, like herself, supported him so he could write a book every four or five years about what mean bullies the white people, like herself, were; while for her part, she had grown old trying to defend the lazy niggers. "If they had to work as hard as I do they'd all die," she concluded.

He looked at his greasy reflection in the mirror and thought, "You don't look a damn bit different, son." There were five toothbrushes on the rack; to one side on a wall shelf of glass a box of talcum powder, comb and brush, colognes and perfumes;

beside the tub one gray and one white bath towel. Inside of the medicine cabinet he found two safety razors, a container of blades, many bottles labeled with a doctor's prescription, a septic pencil and a man's comb, aftershaving lotion, and the bottle of blue tablets which had the shape of dexedrine but not the color. "Man, woman, and doctor," he thought, immediately amending it to, "Statue of modern woman standing atop a drugstore, right hand lifting nude male to prophylactic couch, left hand behind back beckoning to hovering figure of doctor in background with two middle fingers crossed."

When he came from the bathroom she said, as though to a servant, "Jesse! Put on some water for coffee and make some toast." He went into the sitting room without replying and found his shorts among his other clothes heaped in a pile on the floor. She giggled luxuriously at his silent resentment. "Get the paper from outside the door and turn on the television to Gloucester," she directed.

"I've had it now, little sister, for what it was worth," he thought, disdaining to reply. After donning underwear, sox, pants and shoes, he went to the kitchen, poured the remnants of the Scotch and bourbon into a water tumbler, ran it full of water from the tap and drank it down without stopping. On a high shelf beside the stove he noticed an unopened bottle of imported sherry and a half-filled bottle of vermouth. Looking through the refrigerator he found a remnant of grilled steak, a barbecued chicken leg and two fried crab cakes, all of which he ate greedily without bread.

The liquor took immediate effect and he began to feel good, bubbly with laughter inside, but slightly dazed as if everything, both mental and material, were just a wee bit out of line. "What I prescribe for the world is continuous drunkenness," he thought amusedly as he broke two raw eggs into his highball glass, filled it with milk, and drank it down, breaking the egg yolks in his mouth by the pressure of his tongue.

"Jesse!" he heard Kriss call to him from the bedroom.

He felt very indulgent toward her now. Returning to the bedroom, he turned on the small night light. "Yes, baby."

"Did you do what I told you to do?" she asked, laughing up at him with childish humor, and he knew then she'd done it to annoy him.

He pulled the covers from her and in the soft pink light her nude body resembled one of Van Dyke's nudes. Sitting slantwise on the bed he tickled her until she was nearly hysterical, then said, "That's what you get for being so mean," and left her to get the paper and make the coffee and toast.

She arose and turned on the television to Gloucester before taking the paper to the John to begin her morning ritual. He felt wonderful, no sex drives and almost completely senseless, which was the way he would have loved to feel forever, but he could never let a good glow be, so he went back to the kitchen and drank a water tumbler of the vermouth. It put a sharp sardonic edge on his glow and his thoughts came back not vivid but alive and about ten degrees off the line of conformity.

"Want some eggs, baby?" he called, and getting no reply, went to the bathroom door. "Will you have eggs, chicken? Or should I say *do* you have eggs."

"You can poach me an egg on toast." She was brushing her teeth and her voice was muffled. "You'll find them in the icebox. I'm not laying this morning," she added with double-entendre.

"Soup chicken now. Ought to do a Profile Of Woman At Dawn for the *New Yorker*," he was thinking as he returned to the kitchen, fried six slices of bacon and two eggs, poached one egg in vinegared water that came out frayed and uninteresting looking, which he put on a slice of dry toast and served it with a cup of black coffee.

"Your breakfast is ready," he called, then made himself four well-buttered slices of toast, brought his own bacon and eggs to the table and began eating.

He had neglected to turn up the volume of the television and was surprised to look up and find the busts of a man and a chimpanzee on the screen. "Good God! The Russians are here!" he called to Kriss and she came to see the excitement.

"Oh, you must hear this; he's the cutest thing," she said and hastened to turn on the sound.

She pulled the table in front of the archway so both of them could see, sat on the stool beside him, and said with giggling anticipation, "He says the most fantastic things."

He looked up again at the two grimacing faces and after listening for a moment realized that the man was interviewing the chimp.

"Well, what will happen after that?" Gloucester asked the Chimpanzee with a condescending smirk.

"On July 1 responsible officials of the United States will charge that slave labor exists in Russia on a scope unknown in the history of man," the Chimpanzee replied grinningly.

"Not a Russian after all," Jesse thought. "Not even an ape-man. Must be a man-man."

"That's no news," Gloucester protested. "You're supposed to forecast news events."

"All right then," the Chimpanzee replied. "On September 8 a woman named Bella V. Dodd will testify before a Senate Internal Security subcommittee in New York City."

"Who cares?" Gloucester interrupted rudely. "People are always testifying . . ."

"Wait! Wait!" the Chimpanzee said. "Following which the New York City Board of Education will declare that ex-Communists who admit party membership will not lose their teaching positions if they are genuinely repentant." The Chimpanzee looked at Gloucester expectantly. "Doesn't that sound like wonderful doctrine?"

"Get on with the facts and forget the doctrine," Gloucester snarled angrily.

"Just what I was saying, facts not fancy," the Chimpanzee murmured slyly. "On May 21 fascist Spain will be admitted to UNESCO. On June 2 Secretary Trygve Lie will deny that the U.N. is a communist nest. On July 13 U.S. generals on an inspection tour of Yugoslavia will endorse military aid to communist Yugoslavia. On October 14 Senator O'Conor of Maryland will urge the U.N. to dismiss Americans employed by the U.N. who have refused to say whether or not they were communists. On October 15, following the reorganization of the Soviet Directorate, Stalin will say in capitalist countries 'So-called freedom of the individual does not exist any longer.' On October 16 U.S. Secretary of State Dean Acheson will urge the U.N. to continue to fight in Korea as long as is necessary to stop aggression and restore peace and security. On November 8 police will fire on Negro rioters in Kimberly, South Africa, killing fourteen and wounding thirty-nine. African Negroes will be protesting against government segregation of African Negroes in Africa." The Chimpanzee's interest strayed; he began looking about for his bananas. "Police will shoot into a mob of ungrateful African Negroes, impressing them with white man's goodwill toward African Negroes who respect white man's rule in Africa," the Chimpanzee concluded, yawning with an air of extreme boredom. After all, no one was shooting down chimpanzees.

"The little stinker!" Kriss said. "Imagine the U.S. giving military aid to those communists in Yugoslavia!"

"That's what I'll do! I'll write a book about chimpanzees," Jesse exclaimed. Then hastened to ask, "There isn't any chimpanzee problem, is there?"

"Not that I know of," Kriss said. "All of those I've seen—mostly at the zoo—seem to be well satisfied."

"I guess you're right at that," Jesse said. "I've never heard of a chimpanzee being lynched for raping a white woman and so far none have been cited as communists."

"No-o-o," Kriss said thoughtfully. "But I once saw a chimpanzee in the zoo leer at me."

"Damn!" Jesse said. "That lets them out. Leering at a white woman is considered rape in some states. And if I write a love story about chimpanzees some white woman is sure to remember how some chimpanzee leered at her and the critics will say Robinson has written another sordid protest story, why doesn't that black bastard stop and count his blessings."

"You could write about snakes," Kriss suggested. "Everybody hates snakes."

"But I don't know any snakes," Jesse said. "I've seen some in the snakehouse in the Bronx zoo but I can't say I came to know them."

"Probably no romance novelists ever knew any dukes. But they didn't let that stop them," Kriss said.

"I know, but they don't write about duking. They just go on the age-old principle that human conscience is only waist deep."

"Why don't you read them and learn then?" Kriss asked.

"But it's below the waist the color problem lies," Jesse pointed out.

"Lays!" Kriss corrected him. "It's not the *lies* but the *lays* that make the color problem."

"The *lies* make the *lays* and the *lays* make the *lies*," Jesse expounded, feeling very clever. "If there were more *lays* and less *lies* it would soon be solved, or, conversely, if there were more *lies* and less *lays* it would soon be resolved."

With that profound analysis, he went into the bathroom to tie his tie. Everything seemed so extremely normal he forgot to swipe some pills as he had intended. Way in the back of his mind he found himself humming *da-da-dee*. The floor was listing first one way and then the other, keeping everything in normal perspective. When he finished dressing, he kissed Kriss on the neck.

"When will I see you again, baby?"

"Call me Saturday at noon," she said, smiling sweetly. She felt wonderfully sane and cheerful.

"You're going to see your love tonight?" he asked.

She smiled her secret sensual smile.

At the front door he peeped through the Judas window to see if the coast was clear. He heard footsteps and waited until he heard the outer door open and shut. Then he went hurriedly down the corridor, relaxing only when he had safely reached the street.

"Not that I give a damn for myself," he thought. But he didn't know what might result from her neighbors seeing a Negro man coming from her apartment early in the morning.

She cared less about it than he did. But he didn't know that.

William Demby

Doris and the Count *

. . . But now today is yesterday, and a cold dismal rain falls
upon the ancient paving stones outside the country trattoria
where Doris and the Count are eating in silence. There are no
other customers in the small one-room restaurant. The clinking
of knife and fork against plate is amplified in the mummified
quiet generated by the rain. The entrance to the Catacombs is
just across the Appian Way; Doris and the Count have come to
the restaurant—though it is only 5:00 P.M., two hours before
normal opening time—when it began to rain after their visit to
the martyrs' graves. Slowly, almost sacramentally, Doris lifts her
glass of wine and drinks; her gaze turns inward. She is thinking:
"Rome is beginning to give me the creeps, all this antiquity, all
this piling up dead things and dead people on top of each
other, those Catacombs damn sure gave me the creeps, the way
that Irish priest cracked jokes and played with those bones;
saints or no saints, I just don't like . . . I just don't think it's
right . . . there's something spooky and weird about . . . I
don't like no graveyard where you have to pay to see dead peo-
ples' bones . . ."

The Count dabs primly at his thin lips and smiles. He turns
slightly and looks out the window. In this moment the late afternoon sun probes feebly through the low rain clouds slug-
gishly migrating toward the airport, and at once the ancient
paving stones of the Appian Way begin to bloom through the

* From *The Catacombs*, 1966. The title of this selection was supplied by the editor.

fine tinsled drizzle, like a disorderly array of unhatched dinosaur eggs.

Raffaele is a count and looks like a count. He is thirty years old, vigorous of forehead and gesture, he has a broad, well-sculptured nose, small constantly amused and curious eyes, the pupils gray but speckled with gold, and a calm, almost detached, expression on his face which mirrors an inner security anchored solidly in social position and wealth. He dresses like a junior executive in a Manhattan advertising agency, but the cut of his silk shirt is Italian, and he proudly wears the striped tie of an English public school. Raffaele's smile becomes broader: he is about to say something but is waiting cautiously until the correct English words line up paradelike in his mind. Finally the phrase forming in his mind stands at attention. But before he can open his mouth the waiter rushes over to the table to pick up the lipstick-smeared napkin Doris has just dropped on the floor . . .

Raffaele is annoyed and impatient, for the waiter lingers at the table to fill Doris' glass from the green bottle of Soave that reigns slenderly over the midmeal disorder on the table. Instinctively Doris arranges her gold-embroidered shawl around her almost bare shoulders and smiles up at the waiter. The waiter is a darkly handsome youth with absurdly classical features but with the heavy capable hands and grimy fingernails of an automobile mechanic. Now as the waiter shuffles off to his post near the fireplace, in which a pile of kindling wood and crumpled newspapers stands unlighted, Raffaele smiles across the table at Doris. Doris smiles back at him, then turns her attention back to her plate. Her fork movements as she eats the tiny slivers of dark pheasant flesh which laboriously she manages to separate from the breastbone are cautious, stagy. She seems tense, nervous, and for a moment she and the Count chew in unison like twin ventriloquist dummies. Finally Raffaele clears his throat and says (he works for a British airline ticket office in Rome, public relations, and his accent is the melodious tight-lipped accent of an Italian count who has studied in England and now works for a British airline office in Rome): "Why so pensive? Is something bothering you? You *are* free this afternoon, aren't you?"

Doris raises her eyebrows and assumes a comical air of innocence: "Oh, was I pensive? I wasn't aware of being particularly pensive. I thought I was being composed—*decomposed!*" She breaks out laughing, and somehow her dream-secret Negro laughter seems sacrilegious here in this country trattoria on the ancient Appian Way, and the Catacombs with their layers and layers of bone-powder death just across the street. "What I mean is—if you really had to take me sightseeing—and the good Lord knows I have enough sightseeing to my credit to have earned at least five Mortician degrees—why bring me to the Catacombs? Isn't there anything else to see in Rome except churches and tombs?"

"I had my reasons. But to get back to what we were saying a few minutes ago—wherever did you get such a preposterous idea? Why, there must be thousands, perhaps even millions, of Italians who are blond, blonder even than me . . . than I . . ."

"Than me . . . than I . . ." Doris says, giggling.

She is getting slightly drunk from the wine and defiantly she straightens her shoulders. "Than me . . . me is the object of what . . . or than . . . I am . . . the subject of—?"

The Count nervously shifts his weight on the hard seat of the chair. Doris grasps the neck of the bottle and unsteadily fills her glass again. She starts to fill the Count's glass. Almost too abruptly he claps his hand over the glass and says: "Not for me, thank you. I've had enough . . ." But as soon as the words have crossed his lips, he realizes that Doris is offended. Desperately he tries to think of something to say that will mitigate the implied reproach of his tone. As he forces a smile and reaches for the bottle, and pours himself another glass of the cool pale wine, and drinks it energetically, a man among men, an aristocrat drinking with his serfs, discussing football on a rainy Sunday afternoon, he cannot help noting that Doris has withdrawn inside herself again. The agitated field of telepathic energy separating their faces warns him that she is thinking violent thoughts . . .

He's trying to make me, Doris is thinking, as once again the Count begins to dab primly at his thin lips and smiles into her eyes—as absently he brushes bread crumbs off the stylishly narrow lapel of his expensive flannel blazer—and do you know something, girl, after those spooky Catacombs, now why do you think he wanted to take me there? Why, hell, you could get lost down there, saints and martyrs, the sneaky way that Irish priest looked at me and cracked jokes and played with those bones, he's trying to make me, and do you know something, girl, you're going to let yourself get made, why not—?

Again the Count clears his throat . . .

"My ancestors were Swedes . . . they came to Italy during that last disastrous Crusade . . . You've heard of the Crusades, I suppose—?"

"Now look—! I'm not all *that* ignorant. I mean, even if I *do* earn my living as a dancer, after all we Americans do know a little bit about *European* history . . . Doc Kunster: A survey of European History 101—"

"I beg your pardon—"

"No. I was just thinking of my sophomore Humanities professor in college. A refugee from Germany. Everybody said he was queer, but once during comprehensive exams he tried to slip his hand up my dress—"

The Count's laugh is a brittle shadow, his eyes cloud wistfully, his eyelids lower like furtive window shades, his nostrils twitch: "And what did you do, I mean it must have been somewhat embarrassing for you—"

"What did I do? I told him to take his slimy hand out from under my dress, that's what I did, said—"

"And—the er-uh, professor?"

"He started crying, he got on his knees, he begged me not to report him to the president, he said he couldn't help what he did on account of I reminded him of Aïda—she's an Ethiopian queen—I got an A out of the course without even having to finish the exam—"

Raffaele finishes the wine in his glass. He is blushing. He swallows and nervously clears his throat and says: "You know, I

had no idea you had a university degree. Here in Italy, we—"
"I don't. I ran out of money after my sophomore year and had to go to work as a waitress—"
"Oh, what a pity—"
"Oh, I wouldn't say so. It's the first smart thing I did in my life. I might have ended up a social worker—that's what I was studying to be, a social worker—"
A buglike 500 Fiat pulls up into the driveway. Eagerly the waiter rushes to the door. He flicks his napkin against his grease-stained black trousers, pantingly, like a house-bred hound wagging its tail. The Count reaches across the table and takes Doris' hand. It is surprisingly limp and birdlike, very warm, and a tiny nerve is throbbing in the small of the wrist. As Doris turns to look toward the door (the waiter is leading two mud-caked hunters across the room: the taller hunter slips his gun off his shoulders and says as he slumps down wearily on the chair the waiter is holding for him: "*Accidenti che pioggia—!*"), the Count, who is slyly observing Doris, is suddenly reminded of gold and rubies, of black Byzantine madonnas, amulets and incensed prayers. Annoyed at the way the two hunters are boldly ogling her (for through her long warm fingers he can feel her whole body expand like a watch spring suddenly released: aware of the mud-caked hunters' virile devotion, Doris throws her head back and laughs, pulls away her hand, fumbles nervously in the brocade handbag for her lipstick and begins to stripe her pouting lips a waxy ruby red), the Count says, surprised at the uncontrolled tremor of jealousy in his voice: "I'm sure you would have made a perfectly marvelous social worker—I can just see you, visiting lonely old men in their shabby rented rooms, massaging their trodden egos and lecturing them on the need for moral uplift . . ."
"I suppose your idea of social workers is a kind of poor man's call girl—"
"Well, to tell you the truth, I have little sympathy for what you Americans call 'social workers'—especially women. Somehow they all seem part of some international feminine conspiracy to make us men suffer for the drudgery their mothers had

to endure in a young country without servants or slaves, and before the washing machine was invented—"

"Hold on a minute, Count—I'll have you know my mother worked all her life as a maid, and her mother's mother was a slave—so just what in the hell are you talking about, anyway?"

"I'm sorry—"

Raffaele is blushing (he hears one of the hunters say in coarse Roman dialect what sounds like "A—*mazzachepezzodifica, e purecioccolatoè!*"), he stiffens and calls the waiter imperiously: "*Cameriere!*"

The waiter comes rushing to the table, but backtracks to drop a plastic-covered menu on the mud-caked hunters' table: "*Comandi?*"

"*Il conto, per favore—*"

Raffaele looks down at his gold Omega watch. It is nearly five fifteen. He wonders whether he should call the office, but decides against it: Higgins can take care of anything important that comes up. Having made this decision, he relaxes and smiles and suavely says to Doris: "I think you'll like my apartment—"

"Who says I'm going to your apartment?"

"I insist—"

"Well, Count—if you insist—"

Doris laughs again and begins smoothing her skirt. She looks over at the mud-caked hunters; she exchanges inflammatory glances with them. The mud-caked hunters look away like embarrassed schoolboys, the taller hunter stomps his boot on the floor, he calls boisterously for the waiter: "*Ocaminiere, quisimuoredifame!*"

It is three o'clock in the morning. Doris and the Count are asleep in the Count's huge baroque-sculptured bed. Doris is naked. One arm rests limply along the bas-relief contours of her body swathed in crumpled sheets. The Count wears pale yellow silk pajamas and there is a determined smile on his lips as though sleep for him is a far more serious business than wakefulness. He sleeps in an adult version of the prenatal position; his fists, joined together beneath his chin, are tightly clenched.

A wide valley of cotton and cashmere separates them. There is no harmony to their breathing, though neither snores. The only light in the bedroom, more a phosphorescent glow, comes from the circular dial of a radio which has been left turned on. The radio hums like a miniature factory. There is a crucifix over the bed. There are two gilded baroque angels at the foot of the bed. There are no photographs in the room, but a water-color portrait of a circle hangs on the wall; Doris' clothes are spread out carelessly on a silk-covered divan. A white garter belt and a pair of silk stockings lie on the floor next to the bed like relics washed ashore by the tide. Down on the street, four floors below, the night watchman passes; the tires of his bicycle swish smoothly on the sidewalk, he whistles jauntily in time with the jingling of his keys. There is a half-empty bottle of whiskey on the low table in front of the silk-covered divan. One of the two glasses is still almost full. There is an overturned ashtray on the handwoven rug beneath the table. Most of the butts are long and lipstick-rimmed and there are many olive pits mixed with the scattered mound of ashes. Near the overturned ashtray there is a damp liquid stain: does it look like blood? . . .

Suddenly the radio coughs and splutters and Doris stirs in her sleep. She is dreaming. "What are you doing down here at this time of night?" the Irish priest asks. "Don't you know visitors aren't allowed down here in the Catacombs at this time of night?" Doris jerks herself awake. She sits up with a start and looks around the room. Moonlight or the bright glow of a street light filters in an almost perfect rectangular design through the closed shutters. There is a bad fuzzy taste in her mouth and only now does it occur to her that there must have been garlic in the salad. She looks around on the bed table at her side for a cigarette, but the package of Lucky Strikes is empty. Running her tongue over her teeth, forcing a surge of saliva to rise in her mouth to rinse away the bad fuzzy taste, she reaches over and wakes up the Count . . .

"Raffaele . . . Raffaele . . . wake up, what time is it, anyway?"

The Count wakes up, he turns on the bed lamp, in a matter of moments he is well-groomed and smiling—almost as if, in the instant between wakefulness and sleep, he had somehow rushed to the bathroom, urinated, washed, shaved and combed his hair.

"*Buon giorno*," he says, turning over on his side to face Doris, who instinctively pulls the sheets over her small firm breasts, which in the rose glow of the bed lamp have the silken purplish sheen of eggplants.

"What time is it? You don't happen to have a cigarette, do you?"

Raffaele picks up his watch, he holds the dial close to his eye, he shakes it, and says: "It's three o'clock in the morning, and if you open that drawer there, there ought to be some cigarettes in there . . ."

In the drawer there are no cigarettes but there is a long fat cigar wrapped in crackling cellophane. The Count strikes a match and lights the cigar for Doris. She blows out a cloud of fragrant tobacco smoke. The blue smoke clings to her naked shoulders and breasts like morning clouds clinging to valleys and hills. Through the smoke her eyes gleam like moonlight reflected in a well. The Count runs a finger along the slightly sunken curve where the aggressive tilt of her breasts begin. The purple nipples stiffen, they become vibrantly alive. Impulsively Raffaele throws his arms around her waist and buries his head in her lap. He rotates his head in the warm depression, in the fleshy trinity of pelvis and thighs—I am a rhinoceros wallowing in the muddy delta of the Nile . . .

"What I mean," Doris says, as, studiously, in perfect four-four time, she runs her fingers through his brittle close-cropped blond hair, "what I mean is, if you've only been to bed with *one* white woman before—I mean how can you generalize about what white women are like—?"

"Doris . . . Doris . . . *non sono stato mai così felice in tutta la mia vita!*"

"Do you mind handing me that ashtray over there?"

"I'll never go to bed with another white woman as long as I live!"

Without changing position he reaches for the ashtray and

places it on the pillow with a muscle-straining backhand gesture. Doris staidly flicks the flaky white ashes into the amber-colored ashtray. She blows out another cloud of fragrant tobacco smoke and her expression becomes thoughtful as she says: "You're the first white man I've ever been to bed with . . ."

"I don't believe you . . ."

"No kidding, the very first . . ."

"And . . . men of your own . . . race . . . ?"

"Only one . . . and it wasn't in bed . . . it was in the back of a station wagon along the Pennsylvania Turnpike . . ."

"But—"

"You think girls in show business have a lot of affairs; you think just because a girl's a dancer—"

"Doris, *bellezza mia* . . . then you're practically a virgin . . ."

"Not after tonight I'm not—"

Again Doris and the Count make love. Time expands and contracts, consciousness drifts violently from brain to hands and fingers, to unexplored patches of flesh, nerve ends burn with a cold fierce light. Gradually breathing assumes the rectangular minuette cadence of rational thought and life. Tiny beads of perspiration dot the Count's hairline, like a microscopic crown of pearls. He picks up Doris' dead cigar from the floor and lights it. The flame flickers, his hands are shaking. Doris gets up and goes to the window. She pulls open the shutters. The sky has brightened with the approaching dawn. Birds twitter in the majestic pine tree across the street. (Which bird has first heard the rising of the sun?) Graceful and confident is her pose as she stands silhouetted against the glass. At this haunted hour between night and day it is as if Doris has never known the atrocious innocence of clothes . . .

Audre Lorde

Pirouette

I saw
Your hands on my lips like blind needles
Blunted
From sewing up stone
And
    Where are you from
               you said
Your hands reading over my lips for
Some road through uncertain night
For your feet to examine home
Where are you from
               your hands
On my lips like thunder
Promising rain;
A land where all lovers are mute.
And
    Why are you weeping
               you said
Your hands on my doorway like rainbows
Why are you weeping?

I cannot return.

Eldridge Cleaver

The Primeval Mitosis

The roots of heterosexuality are buried in that evolutionary choice made long ago in some misty past—but not so remote that it can't be reached with the long arm of the mind—by some unknown forerunner of Homo sapiens. Struggling up from some murky swamp, some stagnant mudhole, some peaceful meadow, that unknown ancestor of Man/Woman, by some weird mitosis of the essence, divided its Unitary Self in half— into the male and female hemispheres of the Primeval Sphere. These hemispheres evolved into what we know today as man and woman.

When the Primeval Sphere divided itself, it established a basic tension of attraction, a dynamic magnetism of opposites —the Primeval Urge—which exerts an irresistible attraction between the male and female hemispheres, ever tending to fuse them back together into a unity in which the male and female realize their true nature—the lost unity of the Primeval Sphere. This is the eternal and unwavering motivation of the male and female hemispheres, of man and woman, to transcend the Primeval Mitosis and achieve supreme identity in the Apocalyptic Fusion.

Each half of the human equation, the male and female hemispheres of the Primeval Sphere, must prepare themselves for the fusion by achieving a Unitary Sexual Image, i.e., a heterosexual identity free from the mutually exclusive, antagonistic, antipodal impediments of homosexuality (the product of the fissure of society into antagonistic classes and a dying culture and civilization alienated from its biology).

340

Man's continual striving for a Unitary Sexual Image, which can only be achieved in a Unitary Society, becomes a basic driving force of the Class Struggle, which is, in turn, the dynamic of history. The quest for the Apocalyptic Fusion will find optimal conditions only in a Classless Society, the absence of classes being the *sine qua non* for the existence of a Unitary Society in which the Unitary Sexual Image can be achieved.

Each social structure projects onto the screen of possibility the images of the highest type of male and female sexual identities realizable within the limits of that society. The people within that society are motivated and driven, by the perennial quest for Apocalyptic Fusion, to achieve this highest identity, or as close as they can come to the perfection of the Unitary Sexual Image. All impediments to realization of this image become sources of alienation, obstacles in the way of the Self seeking to realize its ultimate identity.

Since each society projects its own sexual image, the Unitary Society will project a Unitary Sexual Image. We can thus postulate, following the model of Marx, that in ancient communal society, which was not cleft into antagonistic classes, there existed a Unitary Society in which a Unitary Sexual Image was in natural coincidence with the way of life of the people. This is the lost innocence of the Garden of Eden.

The Class Society projects a fragmented sexual image. Each class projects a sexual image coinciding with its class-function in society. And since its class-function will differ from that of other classes, its sexual image will differ also and in the same proportion. The source of the fragmentation of the Self in Class Society lies in the alienation between the function of man's Mind and the functions of his Body. Man as thinker performs an Administrative Function in society. Man as doer performs a Brute Power Function. These two basic functions I symbolize, when they are embodied in living men functioning in society, as the Omnipotent Administrator and the Supermasculine Menial.

Since all men are created equal, when the Self is fragmented by the operation of the laws and forces of Class Society, men in the elite classes usurp the controlling and Administrative Function of the society as a whole—i.e., they usurp the administrative component in the nature and biology of the men in the classes below them. Administrative power is concentrated at the apex of society, in the Godhead of the society (pharaoh, king, president, chairman). Administrative power beneath the apex is delegated. Those in classes to which no administrative power has been delegated have the administrative component in their personalities suppressed, alienated, denied expression. Those who have usurped the Administrative Function we shall call the Omnipotent Administrators. Struggling among themselves for higher positions in the administrative hierarchy, they repudiate the component of Brute Power in themselves, claim no kinship with it, and project it onto the men in the classes below them.

All the males in the classes beneath *the* Omnipotent Administrator, or Godhead of the society, are alienated from the administrative component in themselves in proportion to their distance from the apex. That is, they perceive their alienation in terms of their distance from the apex. This perception of their alienation, in terms of the apex, is an illusion. In fact, their alienation must be measured by their distance from the attainment of a Unitary Sexual Image, the take-off stage for the Apocalyptic Fusion. Generally, in a fragmented Class Society, the basic impulse of Omnipotent Administrators is to despise their bodies and glorify their minds.

Those who have been assigned the Brute Power Function we shall call the Supermasculine Menials. They are alienated from their minds. For them the mind counts only insofar as it enables them to receive, understand, and carry out the will of the Omnipotent Administrators.

The Class Society has a built-in bias, which tends to perpetuate the social system. The Omnipotent Administrators, wishing to preserve what they perceive as their superior position and way of life, have, from a class point of view and also on an individual level, a negative reaction toward any influence in the society that tends to increase the number of males qualified to fulfill the functions of administration. When it comes to anything that will better the lot of those beneath him, the Omnipotent Administrator starts with a basic "anti" reflex. Any liberality he might show is an indication of the extent to which he has suppressed his "anti" reflex, and is itself a part of his lust for omnipotence. His liberality is, in fact, charity.

The Supermasculine Menial clearly realizes that the superiority of the Omnipotent Administrators over him is based upon the development of their minds and the power they command as a result. Hence, he starts with a "pro" reflex. He is, for example, pro-universal education at public expense.

Weakness, frailty, cowardice, and effeminacy are, among other attributes, associated with the Mind. Strength, brute power, force, virility, and physical beauty are associated with the Body. Thus the upper classes, or Omnipotent Administrators, are perennially associated with physical weakness, decay, underdeveloped bodies, effeminacy, sexual impotence, and frigidity. Virility, strength, and power are associated with the lower classes, the Supermasculine Menials.

In feudal society, the men of the nobility, who were Omnipotent Administrators by Divine Right, are generally considered to have been weak, delicate, and effeminate, with the affectations of demonstrative homosexuals. The serfs and peasants are considered to have been physically strong, sturdy, hearty, fecund—"supermasculine."

The image of the Omnipotent Administrator, that he is markedly effeminate and delicate by reason of his explicit repudiation and abdication of his body in preference for his mind, is decisive for the image of the woman of the elite classes. *Even though her man is effeminate, she is required to possess and project an image that is in sharp contrast to his, more sharply feminine than his, so that the effeminate image of her man can still, by virtue of the sharp contrast in degrees of femininity, be perceived as masculine.* Therefore, she becomes "Ultrafeminine."

In order to project an image of Ultrafemininity, the women of the elite repudiate and abdicate the Domestic Function of the female (which is, in the female, the counterpart of the function of Brute Power in the male). To enhance her image and to increase her femininity, the domestic component of her nature is projected onto the women in the classes beneath her, and the femininity of the women below is correspondingly decreased. In effect, a switch is made: the woman of the elite absorbs into her being the femininity of the woman below her, and she extirpates her domestic component; the woman below absorbs the elite woman's cast-off domestic component and relinquishes her own femininity. The elite woman thus becomes *Ultrafeminine* while the woman below becomes *Subfeminine*. For the purposes of social imagery, the woman below becomes an Amazon.

Thus, a most weird and complex dialectic of inversion is established in Class Society. The Omnipotent Administrator is launched on a perpetual search for his alienated body, for affirmation of his unstable masculinity. He becomes a worshiper of physical prowess, or he may come to despise the body and everything associated with it. Fearing impotence, impotence being implicit in his negation and abdication of his Body, his profoundest need is for evidence of his virility. His opposite, the Body, the Supermasculine Menial, is a threat to his self-concept (and to compound it all, this perceived threat and resultant fear is reinforced decisively by the fact that the men beneath him are a threat to him *in reality*, because their life goal is to destroy his Omnipotence over them). He views them as his enemies and inferiors, men of a lesser breed than himself and his kind. He despises, hates them. Yet, because of the infirmity in his image and being which moves him to worship masculinity and physical prowess, the Omnipotent Administrator cannot help but covertly, and perhaps in an extremely sublimated guise, envy the bodies and strength of the most alienated men beneath him—those furthest from the apex of administration—because the men most alienated from the mind, least diluted by admixture of the Mind, will be perceived as the most masculine manifestations of the Body: the Supermasculine Menials. (This is precisely the root, the fountainhead, of the homosexuality that is perennially associated with the Omnipotent Administrator.) The dialectic of the Supermasculine Menial is the converse of that of the Omnipotent Administrator. The Supermasculine Menial has an infirmity of the brain because of his alienation from his mind.

Because he despises weakness of the body in himself, the Omnipotent Administrator will have a secret or subconscious aversion to the women of his own class, because of the Ultrafemininity which they have developed to counterbalance his effeminacy. At the same time, he will surpass himself in his efforts to conceal his aversion and make believe that the very opposite is true. He thus makes an icon of his woman and, literally, worships her. He pays obeisance to Her ritualistically while in the chapel of Her presence. Enshrining Her on a pedestal, he goes off seeking confirmation of his insecure masculinity elsewhere. Since the women of the elite tend to become the same, i.e., to project a homogeneous image of Ultrafemininity, they cannot, in the end, satisfy his psychic need—the confirmation of his masculinity. Strength gauges its own potency through a confrontation with other strength. To test it, he must go where it is. He may become addicted to a masculine-imaged sport, become a big-game hunter, outdoorsman, mountain climber. He may find satisfaction enough from some outlet as to have no problem at all which he is aware of as a sexual infirmity. He may be unaware of his impotence because he is blinded by his dazzling success and superiority in another field.

But in his quest for confirmation of his masculinity, a quest which he usually perceives as a search for sexual satisfaction and new conquests, his attention is attracted, with the force of the pull of gravity, to the potent Bodies in the classes beneath him, to the strength. He may sexually exploit the white-collar Bodies at the office; then, on his descent toward the Power Source, he may be drawn to the blue-collar Bodies in the plant. If these Bodies leave him still in the clutches of his lust and insecurity, he will bore deeper and deeper into the lower strata until he finds his sexual Balm of Gilead. There is a Pandora's box of sexual aberrations here.

The Body is tropical, warm, hot: Fire! It is soft, pleasing to the touch, luscious to the kiss. The blood is hot. Muscles are strength. *The basic motion of the women of the elite is flight from their bodies.* The weakness of the female body when contrasted to the strength of the male body is an obvious attribute of femininity as manifested in social imagery. Thus, to enhance and emphasize the femininity of her image—which is mandatory in order that she present a sharp feminine contrast to the effeminate image of her man, the Omnipotent Administrator— she seeks to increase the weakness of her body and stamp out all traces of strength, to differentiate it further from the effeminate form of her man. An appearance of strength in her body is called *ugly*.

Having projected her strength, the domestic component, onto the women beneath her, she achieves an image of frailty, weakness, helplessness, delicacy, daintiness. Silks, ruffles, frills, bangles, and laces are her element. In the realm of sex, because the act of sexual intercourse is both a physical and mental process, a joint venture between the Mind and the Body, her basic contradiction is that she is physically inadequate while mentally voracious, with her mind in extreme conflict with her body. The mechanism of her orgasm, which begins in her body and ends in the psychic depths of her mind, becomes short-circuited in the struggle between her mind and her body.

Sitting at the foot of her bed, like the mute Sphinx on the bank of the Nile, is the Ogre of Frigidity. She is terrified, because of the quality of her life, by the prospect of becoming a life-termer in the prison of frigidity. Her basic fear is frigidity, the state in which her frantic search for Ultrafemininity collides with an icepack death of the soul: where the fire in her body is extinguished by the ice in her mind. The psychic core of her sensuality, the male-seeking pole of her Female Principle, the trigger of the mechanism of her orgasm, moves beyond the reach or range of the effeminate clitoris of her man. Frigid, cold, icy, ice. Arctic. Antarctic. At the end of her flight from her body is a sky-high wall of ice. (If a lesbian is anything she is a frigid woman, a frozen cunt, with a warp and a crack in the wall of her ice.)

In proportion to the intensity of the Ultrafeminine's fear and feel of the ice is her psychic lust for the flame, for the heat of the fire: the Body. The Ultrafeminine, seeking sexual satisfaction, finds only physical exhaustion in the bed of the Omnipotent Administrator, and the odds are against her finding psychic satisfaction there. Her "psychic bridegroom" is the Supermasculine Menial. The Omnipotent Administrator, having repudiated and abdicated his body, his masculine component which he has projected onto the men beneath him, cannot present his woman, the Ultrafeminine, with an image of masculinity capable of penetrating into the psychic depths where the treasure of her orgasm is buried. The sexual act being a joint venture of the Mind and Body, though he satisfy her body and sap its strength, he cannot touch that magic spot in her mind which triggers the mechanism of her orgasm. Bereft of psychic satisfaction, and inhibited by social conventions and mores from embarking on a quest for her sexual fulfillment, yet performing her function as a mother and wife to the Omnipotent Administrator, the Ultrafeminine becomes a psychic celibate.

At the nth degree of the Ultrafeminine's scale of psychic lust (the contours of which few men or women throughout their entire lives ever in fact explore, resort being had to the forms of sublimation) stands the walking phallus symbol of the Supermasculine Menial. Though she may never have had a sexual encounter with a Supermasculine Menial, she is fully convinced that he can fulfill her physical need. It will be no big thing for him to do since he can handle those Amazons down there with him, with his strong body, rippling muscles, his strength and fire, the driving force of his spine, the thrust of his hips and the fiery steel of his rod. But what wets the Ultrafeminine's juice is that she is allured and tortured by the secret, intuitive knowledge that he, her psychic bridegroom, can blaze through the wall of her ice, plumb her psychic depths, test the oil of her soul, melt the iceberg in her brain, touch her inner sanctum, detonate the bomb of her orgasm, and bring her sweet release.

The chip on the Supermasculine Menial's shoulder is the fact that he has been robbed of his mind. In an uncannily effective manner, the society in which he lives has assumed in its very structure that he, minus a mind, is the embodiment of Brute Power. The bias and reflex of the society are against the cultivation or even the functioning of his mind, and it is borne in upon him from all sides that the society is actually deaf, dumb, and blind to his mind. The products of his mind, unless they are very closely associated with his social function of Brute Power, are resented and held in contempt by society as a whole. The further away from Brute Power his mental productions stand, the more emphatically will they be rejected and scorned by society, and treated as upstart invasions of the realm of the Omnipotent Administrator. His thoughts count for nothing. He doesn't run, regulate, control, or administer anything. Indeed, he is himself regulated, manipulated, and controlled by the Omnipotent Administrators. The struggle of his life is for the emancipation of his mind, to receive recognition for the products of his mind, and official recognition of the fact that he has a mind.

In his society, the Mind has been adjudged superior to the Body, and he knows that he is the Body and the Omnipotent Administrator is the Mind. It's Mind over matter, and the Body is matter. He may despise the Omnipotent Administrator for his physical weakness and envy him for his mind; or he may despise his own body and idolize the weak body of the Omnipotent Administrator. He may even strive to attain a weak physical image himself in order to identify with the image of the Omnipotent Administrator. The people at the base of society, where the Supermasculine Menial is, are well known for their reflex of attempting to conform to the style, pattern, manners, and habits of the upper classes, of the Omnipotent Administrators and Ultrafeminines. Just how this works itself out is a problem for analysis by sociologist and social psychologists on the mass level, and the headshrinkers and nutcrackers on the individual level. What we are outlining here is a perspective from which such analysis might best be approached.

The psychic bride of the Supermasculine Menial is the Ultrafeminine. She is his "dream girl." She, the delicate, weak, helpless Ultrafeminine, exerts a magnetic attraction upon him. When he compares her with his own woman, the strong, self-reliant Amazon, lust for her burns in his brain. He recoils from the excess of strength injected into the Amazon by the Domestic Function she performs. Also, since standards of beauty are set by the elite, the Ultrafeminine personifies the official standard of feminine beauty of society as a whole. Influenced by and imbued with this official standard of beauty, while at the same time surrounded by Amazons who do not embody this standard and who are in fact clashing with it, the Supermasculine Menial develops an obsessive yearning and lust for sexual contact with the Ultrafeminine. These yearnings are compounded by the fact that on the whole they are foredoomed to remain unfulfilled. The society has arranged things so that the Supermasculine Menial and the Ultrafeminine are not likely to have access or propinquity to each other conducive to stimulating sexual involvement. In fact, it has not been rare for the Supermasculine Menial and the Ultrafeminine to be severely persecuted, if not put to death, for such sexual contact.

The Amazon is in a peculiar position. Just as her man has been deprived of his manhood, so she has been deprived of her full womanhood. Society has decreed that the Ultrafeminine, the woman of the elite, is the goddess on the pedestal. The Amazon is the personification of the rejected domestic component, the woman on whom "dishpan hands" seem not out of character. The worship and respect which both the Omnipotent Administrator and the Supermasculine Menial lavish upon the image of the Ultrafeminine is a source of deep vexation to the Amazon. She envies the pampered, powderpuff existence of the Ultrafeminine and longs to incorporate these elements into her own life. Alienated from the feminine component of her nature, her reinforced domestic component is an awesome burden and shame of which she longs to be free.

The Amazon finds it difficult to respect the Supermasculine Menial. She sees him essentially as only half a man, an incomplete man. Having no sovereignty over himself, he hasn't that

sovereignty over her which our traditional patriarchal myths
lead her to believe he should have. On a still deeper level, the
urges and needs of the Amazon's psyche move her toward the
source of power, toward the receptacle of sovereignty—an attraction motivated by the Primeval Urge to transcend the Primeval Mitosis. When the Primeval Sphere split into the male
and female hemispheres, the attribute of sovereignty was repos-
ited in the male hemisphere, and this attribute exercises a magnetic attraction upon the female hemisphere. Usurping the Supermasculine Menial's mind, the Omnipotent Administrator
usurped all sovereignty; and because of his monopoly on sovereignty, he is the psychic bridegroom of the Amazon. In another
sense, however, being also attracted to the body of the Supermasculine Menial, the Amazon is lost between two worlds.

In net effect, then, there will exist in Class Society two sets
of competing images. Contending for the crown of masculinity
is one image based on the Body and another based on the
Mind; contending for the crown of femininity is one image
based on weak, helpless Ultrafemininity and another based on
the strong, self-reliant attributes of the Amazon. In a society with
a racially homogeneous population, in which the people at the
top are racially the same as the ones at the bottom, the competing images are not mutually exclusive. A Supermasculine
Menial, for instance, who acquires the training of an Omnipotent Administrator, can become a member of the elite and
function according—assuming the existence of some vertical social mobility, which is not, of course, always the case. But even
if he is prevented from ascending the social ladder in fact, a Supermasculine Menial can at least imagine himself doing so
without first having to transcend any biological barriers. Like-
wise, an Omnipotent Administrator can descend the social ladder, develop his muscles, and hoe the row with the coolest serf
on the manor. The women, too, can descend or ascend, depend-
ing on the merits, without having to breach a biological chain.

But in a society where there exists a racial caste system, where
the people at the top are sharply distinguished from those at
the bottom by race as well as social image, then the two sets of

competing images can come to be considered mutually exclusive. The gulf between the Mind and the Body will seem to coincide with the gulf between the two races. At that point, the fear of biological miscegenation is transposed into social imagery; and since the distinction between the two races is founded in biology, the social distinction between Mind and Body is made sacred. Any attempt by the Supermasculine Menial to heal his wound and reclaim his mind will be viewed as a malignant desire to transcend the laws of nature by mixing, "mongrelizing," miscegenating. Coming from the other side, if a member of the elite should attempt to bridge the gulf, it will be conceived as the rankest form of degeneracy and treason to caste. Deep-seated fears and emotions, which are in fact connected with biological traits and are part of a mechanism to aid racial and ethnic survival, are harnessed to social images and thereby transformed into weapons of the Class Struggle. Race fears are weapons in the struggle between the Omnipotent Administrator and the Supermasculine Menial for control of sexual sovereignty.

The Supermasculine Menial and the Amazon are the least alienated from the biological chain, although their minds—especially the Supermasculine Menials'!—are in a general state of underdevelopment. Still, they are the wealth of a nation, an abundant supply of unexhausted, unde-essenced human raw material upon which the future of the society depends and with which, through the implacable march of history to an ever broader base of democracy and equality, the society will renew and transform itself.

Biographical Notes

WILLIAM ATTAWAY (1912–). Born in Mississippi and educated in Chicago and at the University of Illinois, he is the author of two novels, *Let Me Breathe Thunder* (1939) and *Blood on the Forge* (1941). He has also done extensive writing for radio and television. He now lives in the Barbados with his wife and two children.

JAMES BALDWIN (1924–). Born in New York City and educated in New York public schools, he acquired his reputation first as an essayist, later as a novelist and playwright. Some of Baldwin's major works are the novels *Go Tell It on the Mountain* (1953), *Giovanni's Room* (1956), *Another Country* (1962), and *Tell Me How Long the Train's Been Gone* (1968). He is also the author of three volumes of essays and a collection of short stories.

GWENDOLYN BROOKS (1917–). Born in Topeka, Kansas, and educated in Chicago public schools and Wilson Junior College, she is the author of a number of volumes of poetry, including *A Street in Bronzeville* (1945), *Annie Allen* (1949), *The Bean Eaters* (1960), *Selected Poems* (1963), and *In the Mecca* (1968). She has also written a novel, *Maude Martha* (1953), plus a children's book, and was awarded a Pulitzer Prize in 1950. Married and the mother of two children, she has taught in several colleges in Chicago and is at present on the faculty of Chicago Teachers College, North.

FRANK LONDON BROWN (1927–1962). Born in Kansas City, Missouri, and educated in Chicago public schools, he attended Wilberforce University, Roosevelt University and Chicago Kent College of Law. He was a jazz singer, machinist, union organizer, and activist in civil rights groups. His articles and fiction have appeared in *Downbeat, Ebony,* and *Chicago Review,* and he also wrote a novel, *Trumbull Park* (1959). At the time of his death he was an associate editor of *Ebony* and a director of the Union Leadership Program at the University of Chicago.

CHARLES W. CHESNUTT (1858–1932). Born in Cleveland, the son of a Civil War soldier, he was largely self educated and started teaching public school in North Carolina at the age of sixteen. Upon his return to Cleveland after a short stint of newspaper work in New York, he passed the bar examination and spent most of his remaining years as a court stenographer. His Uncle Julius stories made their first appearance in *The Atlantic Monthly* in 1887. Among his books are two volumes of short stories, *The Conjure Woman* (1899) and *The Wife of His Youth* (1899). He also wrote three novels: *The House Behind the Cedars* (1900), *The Marrow of Tradition* (1901), and *The Colonel's Dream* (1905).

ELDRIDGE CLEAVER (1935–). Born in Little Rock, Arkansas, he attended public school in Los Angeles and passed a number of years in California state prisons for a variety of crimes. Former Minister of Information of the Black Panther Party in California and associate editor of *Ramparts Magazine,* he fled the country in 1969 as a parole violator. His pieces have appeared in *Esquire, Liberator,* and *Mademoiselle.* He is the author of a volume of essays, *Soul on Ice* (1968), and a random collection of political miscellanea published in 1969, *Eldridge Cleaver: Post-Prison Speeches and Writings,* edited by Robert Scheer.

COUNTEE CULLEN (1903–1946). Born in New York City, he was raised in a Methodist parsonage and was educated in New York City public schools, New York University and Harvard. A traditionalist poet and devotee of Keats, Cullen achieved his greatest popularity as a Harlem Renaissance poet in the late 1920's. The best known of his eight books are: *Color* (1925), *Copper Sun* (1927), *The Ballad of the Brown Girl* (1927) and *The Black Christ* (1929). He also wrote a satirical novel, *One Way to Heaven* (1932).

WILLIAM DEMBY (1922–). Born in Clarksburg, West Virginia, and educated at West Virginia State College for Negroes, Fisk University and the University of Rome, Demby has lived for the most part in Italy since 1947, working as a free-lance writer for newspapers, periodicals and film scripts. During periodic returns to the United States, he worked in an advertising agency and a public relations office. He now teaches at Staten Island Community College. Married and the father of one child, Demby is the author of three novels, two of which—*Beetlecreek* (1950) and *The Catacombs* (1965)—have been published in the United States.

WILLIAM E. B. DU BOIS (1868–1963). Sociologist, historian, educator, editor, novelist, poet, biographer and autobiographer, encyclopedist, cofounder of the NAACP and founder of the first Pan-African Congresses after World War I —these are some of the accomplishments of America's greatest black intellectual. Born in Great Barrington, Massachusetts, educated at Fisk, Harvard and the University of Berlin, he achieved his most publicized notoriety early in the century for his militant stand against what he regarded as Booker T. Washington's surrender of the principle of Negro equality. Du Bois's enormous list of book publications extends from 1897 to 1961. A few of his best-known works are *The Philadelphia Negro* (1899), *The Souls of Black Folk* (1903), *Darkwater: The Twentieth Century Completion of Uncle Tom's Cabin* (1920), *The Gift of Black Folk* (1924), *Black Reconstruction, 1860–1880* (1935), *Color and Democracy: Colonies and Peace* (1945). An adviser to Ghana's President Nkrumah, he died in Accra on the day preceding Martin Luther King's March on Washington.

PAUL LAURENCE DUNBAR (1872–1906). Born and educated in Dayton, Ohio, he achieved national fame after William Dean Howells wrote a preface of praise for his third book of poetry, *Lyrics of Lowly Life* (1896). In all, Dunbar wrote six volumes of poetry, the most popular of which were dialect poems depicting happy Negro rustics. In addition, he wrote four books of short stories and four novels. He died of tuberculosis.

JUNIUS EDWARDS (1929–). Born in Alexandria, Louisiana, he received his college education at the University of Oslo, Norway. Author of one novel, *If We Must Die* (1963), dealing with the persecution of a returned Southern war veteran, he has also published a number of short stories. Married, with four children, he now works in an advertising agency.

RALPH ELLISON (1912–). Born in Oklahoma City and educated in Oklahoma City public schools, he attended Tuskegee Institute, where he majored in music. His reviews, essays, and fiction began appearing in the late 1930's, but his celebrated novel, *Invisible Man*, was not published until 1952. He has since produced a collection of essays, *Shadow and Act* (1964), and continues to work on his second novel. He periodically lectures, reads and teaches at various colleges throughout the country.

MARI EVANS. Born and brought up in Toledo, Ohio, she attended the University of Toledo. Formerly an industrial editor, she is presently producer/director/writer for a weekly TV presentation, "The Black Experience." Her poems have appeared in *Negro Digest, Phylon, Black Voices* and *Dialog* as well as a number of other anthologies and textbooks. She is a John Hay Whitney Fellow.

ROBERT HAYDEN (1913–). Born in Detroit, he attended Wayne State University and the University of Michigan. He was research director of Negro history and folklore for the Federal Writers Project in the late 1930's and has been teaching at Fisk University since 1946. His first poems, published in the 1930's, have subsequently appeared in *Poetry, Atlantic Monthly, Phylon* and *Midwest Journal.* Collections of his poetry are *Heart-Shape in the Dust* (1940); *The Lion and the Archer* (with Myron O. Higgins, collaborator, 1948); A *Ballad of Remembrance* (published in England, 1962), and *Selected Poems* (1966). He has won a number of poetry awards, among them the Grand Prize for Poetry at the First World Festival of Negro Arts in Dakar, Senegal, in 1965. He is married and has a daughter.

CHESTER HIMES (1909–). Born in Jefferson City, Missouri, he attended public schools in Cleveland and studied at Ohio State University. He began writing fiction in an Ohio penitentiary while serving a sentence for armed robbery. He is the author of five major novels—*If He Hollers Let Him Go* (1945), *Lonely Crusade* (1947), *Cast the First Stone* (1953), *The Third Generation* (1954), *The Primitive* (1955)—and a popular sex farce, *Pinktoes* (1965). In addition, he has written a number of lively crime thrillers centered in Harlem. He presently lives in Spain.

LANGSTON HUGHES (1902–1967). Born in Joplin, Missouri, he attended public schools in Kansas, Illinois and Cleveland, Ohio, and later studied at Columbia University and Lincoln University. The most prolific black writer of this century to date, he was a poet, novelist, short story writer, playwright, journalist, anthologist, and author of two autobiographies. He first acquired fame as a Harlem Renaissance poet in the late 1920's for his experimental verse celebrating Negro city dwellers. Later, as an established author in all genres, he gave considerable support to the works of many unknown black authors. Some of Hughes's best-known poems may be found in *The Weary Blues* (1926), *Fine Clothes to the Jew* (1927), *Shakespeare in Harlem* (1942), *Montage of a Dream Deferred* (1951), and *Ask Your Mama* (1961). Also popular have been several of his Simple books, published in the 1950's, dealing with a Harlem character named Jesse B. Semple.

JAMES WELDON JOHNSON (1871–1938). Born in Jacksonville, Florida, he attended Atlanta University. In addition to following literary pursuits, he was a lawyer and songwriter and served as consul in Venezuela and Nicaragua. At the time of his death, he was professor of literature at Fisk University. His only novel, *The Autobiography of an Ex-Colored Man* (1912), was at the time of publication widely regarded as nonfiction. He was also well known as a poet and an anthologist of Negro verse and spirituals. His best-known works include *God's Trombones* (1927) and *St. Peter Relates an Incident of the Resurrection Day*. His autobiography, *Along This Way*, was published in 1934.

LEROI JONES (1934–). Born in Newark, he attended Newark public schools and Howard University. He has written five volumes of poetry, three of which were collected in 1969 under the title *Black Magic*. He has also written considerable jazz criticism, short fiction, a novel, social essays, and drama, and has edited two anthologies. In recent years he has aligned himself politically and in his writings with extreme black nationalist positions. Some of his best works are his first two books of poems, *Preface to a Twenty Volume Suicide Note* (1961), and *The Dead Lecturer* (1964); his novel, *The System of Dante's Hell* (1965); his jazz history, *Blues People* (1963); and a one-act play, *Dutchman*, published in 1964.

WILLIAM MELVIN KELLEY (1937–). Born in New York City and educated in private schools and at Harvard, Kelley is the author of three novels: *A Different Drummer* (1963), *A Drop of Patience* (1965), and *dem* (1967). He has taught at

the New School and the State University of New York at Ge-
nesco. He now lives in Paris with his wife and daughter.

AUDRE LORDE (1934-). Born in New York City, she attended the University of Mexico and Columbia University,
where she received a degree in library science. She has been a li-
brarian at Mount Vernon, New York, and poet-in-residence at
Tougaloo College in Mississippi. Her first book of poems, *First
Cities*, was published in 1968.

CLAUDE MCKAY (1891-1948). Born in Sunnville, Ja-
maica, West Indies, he arrived in the United States in his early
twenties and studied at Tuskegee Institute and later at Kansas
State University. His first American poems were published in
Seven Arts. He later worked as an editor on the radical periodical
The Liberator with Floyd Dell and Max Eastman and visited
Russia in 1922 as an observer of the Congress of the Fourth International. Although he wrote three novels and a volume of
short stories in the late twenties and thirties, his best writings
are his early Harlem Renaissance poems, published in 1922 as
Harlem Shadows. A free-lance writer after 1928, he lived many
years abroad. An autobiography, *A Long Way from Home*, was
published in 1937.

MALCOLM X (1925-1965). Born Malcolm Little in
Omaha, Nebraska, he was the son of a militant Baptist
preacher. His formal education consisted of eight grade school
years. Convicted of burglary at the age of twenty, he became
converted in prison to Elijah Muhammad's Muslim movement,
and upon his discharge from prison served the latter as a phe-
nomenally successful missionary and minister among the urban
masses. He broke with Muhammad in 1964 and attempted to
establish his own black organization with international ties. He
was assassinated at a rally in Harlem in 1965, leaving behind a
pregnant wife and four children. Various of his speeches have
been published since his death, but the most inclusive collec-

tion remains *Malcolm X Speaks* (1965). An autobiography he had been preparing was published in 1965.

ALBERT MURRAY (1916–). Born in Nokomis, Alabama, he attended Tuskegee Institute as well as classes at the University of Michigan, the University of Chicago, the University of Paris, Northwestern and New York University. A retired Air Force major and occasional teacher and lecturer, he has written a number of book reviews, stories, essays, and criticism for *New World Writing, New Leader, Book Week, Life, Harper's* and other periodicals. At present he is at work on a book of fiction and a full-length study of aesthetics.

DIANE OLIVER (1943–1966). Born in Charlotte, North Carolina, she attended the University of North Carolina in Greensboro and the Writer's Workshop of the University of Iowa. Her stories have appeared in *Red Clay Reader, Negro Digest, The Sewanee Review* and *New Writing of the Sixties*. She died in an automobile accident at the age of twenty-three.

JEAN TOOMER (1894–1967). Grandson of F. S. Pinchback, the "carpetbag" governor of Louisiana, he was born and educated in public schools in Washington, D.C., and later attended the University of Wisconsin and the City College of New York. His novel, *Cane* (1923), one of the earliest and most praised works of the Harlem Renaissance, celebrated négritude and consisted mainly of some of the short fiction, plays and poems he had published earlier in avant-garde periodicals. Drawn to mysticism, he was a disciple of Gurdjieff in the 1920's and became a Quaker the following decade. After *Cane*, his published writings were negligible. He was married twice in the 1930's and had a child by his first wife.

JOHN A. WILLIAMS (1925–). Born in Jackson, Mississippi, he grew up in Syracuse, New York, and attended Syracuse University. In addition to serving in the navy during the war, he has had business and advertising experience, and has served as Information Director for the American Committee on Africa. He has edited anthologies and written television scripts as well as writing poetry, novels, travel accounts, essays and book reviews. His novels are *The Angry Ones* (1960), *Night Song* (1961), *Sissie* (1963), and *The Man Who Cried I Am* (1967). He is married and lives in New York.

RICHARD WRIGHT (1908–1960). Born near Natchez, Mississippi, he had nine years of schooling in various parts of the South. He joined the Communist Party in Chicago in 1933 and remained a Party member for about nine years, contributing poetry, articles and stories to a variety of left-wing publications. In 1947 he moved permanently to Paris, where he came to support several African and anticolonialist political and cultural movements. At his death he left a wife and two daughters. His first published novel, *Native Son* (1940), aroused enormous interest. Some of his other important fictional works are his novellas, collected in *Uncle Tom's Children* (1940); his novels, *The Long Dream* (1958) and *Lawd Today* (1963); and a collection of stories, *Eight Men* (1961). (*Eight Men* and *Lawd Today* were published posthumously.) His best-known nonfictional works are *12 Million Black Voices* (1941), a folk history of the Negro; and *Black Boy* (1945), an autobiography.